Lionel,
Thank you for the inspiration
you have given me.

Best Wishes

Michael J.
04 April, 1995

AVIATION INDUSTRY QUALITY SYSTEMS

Also available from ASQC Quality Press

Managing Records for ISO 9000 Compliance
Eugenia K. Brumm

ISO 9000: Preparing for Registration
James L. Lamprecht

Supplier Management Handbook
James L. Bossert, editor

The ASQC Total Quality Management Series

> *TQM: Leadership for the Quality Transformation*
> Richard S. Johnson
>
> *TQM: Management Processes for Quality Operations*
> Richard S. Johnson
>
> *TQM: The Mechanics of Quality Processes*
> Richard S. Johnson and Lawrence E. Kazense
>
> *TQM: Quality Training Practices*
> Richard S. Johnson

To request a complimentary catalog of publications, call 800-248-1946.

AVIATION INDUSTRY QUALITY SYSTEMS

ISO 9000 and the
Federal Aviation Regulations

Michael J. Dreikorn

ASQC Quality Press
Milwaukee, Wisconsin

Technoqual Standards International
Wichita, Kansas

Aviation Industry Quality Systems: ISO 9000 and the
Federal Aviation Regulations
Michael J. Dreikorn

Library of Congress Cataloging-in-Publication Data
Dreikorn, Michael J., 1961–
   Aviation industry quality systems: ISO 9000 and the Federal
Aviation regulations / Michael J. Dreikorn.
      p.   cm.
   Includes bibliographical references (p.   ) and index.
   ISBN 0-87389-331-X (alk. paper)
   1. Airplanes—Design and construction—Quality control—Standards—
United States. 2. ISO 9000 Series Standards. 3. Aircraft
industry—Production standards—United States.   I. Title.
TL671.28.D74   1995
629.134'1'021873—dc20   94-43754
                                                              CIP

ISBN 0-87389-331-X

ASQC Mission: To facilitate continuous improvement and increase customer satisfaction by identifying, communicating, and promoting the use of quality principles, concepts, and technologies; and thereby be recognized throughout the world as the leading authority on, and champion for, quality.

For a free copy of the ASQC Quality Press Publications Catalog, including ASQC membership information, call 800-248-1946.

  Printed on acid-free recycled paper

 ASQC
Quality Press
611 East Wisconsin Avenue
Milwaukee, Wisconsin 53202

 Technoqual Standards International
P.O. Box 12770
Wichita, Kansas 67277

This book is dedicated to all those professionals who are committed to keeping aviation safe.

CONTENTS

FIGURES

PREFACE

To present date, quality professionals within the aviation industry have had to learn the ropes of the industry through trial and error and by learning from the experienced members of the industry. There has not been a source text available to draw upon. Having grown up in the industry, I too found that making preventable mistakes was both frustrating and sometimes embarrassing. With the growing interest in the ISO 9000 quality standards, I began a quest to find information on how these new international quality standards compare with the special and sometimes stringent requirements of commercial aviation. Having found that there were no published materials on the intermixing subject, I found it compelling to transfer both by experience and research into a manuscript in such a fashion that other aviation professionals would benefit from it. This is the first book of its kind that is designed to support the aviation professional in the field, the quality auditor, the management of aviation organizations, and those wishing to become more familiar with the ever-changing requirements of aviation quality systems.

This book is designed to provide the reader with the informational tools and models needed to develop a quality assurance system in the commercial aviation industry. Though the emphasis is placed upon coupling of the federal aviation regulations (FARs) and the ISO 9000 quality standards, the content can also be utilized to develop internal quality systems that comply with the Federal Aviation Administration (FAA) requirements without the ISO 9000 quality standards. Additionally, contractors that currently produce under one of the military specifications, particularly MIL-Q-9858A, can benefit from this book. By implementing the requirements of a production certificate approval and those of ISO 9001 (ANSI/ASQC Q9001-1994), such organizations will meet the generic requirements of the Department of Defense and the National Aeronautics and Space Administration (NASA). Additional contract clauses must be considered separately within stand-alone quality plans. For manufacturers outside of the United States this book will be helpful as well. First, by clarifying the sometimes confusing requirements of the FARs and providing models, foreign manufacturers will be provided a useful tool in developing internal quality systems to meet their U.S. customers' requirements. Second, the requirements of most other civil airworthiness authorities are quite similar to those of the FAA. This is particularly true for foreign manufacturers who operate under the requirements of the

European Joint Airworthiness Authority (JAA). Many of the JAA requirements are identical to the FARs.

By design, this book has 21 chapters that outline each of the major requirements of the ISO 9000 quality standards. Chapter 1 provides a background of the development of the aviation industry to include the birth of aviation regulation and quality systems. This background is necessary to ensure that those who are not so familiar with the industry understand why regulation is there and how it evolved, and to display how the aviation industry concerned itself with quality control early and improvement later. In each of the following chapters, comparisons are made between the individual elements of the international quality standards and those of the FAA. The book is concluded with some assumptions by the author with regard to the future of aviation quality systems. A glossary at the end of the book defines the primary acronyms used in the aviation industry as well as in this book. Appendix A is provided as a cross-reference to the various FARs and international quality standard requirements, as well as to the evaluation criteria of the Aircraft Certification System Evaluation Program (ACSEP).

Throughout this book, the three levels of the international quality standards are displayed, as applicable, and the various system requirements of the FAA approvals are shown in comparison. Though ISO 9003 (ANSI/ASQC Q9003-1994) has very limited applicability in the aviation industry it is also displayed in each of the chapters. This is because in some cases subcontractors and suppliers will be unable to comply with the more stringent requirements and alternative controls must be found. In some cases ISO 9003 (ANSI/ASQC Q9003-1994) is an acceptable alternative, providing the applicable FAR requirements are met.

The reader may feel that there is some repetition or redundancy in the text; this is intentionally so. Each chapter is designed to stand alone. This stand-alone method will allow this book to be used as both a training tool and a reference text. The best method for using this book as a tool is to read it once completely, then refer to the individual chapters/elements as needed.

In all of the primary chapters, models are provided to promote a better understanding of implementation and create transparency of the requirements. The reader must understand that the models provided are not the only means of implementation and compliance, but rather are proven methods. Additionally, the content is based on the revision level of the standards at print time. Because these requirements change, it is suggested to ensure revision applicability prior to full implementation. As a rule, the international quality standards are updated every five years; however, this last revision took seven years to become published. This book is based on the 1994 revisions of the standards.

The federal aviation regulations are consistently being reviewed for updating, but those of the manufacturing approvals are revised rarely. The advisory circulars that provide clarity of the federal aviation regulations are updated more regularly, sometimes on an annual basis and other times more or less frequently, depending on the content. Those advisory circulars that cover evolving subject matter or those that list names and/or locations will be subject to change on a more regular basis. It is strongly recommended for organizations to develop internal libraries of federal aviation regulations and advisory circulars. The federal aviation regulations are available for a fee on a subscription basis from the Government Printing Office. The advisory circulars, for the most part, are free of charge and can be obtained from the FAA by filling out an order card. Keep in mind that it will literally take years to develop a complete reference library. Industry professionals also are urged to develop their own private libraries.

Chapter 1

HISTORY OF AVIATION QUALITY SYSTEMS

Greek mythology tells us that Daedalus and Icarus, father and son, were held as prisoners by King Minos on the island of Crete. Daedalus studied birds' flight and made for himself and his son pairs of wings. He used framework of wood covered with cloth, and with melted wax he attached feathers. Before the escape, Daedalus warned his son that if he flew too close to the sea, the spray would wet his feathers and make flying difficult; and Icarus was warned that if he climbed too high, the heat from the sun would melt the wax that held his feathers and flying would be impossible.

In their escape Icarus flew too close to the sea, got his feathers wet, and barely remained airborne. He then flew too high; the sun melted the wax, he lost his feathers, and fell to his death in the sea.[1] This may have been the first forewarning of a need for procedural control over a process as well as a prophecy of a procedural noncompliance.

The aviation industry and the people within the industry have always been considered a little different than others. This may be attributable to the hundreds, or even thousands, of years attempting to do what many considered was impossible. Though this book is designed to provide an understanding of how the international quality standards compare to the requirements of the various federal aviation regulations for commercial aviation manufacturers, designated alteration stations, and repair stations, it is important that personnel working within this field understand the history of their industry. This also will provide some insight as to how and why regulation was implemented into the aviation industry. We cannot begin to focus on the future without understanding our past. This chapter will provide an insight into where we have been in the aviation industry.

THE HISTORY OF FLIGHT

Through the ages people have made many attempts to fly. In these attempts, they have created various types of aircraft. Though the majority of these contraptions could not really be considered aircraft because they never realized sustainable flight, some did and the process of the aircraft evolution was on. The first documented event of crewed flight was in Versailles, France. In 1782 the brothers Montgolfier built a balloon of linen, lined with paper, that was capable of sustaining flight. During a command performance at the court of King Louis XVI, the king's historian, Pilatre de Rozier, became the first man ever to fly. The development of the balloon continued, and it was even used in military applications during the American Civil War.

The first dirigible was built in 1816 by an English scientist by the name of Sir George Cayley. Through the evolution of the dirigible, people developed an understanding of controlled flight. The result of Cayley's invention led to construction of the great airships, like the Hindenburg.

Cayley also experimented with designs of fixed wing aircraft and the uses of rudders and elevators. He theorized that a cambered surface gives more lift than a flat one, that there is a low pressure area on top of the cambered surface. This led to the development of successful gliders, making Cayley the father of modern aerodynamics. During the glider era, men like Otto Liliental, Percy Pilcher, and Lawrence Hargrave also became the brave pioneers of flight.

In 1841 another Britisher, by the name of William Henson, designed the first propeller-driven airplane. The design was of a monoplane aircraft with a 150-foot wingspan, tricycle landing gear, and a tail plane. However, the design was never produced as a full-scale aircraft. In 1857 a French naval officer, Felix du Temple, also created a propeller-driven design; however, the full-scale aircraft was unable to accomplish staffed flight. During this same time, Russia made a claim that Captain Alexander Mozhaiski had accomplished flight. However, there was no evidence and it was suspected that Captain Mozhaiski had accomplished downhill flight as a glider.

In 1866 the Aeronautical Society of Great Britain was formed. This represented the first organized activity dedicated to the research of aviation. During its first meeting, F. H. Wenham, a marine engineer, submitted the results of his research in aerodynamics. His findings substantiated Cayley's theories and the cambered surface wing. Wenham is also credited with building the first wind tunnel.

Alphonse Penaud, a young French person, without reading the papers of Sir Cayley, also had discovered the effects of dihedral and a tail. He also learned that he received additional stability with a negative angle of attack on the tail plane. Penaud had designed an aircraft of considerable advancement, including such features as a single control to move both rudder and elevators, retractable landing gear, a glass canopy, and an engine enclosed within the fuselage. However, because of the lack of an available engine and an unfavorable reception at an 1871 Paris display, he gave up and committed suicide.

Clement Ader, another French person, made claims in 1890 to have flown 165 feet in a steam-powered aircraft. However, the event was not properly witnessed and could not be repeated. He was later considered a fraud.

In 1894 Hiram Maxim, an English inventor, proved the theory of thrust. With a test bed that had a 4000-square-foot lifting area, Maxim powered his two eighteen-foot-diameter propellers with two 180-horsepower steam engines. In July Maxim powered his throttles a little too far, and his machine tore through the guard rails, lifting into the air. Maxim quickly reduced the throttles and dropped to the ground. This was a wise act because the machine had no directional controls. With his machine severely damaged, Maxim announced, "I've done it! I've proved that there is lift and thrust for flight. The rest is easy." However, he never pursued controlled flight.[2]

Samuel Pierpont Langley was close to being the first person to design and build a heavier-than-air aircraft that was capable of carrying a person in flight. He was a noted astronomer who became secretary of the Smithsonian Institution. Langley, like the others who pioneered flight, was fascinated with the concepts of flight. He experimented with models that he had created with very good results. However, as many before him, he was plagued by the lack of a capable engine. With help from his assistant, Charles Manly, he attempted to produce the engine they needed. In October of 1903, a 125-pound, 53-horsepower engine was installed into Langley's machine, the aerodrome. On 7 October and again on 8 October Manly attempted to fly the aerodrome, catapulted from a converted houseboat in the Potomic River. Both times Manly failed but returned from the water unhurt. Two weeks later two young bicycle shop owners succeeded where many great inventors and scientists had failed.

On 17 December 1903 the brothers Wilbur and Orville Wright, Americans, flew the first propeller-driven heavier-than-air aircraft. The first flight had a distance of 120 feet, at an altitude of 10 feet, airspeed of 30 mph, and a duration of only 12 seconds. This accomplishment proved the theories of flight and led the way for the expedient improvement of designs. Within the next 10 years aviation realized such great leaps in technology that an emerging industry was created; so was the first legislation.

THE BIRTH OF AVIATION REGULATION

With the continued development of the aircraft, entrepreneurs found some profitable applications for them. In January 1914 P. E. Fansler started the first airline. Fansler used a Benoist seaplane, with A. Janus as pilot, to carry passengers from Tampa to St. Petersburg, Florida. This turned what used to be an entire day's journey into a 20-minute hop. However, at the introduction of this airline, the government had not yet established certification criteria for pilots, mechanics, airlines, or manufacturers. Passengers were placing their safety in the hands of the airlines.

The United States government also had discovered a use for these flying machines—in military applications. In reality, the government had been using aviation assets in its military since the days of the Civil War, with the implementation of hot air balloons used as spotters. However, with the onset of World War I, this interest was magnified.

In July 1914, under the direction of the Equipment Division of the U.S. Army Signal Corps, the Aircraft Production Board (PAB) was established. This board was to advise the armed services on production methods and provide information on materials for aircraft. This was the first governmental action to control quality and schedules within the aviation industry. During World War I, the government appropriated $640 million, up to that date the largest amount ever appropriated by Congress for any one thing. This allowed the industry the needed assets to evolve further. Unfortunately, the leadership of the PAB had no experience in aviation and was found to be corrupt. As a result, President Wilson removed aviation from the Signal Corps and appointed John D. Ryan as director of the Air Service and second assistant secretary of war. The Aircraft Production Board was dissolved and W. C. Potter was placed in charge of the newly formed Bureau of Aircraft Production. Aviation realized dramatic results as the program leaped forward.

In 1915 the president of the United States formed the National Advisory Committee for Aeronautics (NACA) to advise him on matters relating to aviation. This committee served the nation well in many difficult situations. The president appointed members "to supervise and direct the scientific study of the problems of flight, with view to their practical solutions."[3] As technology entered the era of space applications, it became apparent that NACA was no longer efficient to handle the task ahead. This was because the army and navy had duplications of effort and research and were competing with each other. On 1 October 1958 the United States space effort was centralized when NACA became the National Aeronautics and Space Administration (NASA) and became responsible for the entire space effort.

Wars excite the need for the advancement of technology, and World War I was no exception. However, because of patent restraints, many manufacturers were hesitant to develop new aircraft in fear of being sued. This is because the patents that were issued were so vague that the simplest of designs could violate them. In July 1917 the Manufacturers of Aircraft Association (MAA) was established to administer a cross-patent agreement. A blanket fee was paid by members of the association that enabled them to use one or all of the patents managed by the MAA. The collected fees would then be apportioned among the patent holders. So, in the end, both the manufacturers and the patent holders had a win–win deal. However, it should be noted that membership in the MAA was purely voluntary, and not legislated by the government. But with the influence of the industry as a whole, nonmembership meant certain failure. Because of the team effort, by the end of World War I the aviation industry increased the size of its workforce from 5000 to 175,000 workers.

The Air Mail Act of 1925, also known as the Kelly Bill, was passed and was another boost to the aviation industry. Congress believed that it would be economically profitable to turn air mail over to private enterprise. This was the beginning for government spending in the private sector of the aviation industry.

The first real legislation to control the civilian sector of aviation came with the passing of the Air Commerce Act of 1926. This act laid the foundation for all the government regulation to come. The four basic aims of the act were

1. To license aircraft and pilots (initially only for airlines; however, the act was quickly revised to include all planes and pilots)
2. To make rules for the control of air traffic
3. To investigate accidents to determine cause and establish measures of prevention
4. To test new aircraft and engines for safety[4]

This was the legislation that brought order to the aviation industry. Prior to the bill's passage, anyone could fly, build, or maintain an aircraft. This new law also made insurance companies more willing to provide coverage.

During the late 1920s and early 1930s, the carriage of air mail by airlines was brought into a bad light. Corruption and unfair contract grants were giving aviation a bad name. President Roosevelt, in January 1930, returned the carriage of mail back to the army. The army's aircraft and personnel were not prepared for the task; however, they performed admirably. Unfortunately, four army pilots were killed in crashes while carrying mail. Much like in today's media, the deaths were highly publicized thus creating heavy pressure upon the president to stop the army's participation. On 12 June 1934 the Air Mail Act of 1934 was passed, returning the carriage of air mail to the airlines. The new law established the Interstate Commerce Commission and provided it the authority to set rates for the carriage of mail by airlines, based on mileage with a sliding scale on load.

The 1930s brought adversity and depression; they also brought the airlines together as an alliance. Together they formed the Air Transport Association (ATA) through which the airlines were able to present a united front. In all actuality, the ATA could be credited for prompting the government to take control of civil aviation. The ATA issued a statement to the news media that unless the federal government aided and regulated the airline industry any deaths from airline crashes would be the government's fault.

On 1 July 1937 $7 million was allocated by the government to modernize the airway system, with most of the funds dedicated to the standardization of radio frequencies. On 23 June 1938 President Roosevelt signed the Civil Aeronautics Act of 1938 into law. The act created the Civil Aeronautics Authority (CAA) with the responsibility for all civil aviation. The authority was governed by a five-member board with the office of the administrator, who was responsible for the executive and operational aspects of the authority, located within the authority. The board dealt with economic and safety issues, with a three-person safety board for the latter. Two years later, on 30 June 1940, the Civil Aeronautics Board (CAB) was established to control the rights of airlines and the routes they traveled.

With the threat of World War II, President Roosevelt, on 16 May 1940, called for the production of 50,000 aircraft. These aircraft were initially needed to bolster the English air forces, but were later required to build up the U.S. Army Air Corps. Prior to this dramatic increase in production, several actions had to be taken by the industry. Existing factories had to expand, new facilities had to be built, personnel had to be recruited and trained, and new production processes had to be developed.

The method of production at this time was primarily the job shop method. This meant that one machine had various uses and required considerable set-up and tear-down time for each part run. This also allowed for numerous inconsistencies between the various batches. For small production runs this method was acceptable; however, for the push realized in the early 1940s a quicker method of production was needed. The industry quickly shifted to the assembly line method of production. Additionally, to produce the aircraft on the scale required, manufacturers had to use suppliers as never before imagined. In doing so, problems in quality control arose. Manufacturers dealt with the control of suppliers in various ways. Wright Aircraft insisted that all assembly was to be performed at the home plant to ensure the final product met its standards. Pratt and Whitney went about it in a different way. It licensed its subcontractors to assemble the product and sent its own experts to the subcontractors to assist with quality control issues. This represented the first formal control over supplier operations by aircraft manufacturers as well as the implementation of source inspection.

During World War II, individual military activities also began to create their own standards for process and system control. These standards were created for the control of such products as aircraft tires, glass, plastics, sheet metal, and practically anything else one could think of. The standards also were created to control the quality systems of their subcontractors. These standards are still around today and, of course, have been revised with the advancement of technology. Presently, the Department of Defense controls its suppliers' quality systems under military standards MIL-I-45208 or MIL-Q-9858A, and the corrective action process under MIL-STD-1520C. (These military standards are referred to as "mil-specs" within the industry.) However, in 1993 the Department of Defense, together with NASA, announced that it will begin to accept registration to ISO 9001 (ANSI/ASQC Q9001-1994) as evidence of an acceptable quality system.[5]

In 1942, West Coast aircraft manufacturers formed the War Production Council. The council consisted of representatives from each member company. During their periodic meetings, they discussed production methods and their associated problems. This council helped aviation greatly because techniques and process methods were shared with member companies and the duplication of technology research was prevented. Eventually, this group sharing spread to the rest of the United States.

The Federal Aviation Agency (FAA) replaced the CAA with the passing of the FAA Act of 1958. The aim of the act was to improve air traffic control and other aspects relating to air safety. The FAA assumed the responsibilities for the modernization of airways and the management of national airspace and continued to license aviators, including mechanics. The CAB retained the task of investigating the probable cause of aviation accidents and continued its role of economic regulation of the airlines.[6]

The Department of Transportation Act of 1966 created a separate government department, the Department of Transportation (DOT), to centralize federal transportation agencies and to help cope with the transportation problems in the United States. The FAA was placed under the DOT and renamed the Federal Aviation Administration (FAA). This same act also created the National Transportation Safety Board (NTSB) which took over the accident investigation responsibilities of the CAB, as well as the responsibility for investigating accidents in other modes of transportation. The NTSB was not in the DOT or under the Secretary of Transportation, but it did receive administrative support from the DOT.

When the Independent Safety Board Act of 1974 passed, on 1 April, the NTSB began operations as an independent agency. This allowed the NTSB the extra freedom and, most importantly, the budget to further its activities in transportation safety.

October of 1978 brought the passing of the Airline Deregulation Act. The act was a controversial one. Many of its opponents argued that without regulated control over the airlines' pricing and routes, the country's transportation infrastructure would fail. However, its supporters argued that without regulation a healthy competitive market would arise and the consumer would benefit from lower prices. The passing of this act bound the CAB into obsolescence in 1985.

The International Air Transportation Act of 1979 passed in 1980 to promote competition in the international marketplace. The primary goal of the act was to place maximum reliance on competitive market forces to achieve efficient service allowing more people to travel to more places at lower prices.[7] The act also provided verbiage that prevented foreign carriers and their governments from placing unreasonable restrictions on U.S. carriers, resulting in their inability to compete effectively. In a way, this could be viewed as a step toward global standardization.

Since 1980, there have not been any other substantial changes in regulation. However, with the evolution of a global economy, change should be expected. Airlines have seen regulation grow to the point of choking the industry, then fall to the levels of today. Presently airlines enjoy the operational freedom to select their routes and set their fares. Their maintenance activities are still strongly regulated, and rightfully so in the name of safety. From the manufacturers' viewpoint, government regulation has not been reduced but has actually proliferated. Though not displayed in this chapter, the FAA has established regulations to control the design, production, certification, and even the sale of aircraft. Additionally, these regulations cover a broad spectrum of concerns ranging from safety and clean environment to foreign policy.

THE INTERNATIONAL STANDARDS

In 1947, the United Nations created the International Organization for Standardization. With its headquarters in Geneva, Switzerland, it presently has representatives from over 90 countries. The United States is represented by the American National Standards Institute (ANSI). The International Organization for Standardization was established to develop international standards for products, materials, and processes, to promote global standardization. Though not planned, the documents this international organization developed came to be known as the ISO standards. This may be partly because *iso* is a Greek word meaning *equal.*

Between 1979 and 1987, a considerable amount of discussion took place within the European Community (EC) regarding the standardization of quality management systems. As a result of these discussions, in 1987, the ISO 9000 series of quality standards was published by the International Organization for Standardization. These standards adopted the characteristics of various national quality standards, and to say they originated from one national source would not be fair to the various nations that helped mold them. As a matter of fact, many non-EC nations contributed to the development of the standards.

The primary difference between the ISO 9000 series and many other quality standards is that the ISO standards are internationally recognized. Additionally, the ISO 9000 series looks at the management system of a company and how it ensures quality,[8] whereas the majority of the other quality standards place emphasis on the quality inspection systems. Though the popular MIL-Q-9858A quality standard requires manufacturers to develop a quality system that ensures adequate quality throughout all areas of contract performance, it does not place as much emphasis on management interaction as the international quality standards. Another major difference between ISO 9000 series standards and other quality standards is their diverse applicability. With the 1994 revisions to the ISO 9000 series, its diverse applicability has been even more clarified. In the United States the ANSI/ASQC Q9000 series was published and is equivalent to the ISO 9000 series. From this point on, reference to these international/national standards, in their document form, will be made in the U.S. version. However, we will continue to call them international standards.

Compliance with the international quality standards is voluntary in that there are no direct legal requirements to adopt them (only contractual requirements). The international quality standards are a second-party assessment standard. This means that the customer may stipulate the conformance requirement in the contract or purchase order. However, many organizations have found that registration to the international standards provides both a method of ensuring a good internal quality system as well as a great marketing tool. Because of these voluntary conformities, as well as the inability of customers to provide audit teams, third-party auditing and registration have become pretty much the norm.

When an organization becomes registered, it is required to maintain control over its suppliers. The easiest way for most companies to do so is to require their suppliers to be registered to the international quality standards. In many cases, customers have already begun to refuse solicitations from suppliers who are not registered to the ISO 9000 series. This has been excited by the unification of the European economy. There is now a total market of approximately 350 million consumers in Europe. In comparison, there are 250 million consumers in the United States and 270 million consumers in countries of the former Soviet Union. The marketability of such a standard becomes obvious when Europe is viewed as a whole (520 million consumers). As U.S. companies gradually adopt the international quality standards, they will also require their suppliers to conform. Registration or compliance to the international quality standards may not only open the door to new market places, but may also ensure the retainability of present clients. Beyond the marketing aspects lay other benefits. Because of its structure, implementation of the international quality standards will most certainly improve an organization's internal processes. Eventually, such process improvements will have positive effects on cash flow.

As will be discussed in the following chapters, companies register their systems to the international quality standards for various reasons. If ISO 9000 is successful on a global scale, consumers would be more assured that the product they are buying is what was promised. Keep in mind, though, that registration to one of the international quality standards conforms only the quality system that produced the product and not the product itself. One of the major benefits to manufacturers is that because of voluntary third-party registration the majority of the second-party audits may no longer be needed. When this is taken into consideration, larger manufacturers will find that millions of dollars of their budget may now be available for something else, like product development. However, aviation manufacturers will need to keep in mind that the requirements of the FAA, and other governmental and customer requirements, are not enforced by the international quality standards, and the assurance of these additional requirements remain the manufacturers' responsibility. In the following chapters, you will find that there are many similarities between the international quality standards and the quality control requirements of the FAA. There are also some important differences that will be outlined as you read further in this book. The purpose of this book is to display the comparisons of the international quality standards to the federal aviation regulations (FARs) and provide examples of compliance. The examples provided are not the only method of compliance, but they are proven methods. Each organization must establish its own systems in such a fashion to meet the requirements of both its commodity and of the applicable standards and regulations.

SUMMARY

The history of aviation is a long one—starting in the days of mythology and continuing on into today. As aviation grew from sport to industry, it was initially self-governing and learned primarily through trial and error. As the industry grew, airlines realized that without outside regulation, the industry would become unsafe, so they asked the government for leadership. Though the government control over the industry was gradual at first, and not without some pitfalls, it now controls the designs, manufacturing, and maintenance of the entire industry through the issuance of FARs. Additionally, FARs provide the requirements for the certification of airlines, pilots, mechanics, and other personnel who have direct influence on the safe operation of the aircraft.

In controlling the manufacturing and design aspects of the industry, quality standards have developed to standardize the requirements. Initially, these quality standards came in the form of military standards that were issued by military departments in procuring their equipment. Later, civil manufacturing units took over these same standards as their own, and controlled their suppliers accordingly. In an effort to standardize quality systems on a global scale, the International Organization for Standardization developed the ISO 9000 series. The American National Standards Institute and the American Society for Quality Control (ASQC) published the ANSI/ASQC Q9000 series, which is the U.S. version of the ISO 9000 series, to promote national recognition of the standards. In reviewing the history of aviation, it would appear that the government has a tendency to relinquish control when the industry is capable of controlling itself and desires it. The international quality standards provide the tool upon which a globally standardized system can be built.

NOTES

1. Carl A. Brown, *A History of Aviation* (Daytona Beach: Embry-Riddle Aeronautical University, 1980), 1.

2. Ibid., 17.

3. Ibid., 67.

4. Ibid., 87.

5. "ISO 9000 Supports Growing at NASA, DoD, FAA," *Quality Systems Update* 3, no. 6 (June 1993): 13.

6. V. Foster Rollo, *Aviation Law: An Introduction* (Lanham, Md.: Maryland Historical Press, 1985), 253.

7. Nawal K. Taneja, *Airlines in Transition* (Lexington, Mass.: Lexington Books, 1981), 59.

8. Richard B. Clements, *Quality Manager's Complete Guide to ISO 9000* (Englewood Cliffs, N.J.: Prentice Hall, 1993), 3.

Chapter 2

QUALITY SYSTEMS

Regardless of the size, type, or location of a business, if it supplies a product or service, that which is delivered must be of an acceptable quality. If it is not, then the management has failed the company, its customers, and its investors. A company can only remain viable as long as customers are willing to purchase that which is produced. For these reasons, companies adopt quality standards and establish internal quality systems.

Within the aviation industry, companies have little choice on whether or not they wish to establish a quality system. The requirements for establishing a quality control system are documented within the individual manufacturing approval requirements of the FARs and are a fact of law. However, companies do have the option on whether or not they wish to implement a quality assurance system that exceeds the requirements of the individual FARs.

By implementing additional procedures and control criteria, that place assurance of conformity early in the individual processes, the possibility of later, more costly, nonconformance is diminished. These preventive processes are not restricted to the manufacturing cycle. They can be implemented within the contract review, procurement, scheduling, facility maintenance, or any other activities that are susceptible to variances and noncompliance within their individual process flows. Because of its adaptability and global acceptance, the ISO 9000 quality standards have became very popular. These international quality standards can be applied to any commodity or process and, if properly implemented, can provide positive results, in both capability and capacity. These positive results eventually will have positive effects on the bottom line.

Within this chapter the requirements of the international quality standards, as well as the requirements of the FAA, will be discussed with regard to aviation manufacturing approvals.

THE INTERNATIONAL STANDARDS

The international quality system standards were developed in three varying levels: ISO 9001, ISO 9002, and ISO 9003. However, there are additional standards within the ISO 9000 series. ISO 8402 provides the definitions of the vocabulary used within the standards. ISO 9000-1 was created to provide the guidelines for selecting one of the three quality system standards to fit the individual organization and commodity. ISO 9004-1 provides the background and intent of the series of standards, and is helpful in interpreting the ISO 9001, ISO 9002, and ISO 9003 standards. Figure 2.1 illustrates the flow of the international standards. (The core standards for the series are shown; however, there are other international standards that are complementary.)

ANSI and ASQC have established a joint venture in recognizing these standards within the United States. They are referred to as ANSI/ASQC Q9000-1-1994 (ISO 9000-1), ANSI/ASQC Q9001-1994 (ISO 9001), ANSI/ASQC Q9002-1994 (ISO 9002), ANSI/ASQC Q9003-1994 (ISO 9003), and ANSI/ASQC Q9004-1-1994 (ISO 9004). The ANSI/ASQC documents are the U.S. version of the ISO documents. For the purpose of this book, and to promote U.S. recognition of the standards, these quality standards will be referred to by their U.S. titles. However, to create global applicability they will also be referred to as the international quality standards.

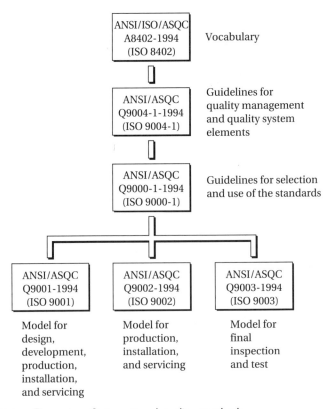

FIGURE 2.1.   *The series of international quality standards.*

Presently, the ASQC is jointly administering the U.S. ISO 9000 registration scheme, under a subdivision called the Registrar's Accreditation Board (RAB), together with ANSI. The ANSI/RAB team is responsible for accrediting quality system registrars. The RAB certifies auditors, lead auditors, and course providers. Additionally, there are numerous registrars operating in the United States under the accreditation of foreign national quality schemes. Qualified U.S. citizens also may be certified under one of the foreign schemes as an auditor (assessor) or lead auditor (lead assessor), as well as an internal assessor. The most popular is the Institute for Quality Assurance—International Register of Certificated Auditors (IQA-IRCA), formally named the Registration Board for Assessors (RBA), in the United Kingdom. It must be clarified that no scheme is easier or better than the other in achieving accreditation or certification; each of the accredited bodies have virtually the same qualification requirements. It has purely been a matter of global recognition. However, as a result of discussions in Geneva, the Quality Society of Australasia (QSA), the IQA-IRCA, and the RAB have agreed to recognize each other's certifications for assessors/auditors and lead assessors/auditors, as well as training organizations certified under the individual certification bodies.[1]

The 1994 revision made significant changes in the international quality standards. The most affected was ANSI/ASQC Q9003. ANSI/ASQC Q9003 has 18 elements for a quality inspection system (changed from 12 in the 1987 revision). Though this standard has 18 elements, the control of the system is limited to final inspection and test of the product. Because this standard does not control in-process activities, it is not very applicable to the aviation industry, and its implementation is not recommended for manufacturers. It may be implemented for small assembly facilities that have no design, procurement, or servicing activities.

ANSI/ASQC Q9002 has 19 elements for a quality assurance system and ANSI/ASQC Q9001 has 20, as shown in Figure 2.2. Each of the individual elements are mostly identical in their wording. The main difference between these two quality standards is that ANSI/ASQC Q9001 has the requirement for the control of design and ANSI/ASQC Q9002 does not. In the aviation industry, there is a mixed bag. Some manufacturers operate solely as a supplier or subdivision and have no control over the design. (Prior to the 1994 revisions, ANSI/ASQC Q9002 had no requirements for the control of servicing.) These manufacturers would pursue compliance to the requirements of ANSI/ASQC Q9002. However, manufacturers who create and control their own designs, whether of an aircraft, engine, propeller, galley, landing gear, cargo system, or anything that is proprietary, will be required to perform to the requirements of ANSI/ASQC Q9001.

	ANSI/ASQC Q9001-1994 (ISO 9001)	ANSI/ASQC Q9002-1994 (ISO 9002)	ANSI/ASQC Q9003-1994 (ISO 9003)
Management responsibility	*	*	*
Quality system	*	*	*
Contract review	*	*	*
Design control	*		
Document and data control	*	*	*
Purchasing	*	*	*
Control of customer-supplied product	*	*	*
Product identification and traceability	*	*	*
Process control	*	*	*
Inspection and testing	*	*	*
Control of inspection, measuring, and test equipment	*	*	*
Inspection and test status	*	*	*
Control of nonconforming product	*	*	*
Corrective and preventive action	*	*	*
Handling, storage, packaging, preservation, and delivery	*	*	*
Control of quality records	*	*	*
Internal quality audits	*	*	*
Training	*	*	*
Servicing	*	*	
Statistical process control	*	*	*

FIGURE 2.2.   *The elements of the international quality standards.*

Each of the individual system elements stated in the international standards provides a clear and concise description of the requirements. In some instances, notes are provided for additional clarification. However, notes within the international quality standards are not mandatory requirements, and are only provided as a means of clarification. Each of the chapters of this book provides models that will meet the requirements of the individual elements; however, they are not the only method of compliance. Each manufacturer, and this includes those companies who only provide services, must develop its own methods of compliance to the international quality standards and FARs as applicable to it and its commodity.

For aviation manufacturers, it should not be a mystery as to which level of the international quality standards they should apply. Discounting ANSI/ASQC Q9003 as an acceptable quality standard is probably the first thing the majority of aviation manufacturers should do. However, for those who absolutely want a system that complies with ANSI/ASQC Q9003, they will find that because of FAR requirements, they will be required to implement additional controls, in excess of ANSI/ASQC Q9003. This will place these manufacturers close to complying with ANSI/ASQC Q9002. So, in essence, it makes little sense for an FAA-approved manufacturer to pursue ANSI/ASQC Q9003 conformance. However, for the sake of being complete and for those organizations who procure no materials, create no designs, and are not required to service their products, the ANSI/ASQC Q9003 requirements also will be displayed within the contents of each chapter of this book. The remaining manufacturers should concentrate on ANSI/ASQC Q9001 or ANSI/ASQC Q9002 compliance.

All manufacturers, including those pursuing ANSI/ASQC Q9003, shall establish and maintain a quality system as a means of ensuring that their product conforms to specified requirements. This shall include the preparation of a documented quality manual in accordance with the applicable international quality standard. The quality manual shall include or make reference to the quality system procedures and outline the structure of the documentation used in the quality system. ISO 10013 was developed to provide guidance in the development of such a quality manual. As will be discussed throughout this book, the international quality standards place strong emphasis on documentation and audit.

To augment the controls of the quality manual, quality procedures are needed. The international quality standards state that "the range and detail of the procedures that form part of the quality system depend on the complexity of the work, the methods used, and the skills and training needed by personnel involved in carrying out the activity."[2] These procedures must be consistent with the requirements of the international quality standards and the manufacturer's documented quality policy. The manufacturer must ensure that these procedures, as well as the entire quality system, are effectively implemented. However, written procedures are only mandatory when their absence would adversely affect quality, or as specifically stated in the international quality standards or FARs.

The documentation should be structured as displayed in Figure 2.3. The applicable standards and regulations flow into the quality assurance manual (QAM). Procedures are created to document detailed requirements of individual processes or activities from the requirements of the QAM. Additionally, if there are special customer requirements, these can be incorporated into procedures or, the next level, plans.

The 1994 revisions of the international quality standards brought with them additional clarification for the requirements of quality planning. Plans and work instructions should be detailed instructions of how to perform a certain process, operation, test, inspection, or task, and must be consistent with the quality system. These documents can and should document the acceptance of these actions. Special inspection plans/records referring to these documents also can be created. Once documents that reflect acceptance of a process, operation, inspection, test, or task are completed, those documents become *quality records.* These quality records shall be maintained in appropriate file (reference chapter 17) and will provide the majority of the objective evidence during both internal and extrinsic audits.

The quality planning element of the international quality standards goes beyond just the creation of plans and procedures. It is more of a process activity that considers the global quality planning efforts of all operations. It actually requires organizations to be proactive in heading off unwanted surprises. The 1994 revisions require manufacturers to give consideration to the following activities, as appropriate, in meeting the specified requirements for products, projects, or contracts.

(a) The preparation of quality plans;

(b) The identification and acquisition of any controls, processes, equipment (including inspection and test equipment), fixtures, resources, and skills that may be needed to achieve the required quality;

(c) Ensuring the compatibility of the design, the production process, installation, servicing, inspection and test procedures, and the applicable documentation;

(d) The updating, as necessary, of quality control, inspection, and testing techniques, including the development of new instrumentation;

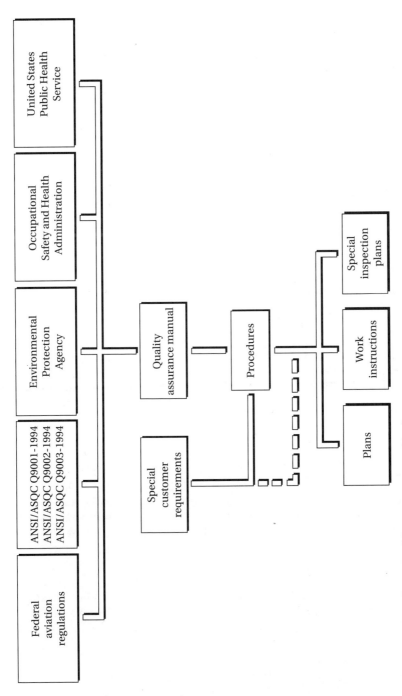

FIGURE 2.3.   The tiers of documentation and its flow.

(e) The identification of any measurement requirement involving capability that exceeds the known state of the art, in sufficient time for needed capability to be developed;

(f) The identification of suitable verification at appropriate stages in the realization of product;

(g) The clarification of standards of acceptability for all features and requirements, including those which contain a subjective element; and

(h) The identification and preparation of quality records.[3]

Most of the noted activities should be accomplished within the contract review process, but will also require follow-up audit to ensure effectiveness.

The effective implementation of the control procedures and plans are assured though audits. Audits are one of the most powerful tools a manufacturer could develop. Through audits, both internal (own systems) and external (suppliers' systems), processes can be verified and their capability assured. Assurance of the process may eventually reduce the number of inspectors needed, however, increasing the number of auditors. However, performing as an auditor is not always a full-time job. Individuals within disciplines outside of quality assurance can be trained in the correct methods of auditing and can assist quality assurance personnel in the performance of internal or external audits. This increases the awareness of personnel outside of quality assurance of the importance of quality controls. Quality assurance would eventually evolve from a policing activity to an auditing activity, and should provide a continued leadership role within the company.

During the development of the quality system, it should not be forgotten that the international quality standards are complementary, not alternative, to the technical specified requirements. In the case of the U.S. aviation industry, this means that the individual FARs have precedence over the international quality standards. The intent of the international quality standards was for them to be implemented as is; however, on occasion they may need to be tailored by adding or deleting certain quality system requirements for specific contractual situations. ANSI/ASQC Q9000-1-1994 provides guidance on such tailoring. Within the U.S. aviation industry, and as outlined in this book, the manufacturer will find that the international quality standards are very complementary to the FARs and, in most cases, existing FAA-approved quality systems actually will require only moderate modification to meet the requirements of the international quality standards.

When manufacturers feel that they have complied with the requirements of the applicable international quality standard, they may pursue registration through an accredited registrar. However, as of this writing, unless required by contract, registration is optional. Some manufacturers may wish to use the international quality standards as their core model, and not pursue, or delay pursuance of, registration. But when registration is sought, the manufacturer should select a registrar in the same manner as it would any other special processor. Just because a registrar is accredited does not mean that the registrar is experienced in your industry. To ensure the registration process is performed knowledgeably, the manufacturer should ensure that the registrar is fluent in the requirements of the FAA or applicable civil air authority. This also includes the lead auditor and auditors the registrar sends to perform the third-party (extrinsic) audits. It may not be a bad idea for manufacturers to perform process audits of their own on the prospective registrar. Such an audit could include a review of the registrar's experience in aviation systems, the experience of its auditors and lead auditors, and the assurance that the registrar has its own, or has access to someone else's, library of FARs and advisory circulars. Advisory circulars are supplemental publications to the FARs, but are nonbinding. These documents provide the official FAA interpretation of the FARs.

A good indicator that the registrar has experienced personnel is when the registrar's auditing personnel are certified by the Aerospace Sector Certification Scheme (ASCS), under the authority of the IQA-IRCA, in the United Kingdom. Under this scheme, each assessor or lead assessor candidate has his or her experience in aerospace reviewed by the ASCS board, prior to certification. This process increases the confidence in the quality and experience of the aerospace/aviation auditor. As of this writing, the RAB, in the United States, has not yet established special criteria for the verification of this special experience.

MANUFACTURING APPROVALS UNDER THE FEDERAL AVIATION REGULATIONS

The FAA has developed quality control regulations for various types of aviation manufacturers. The majority of the regulations are located in Part 21 of the FARs. However, there is also reference to other FAR parts for identification, servicing, maintenance, and repair station activities. This book outlines the requirements of the various types of manufacturing approvals, with regard to their respective quality control systems, as well as the quality system requirements for the designated alteration station and the repair station.

There are basically four different FAA approvals for an aviation manufacturer, and they are found in FAR Part 21.

1. *Production Under Type Certificate Only* (also known as an Approved Production Inspection System—APIS), under FAR Part 21 Subpart F, is granted to qualified manufacturers who hold a type certificate design approval for a product they have designed and have had their quality system qualified for their manufacturing facility by the FAA. These certifications are normally held only by airframe, engine, and propeller manufacturers. However, for various reasons, most manufacturers will prefer to apply for a Production Certificate. There is no actual certificate; the certification is issued in the form of a letter.

2. *Production Certificates* (PC) (Figure 2.4), under FAR Part 21 Subpart G, are granted to qualified manufacturers who hold a Type Certificate, a licensing agreement with a Type Certificate holder, or a Supplemental Type Certificate. As will be discussed later in this book, Production Certificates are usually preferred over certification under a Production Under Type Certificate Only (APIS) approval. This is mainly because of the requirements for final acceptance of the product and issuance of certifications.

3. *Parts Manufacturer Approvals* (PMA), under FAR Part 21 Subpart K, are granted to qualified manufacturers who produce products under a Supplemental Type Certificate, or under a licensing agreement with a holder of a Supplemental Type Certificate. Though it is commonly thought that PMA manufacturers only produce small parts and appliances, they also manufacture complete systems. This could include galley systems, cargo loading systems, and on-board entertainment systems. In addition to the standard FAA quality requirements, PMA manufacturers also have special product identification requirements. Like the APIS approval, the PMA approval is also in the form of a letter, but also has a supplemental sheet documenting the approved part numbers to be manufactured (Figure 2.5).

4. *Technical Standard Order* (TSO) *approvals,* under FAR Part 21 Subpart O, are issued to qualified manufacturers as a design and production approval for products that have been found to meet the requirements of a TSO. TSOs are FAA-established design parameters for materials, parts, processes, and appliances that are used on civil aircraft. After a manufacturer has developed its own design that complies to the TSO specification, and its quality control system conforms to the requirements of the subpart, it may apply for TSO certification. Like the special product identification requirements for the PMA manufacturers, TSO manufacturers also must apply special identification to their products. Certification of TSO manufacturers also is issued in letter form.

The United States of America
Department of Transportation

Federal Aviation Administration

Production Certificate

Number 6CE

This certificate, issued to
Aviation Company X, Inc.

whose business address is
1234 W. Main Street
Wichita, Kansas, 67213

and whose manufacturing facilities are located at
4321 South Street
Derby, Kansas, 67777

authorizes the production, at the facilities listed above, of reasonable duplicates of airplanes *which are manufactured in conformity with authenticated data, including drawings, for which Type Certificates specified in the pertinent and currently effective Production Limitation Record were issued. The facilities, methods, and procedures of this manufacturer were demonstrated as being adequate for the production of such duplicates on date of* 05 August, 1994

Duration: *This certificate shall continue in effect indefinitely, provided, the manufacturer continuously complies with the requirements for original issuance of certificate, or until the certificate is canceled, suspended, or revoked.*

Date issued:
05 August, 1994

By direction of the Administrator
I. M. Aviation
Chief, Engineering and Manufacturing Division

This Certificate is not Transferable, AND ANY MAJOR CHANGE IN THE BASIC FACILITIES, OR IN THE LOCATION THEREOF, SHALL BE IMMEDIATELY REPORTED TO THE APPROPRIATE REGIONAL OFFICE OF THE FEDERAL AVIATION ADMINISTRATION.

Any alteration of this certificate is punishable by a fine of not exceeding $1,000, or imprisonment not exceeding 3 years or both
FAA FORM 8120-4 (12-69) SUPERSEDES FAA FORM 333

FIGURE 2.4.   *Sample FAA form 8120-4, Production Certificate.*

Production Approval Listing—Supplement No. 1

Parts Manufacturer Approval No. PA920001CE

Federal Aviation Administration—Parts Manufacturer Approval

Aviation Company X, Inc.
1234 W. Main St.
Wichita, Kansas 67213
316-729-7948

Nomenclature and part no.	Approved replacement for	FAA design approval means	Installation eligibility
Mechanism 1234567-7 Rev. D	Mechanism 596432-1	Identicality by licensing agreement with Engineering Structures, dated 12/07/92, approval no. AA1234XX, dwg. no. 1234567-7, rev. D, dated 07 Aug. 1992 or later FAA-approved drawing.	Boeing 757-200
Mechanism 1234567-8 Rev. D	Mechanism 596433-1	Identicality by licensing agreement with Engineering Structures, dated 12/07/92, approval no. AA1234XX, dwg. no. 1234567-8, rev. B, dated 24 Sept. 1992 or later FAA-approved drawing.	Boeing 757-200

----------------------------End of listing----------------------------

Note: The procedures that have been accepted by the type certificate holder and their cognizant FAA Aircraft Certification Office, for minor changes to original parts used on type certification products, are also acceptable for incorporating the same minor changes on identical FAA-PMA replacement parts. The FAA PMA holder shall be able to show traceability relating to the TC or STC holder on all minor changes incorporated by this procedure. When these procedures are no longer applicable because of completion of the production contract or termination of the licensing agreement or equivalent, all subsequent design changes to the PMA parts would require FAA approval by the ACO who has jurisdiction of the PMA holder.

I. M. Aviation
Manager, Small Airplane Directorate

FIGURE 2.5. *Sample PMA supplement sheet.*

The United States of America

Department of Transportation
Federal Aviation Administration

Production Limitation Record

The holder of
Production Certificate No. 6CE

may receive the benefits incidental to the
possession of such certificate with respect to

AIRCRAFT, AIRCRAFT PROPELLERS, OR AIRCRAFT ENGINES,
AS APPLICABLE

manufactured in accordance with the data forming the
basis for the following Type Certificate(s) No.

TYPE CERTIFICATE	MODEL	DATE PRODUCTION AUTHORIZED
A 920CE	ABC 2047R	August 05, 1994
A 9CE	ABC 258D	August 05, 1994
STC 492CE	Drawing List HC-B2YK-6	August 05, 1994

(Note: Any number or columns may be used provided the material is
neat and legible. Additional PLR's may be used as necessary
and numbered "1 of 2", "2 of 2", as appropriate to the number of pages required.)

LIMITATIONS:

(If any, note as required.)

By Direction of the Administrator

August 05, 1994   I. M. Aviation

Date of issuance   Chief, Engineering and
                                   Manufacturing Branch
FAA FORM 8120—3 (7-67)

FIGURE 2.6.   *Sample FAA Form 8120-3, Production Limitation Record.*

Each of the FAA manufacturing approvals is only extended to those part numbers identified on the applicable documents for that certification. Figure 2.6 displays FAA Form 8120-3, Production Limitation Record. This form documents the approved part numbers a Production Certificate holder may deliver. However, as new designs are created, these production approvals may be amended to cover new or changed part numbers.

There are also quality control requirements for companies who manufacture parts for alterations of aircraft. These approvals are called *designated alteration stations* (DAS) and are issued under FAR Part 21 Subpart M (Figure 2.7). Air carriers are the most common recipient of such approvals; however, DAS approval also may be obtained by domestic repair stations, commercial operators, and manufacturers of FAA-approved products. When approved, the holder may issue Supplemental Type Certificates, issue experimental certificates, and amend standard airworthiness certificates. As this approval is always in addition to another FAA-approved system, the majority of the quality requirements come from that initial FAA-approved system. However, when under audit, internal or extrinsic, the DAS should be audited separately from the core facility.

Repair stations are certified under FAR Part 145 (Figure 2.8) and have special quality requirements, different from the other approvals. Though repair stations are not in reality manufacturers, they are certified to perform the servicing, modification, and repair on the aircraft or components produced under a manufacturing approval. Unless specifically stated, when reference is made to manufacturers in this book, repair stations are also included. As FAA manufacturing approvals are based on approved part numbers, repair station approvals are based on specific ratings. There are six different ratings, and each of these have subratings. So the actual rating approval can be very specific. For example, a class 2 airframe rating authorizes the holder only to perform repairs and maintenance on the composite construction of large aircraft, or a class 3 instrument rating allows repair and maintenance only on gyroscopic products. It is important for quality system auditors to understand the authorizations of each rating prior to the performance of the audit.

The FAA requires that manufacturers establish a total quality control system that provides control over all phases of manufacture, including the manufacture of all supplier-furnished articles. The control exercised by the manufacturer over articles furnished to the manufacturer by a supplier that holds its own FAA approval (PC, APIS, PMA, TSO) for the article may be limited to the approval of the supplier's material review systems and design changes, and to the manufacturer's usual incoming quality control procedures employed after articles are received from an outside source.

As in quality system evaluations by the third-party quality system registrar, each of these manufacturing approvals is granted by the FAA

UNITED STATES OF AMERICA
DEPARTMENT OF TRANSPORTATION
FEDERAL AVIATION ADMINISTRATION

Air Agency Certificate

Number CBA456L

This certificate is issued to
Aviation Company X, Inc.

whose business address is
1234 W. Main Street
Wichita, Kansas, 67213

upon finding that its organization complies in all respects with the requirements of the Federal Aviation Regulations relating to the establishment of an Air Agency; and is empowered to operate an approved Designated Alteration Station

with the following ratings:
Airframe

This certificate, unless canceled, suspended, or revoked, shall continue in effect Indefinitely.

By direction of the Administrator

Date issued:
05 August 1994

I.M. Aviation
Engineering Cheif

This Certificate is not Transferable, AND ANY MAJOR CHANGE IN THE BASIC FACILITIES, OR IN THE LOCATION THEREOF, SHALL BE IMMEDIATELY REPORTED TO THE APPROPRIATE REGIONAL OFFICE OF THE FEDERAL AVIATION ADMINISTRATION

Any alteration of this certificate is punishable by a fine of not exceeding $1,000, or imprisonment not exceeding 3 years, or both

FAA Form 8000-4 (1–67)   SUPERSEDES FAA FORM 390.

FIGURE 2.7.   *Sample FAA Form 8000-4, displayed as a designated alteration station approval.*

UNITED STATES OF AMERICA
DEPARTMENT OF TRANSPORTATION
FEDERAL AVIATION ADMINISTRATION

Air Agency Certificate

Number AB1A345J

This certificate is issued to
AVIATION COMPANY X, INC.

whose business address is
1234 W. Main Street
Wichita, Kansas, 67213

upon finding that its organization complies in all respects with the requirements of the Federal Aviation Regulations relating to the establishment of an Air Agency, and is empowered to operate an approved REPAIR STATION

with the following ratings:

SPECIALIZED SERVICE
INSTRUMENT CLASS 1, 2, and 4.

This certificate, unless canceled, suspended, or revoked, shall continue in effect INDEFINITELY

By direction of the Administrator

Date issued :

05 August, 1994   I.M. Aviation

This Certificate is not Transferable, AND ANY MAJOR CHANGE IN THE BASIC FACILITIES, OR IN THE LOCATION THEREOF, SHALL BE IMMEDIATELY REPORTED TO THE APPROPRIATE REGIONAL OFFICE OF THE FEDERAL AVIATION ADMINISTRATION

Any alteration of this certificate is punishable by a fine of not exceeding $1,000, or imprisonment not exceeding 3 years, or both

FAA Form 8000-4 (1-67)   SUPERSEDES FAA FORM 390.

FIGURE 2.8.   *FAA Form 8000-4, displayed as a repair station approval.*

after an analysis of the quality control system has been performed. The FAA has released a series of documents that promote the development of complete quality assurance systems in aviation manufacturing facilities. These documents define a conforming quality assurance system in excess of the FARs and are designed to replace the earlier FAA quality evaluation programs such as the Quality Assurance Systems Analysis Review (QASAR). The draft advisory circular (AC) 21-ACSEP was the first in a series of documents released to provide information and guidance on the Aircraft Certification System Evaluation Program (ACSEP). This draft AC was released for coordination and comment and described the methodology the FAA intended to use in the evaluation of potential manufacturers and for recurring evaluations of existing manufacturers. This AC was detailed in its requirements for the evaluation of manufacturing facilities and included the actual evaluation audit plan.

In August 1994, AC 21-39 was released to replace AC 21-ACSEP. AC 21-39 retained much of the draft's wording but no longer contained the evaluation audit plan. This audit plan was revised and released in FAA Order 8100.7. The criteria of the ACSEP audit are far in excess of the FAR requirements and it should be remembered that the ACs are not law and FAA orders are only intended for internal use to the FAA. However, the FAA's objective is to standardize the evaluation criteria for aviation manufacturers. The standardized evaluation criteria of ACSEP are "questions developed for each evaluation subsystem the FAR ACSEP evaluation teams use to plan and document the evaluation. The part 21, 43, and 145 requirements, appropriate FAA AC's and directives, international standards (ISO 9000) and specifications, and established industry practices (TQM, SPC) are the basis for these questions."[4]

Though the implementation of the ACSEP criteria is not mandatory, they may eventually find their way into required criteria. Under the objectives of AC 21-39 it states that the "survey of the application by PAHs [manufacturers] of evaluation subsystem functions [is] not required by applicable regulations or FAA-approved data to identify national trends that may require development of new or revised FAA regulations, policy, and guidance."[5] So if the FAA finds that the ACSEP criteria are in the best interest of public safety they may eventually become law.

All manufacturing approvals are handled through the individual manufacturing inspection district offices (MIDO) that have geographical jurisdiction. The DAS is handled through the FAA engineering office (ACO), and the repair station is handled through the flight standards district office (FSDO). Each of the approvals has its own special form letter or form that must be submitted to the FAA by the requesting organization, stating the request for approval, under the applicable approval requirements. Figure 2.9 displays an example of a PMA request, and Figure 2.10

Aviation Company X, Inc. _____ **ACXI**
1234 W. Main Street
Wichita, Kansas 67213
316-729-7948

3 January 1995

Department of Transportation
Federal Aviation Administration, Central Region
Small Airplane Directorate
Attn: ACE 108, Mr. P. I. Inspector
601 East 12th Street
Kansas City, Missouri 64106

Dear Mr. Inspector:

As instructed by the Wichita FAA office, I am forwarding my request for PMA authority
to you. We are requesting FAA-PMA approval for the production of the Boeing 757-
200 Galleys, for which Aviation Company X, Inc. (ACXI) has obtained design approval
through a licensing agreement with Engineering Structures, Inc. (ESI). ESI has instructed
ACXI to perform all MRB and design control issues, in accordance with the established
procedures of the ASXI quality assurance manual. The applicable part numbers are
as follows:

1234567-7   Rev. D
1234567-8   Rev. B
1234567-9   Rev. G

Design approval number AA1234XX

I certify that Aviation Company X, Inc. has established at 1234 W. Main Street, Wichita,
Kansas 67213, a fabrication inspection system that complies with and as required by
FAR 21.303(h) for this production activity. A latest revision copy of the quality assurance
manual, document no. 1000, has been previously supplied to the Wichita FAA office,
as well as a complete set of quality assurance procedures. If you have any questions
or comments, please feel free to contact us at any time.

With best regards,

J. P. Flyer
Director, Quality Assurance

Ref. L95-005

FIGURE 2.9. *Sample application letter for PMA.*

displays FAA Form 8110-12, application for Production Certificate approval. This letter or form initiates the entire cycle and opens an FAA file.
An FAA principal inspector (PI) will be assigned to the project. Though the
FAA may request that a copy of the quality assurance manual and affili-
ated procedures be supplied with the application letter or form, it is recommended to send the quality assurance manual and procedures only
after a PI has been assigned. Additionally, it is recommended that telephone discussions and face-to-face inquiries be documented in letter
form. This will provide an activity trail that can be followed in case the PI
is transferred to another project, which may happen from time to time.

No certificate may be issued unless a completed application
form has been received (14 C.F.R. 21)

U.S. DEPARTMENT OF TRANSPORTATION FEDERAL AVIATION ADMINISTRATION APPLICATION FOR TYPE CERTIFICATE, PRODUCTION CERTIFICATE, OR SUPPLEMENTAL TYPE CERTIFICATE		*FORM APPROVED* O.M.B. No. 04-R0078

1. Name and address of applicant Aviation Company X, Inc. 1234 W. Main Street Wichita, Kansas, 67213	2. Application made for – ☐ Type Certificate ☒ Production Certificate ☐ Supplemental Type Certificate	3. Product involved ☒ Aircraft ☐ Engine ☐ Propeller

4. TYPE CERTIFICATE *(Complete item 4a below)*

a. Model designation(s) *(All models listed are to be completely described in the required technical data, including drawings representing the design, material, specifications, construction, and performance of the aircraft, aircraft engine, propeller which is the subject of this application.)*

5. PRODUCTION CERTIFICATE *(Complete items 5a–c below. Submit with this form, in manual form, one copy of quality control data or changes thereto covering new products, as required by applicable FAR.)*

a. Factory address *(If different from 1 above)* 4321 South Street Derby, Kansas, 67777	b. Application is for – ☒ New Production Certificate ☐ Additions to Production Certificate *(Give P.C. No.)*	P.C. No.
c. Applicant is holder of or a licensee under a Type Certificate or a Supplemental Type Certificate *(Attach evidence of licensing agreement and give certificate number)* ⟶		T.C./~~XXXX~~ No. A 920CE

6. SUPPLEMENTAL TYPE CERTIFICATE *(Complete items 6a–d below)*

a. Make and model designation of product to be modified

b. Description of modification

c. Will data be available for sale or release to other persons? ☐ YES ☒ NO	d. Will parts be manufactured for sale? *(Ref. FAR 21.303)* ☒ YES ☐ NO

7. CERTIFICATION – I certify that the above statements are true.

Signature of certifying official J.P. Flyer	Title Director Quality Assurance	Date 15 July 1994

FAA Form 8110-12 (3-80) SUPERSEDES PREVIOUS EDITION

FIGURE 2.10. *Sample FAA Form 8110-12, Application for Production Certificate.*

When the quality assurance manual is being reviewed, the FAA will be ensuring that all of the quality elements required by the individual manufacturing approval regulations are addressed. The quality assurance manual should be arranged in manual form, with a suitable index, and should cover each portion of the quality control requirements, of the applicable subpart, in English. This is also an international quality standard requirement. When references are made to other company documents, or data are utilized, the manual should briefly summarize the procedure, method, or system that is referenced. Additionally, any such referenced material becomes part of the data approved by the FAA. The individual elements of the FAA requirements for an approved quality control system are discussed in detail within the appropriate chapters of this book. However, all *changes* to an approved quality system must be approved by the FAA prior to their implementation. The quality system registrar may request the same.

After a review of the quality assurance manual and procedures is complete and satisfactory, the PI will schedule a conformance evaluation of the facility. This will usually be twofold—quality system and product. Typically, the quality system audit is performed prior to any product surveillance; however, there may be exceptions. Like an ANSI/ASQC Q9000 quality system audit, the FAA evaluation is performed in accordance with the applicable standards, in this case the FARs. The current method of evaluation is through the use of the ACSEP criteria. However, for some smaller manufacturers a simpler audit plan may be developed to suit their limited operations.

The controls the FAA places on a particular company depend on the product and size of that company. The FAA categorizes parts and assemblies into two types—priority and nonpriority. As described in FAA Order 8100.7, priority parts and assemblies are those that "if it were to fail, could reasonably be expected to cause an unsafe condition in an aircraft, engine, or propeller."[6] Nonpriority parts are those that are not priority parts.

The FAA also categorizes parts and assemblies into three groups.

Group I: Production Certificate and associate facilities. Approved Production Inspection System, and their satellite MMFs [manufacturer's maintenance facilities].

Group II: Parts Manufacturer Approval [priority parts] and associated facilities, Technical Standard Order Authorization and associate facilities, and their associated MMFs.

Group III: Parts Manufacturing Approval [nonpriority parts] and associated facilities, and their satellite MMFs. [15, para. (25)(a)]

Group I and group II manufacturers will have their facilities evaluated by the FAA every 24 months and group III is evaluated every 48 months. The actual time spent by the FAA at the manufacturer's facility performing the evaluation is dependent upon "the quality and engineering procedures and processes required to be in place, the number of applicable evaluation subsystems [elements], the size and physical layout of the facility to be evaluated [single or multiple locations], and product complexity" [15, para. (25)(b)]. However, the rule of thumb the FAA uses for scheduling, as outlined in FAA Order 8100.7 is

> *Small facility with less than 100 total full-time persons: 1 to 5 days on site.*
>
> *Medium facility with 100 to 400 total full-time persons: 3 to 5 days on site.*
>
> *Large facility with 400 to 2000 total full-time persons: 5 to 10 days on site.*
>
> *Very large facility with over 2000 full-time persons: 7 to 15 days on site. [15, para. (25)(b)]*

The size of the FAA audit team will be dependent on the size and complexity of the facility and product. The team will be of sufficient size to achieve confidence that compliance to the applicable FARs and FAA-approved data will be fully evaluated. Again, FAA Order 8100.7 offers a rule of thumb.

> *Small facilities: Team leader and 2 to 3 evaluators.*
>
> *Medium facilities: Team leader and 3 to 5 evaluators.*
>
> *Large facilities: Team leader and 5 to 10 evaluators.*
>
> *Very large facilities: Team leader and up to 10 evaluators. [20, para. (26)(c)(2)]*

FAA Order 8110.7 also provides guidelines on extending such audit intervals. The FAA auditor is required to consider lengthening or shortening the evaluation frequency after each completed ACSEP evaluation. ACSEP findings, prior history, and unsatisfactory progress of any required corrective actions are to be part of this consideration.

The FAA may consider lengthening the evaluation frequency if a facility has

> *(a) A continuing trend of small numbers of findings and prompt, effective corrective action. Trends may be identified through a sequence of several evaluations at a specific facility, which may occur as a combination of PI, district, and ACSEP evaluations.*
>
> *(b) An internal audit program acceptable to the FAA. For the purposes of lengthening frequency, an acceptable internal audit program should, as a minimum, evaluate all the major systems identified in paragraph 53 of FAA Order 8100.7 and be documented. A facility's internal audit program should ensure:*

> *(1) Facility audit personnel are trained in auditing concepts, principles, and techniques. In addition, audit personnel should not have direct responsibilities in the areas audited.*
>
> *(2) Audits are scheduled and accomplished on a periodic basis.*
>
> *(3) Audit results are documented and indicate when follow-up action should occur. The manager responsible for the area audited, and corporate management, should review audit results.*
>
> *(4) Corrective actions are verified for satisfactory completion.*
>
> *(5) Internal audit reports are made available for FAA review on-site at the facility. [17, para. (25)(f)(1)]*

For group I and II facilities the interval lengthening may not be more than six months. Group III manufacturers may not have their evaluation intervals lengthened more than one year.

The FAA may consider shortening the evaluation frequency when the following conditions exist at a facility.

> *(a) An ACSEP evaluation identifies a large number of findings, especially if many are safety-related.*
>
> *(b) There is a continuing trend of large numbers of findings. Trends may be identified through a sequence of several evaluations at a specific facility, which may be a combination of PI, district, and ACSEP evaluations.*
>
> *(c) Corrective action is untimely or ineffective. [18, para. (25)(f)(3)]*

The evaluation frequency may be shortened to the extent necessary to obtain confidence that the facility is complying with the applicable FAR(s).

Like the international quality standards, the ACSEP evaluations also have major system elements for evaluation as well as subsystems. Paragraph 53 of FAA Order 8100.7 provides a description of these major systems (major elements) and subsystems (subelements).

> *(a) The major systems are those most likely to be found at the majority of PAH, associate facility, and priority part supplier facilities and that have the greatest potential to impact the integrity of the FAA-approved design and product quality. The 6 major systems are:*
>
> *(1) **Management**—The system responsible to establish policy for and to control engineering, manufacturing, quality, and service/product support activities utilized to obtain and maintain control of FAA-approved design in the completed product.*

*(2) **Engineering**—The system responsible to establish proce-dures for and to control continued integrity of the FAA-approved design data subsequent to initial FAA approval.*

*(3) **Manufacturing**—The system responsible to establish pro-cedures for and to control manufacture of products, and parts thereof, to FAA-approved design.*

*(4) **Quality**—The system responsible to establish procedures for and to verify:*

> *(a) Product and part conformity to FAA-approved design and condition for safe operation.*
>
> *(b) Manufacturer's Maintenance Facility functions.*

*(5) **Service/Product Support**—The system responsible to es-tablish procedures for and control activities related to main-tenance of FAA-approved design after the completed product is delivered.*

*(6) **Communication with FAA**—The system responsible to es-tablish procedures for and control activities requiring FAA notification. [15, para. (53)]*

In addition to the six major systems there are also 17 subsystems in an ACSEP evaluation. These subsystem evaluations audit the organiza-tion's control over

- Organization and responsibility
- Design data control
- Software quality assurance
- Manufacturing processes
- Special manufacturing processes
- Statistical quality control (SQC), also known as statistical process control (SPC)
- Tool and gauge
- Testing
- Nondestructive inspection
- Supplier control
- Nonconforming material
- Material handling/storage
- Airworthiness determination
- FAR reporting requirements
- Internal audit

- Global production
- Manufacturer's maintenance facility (MMF) [1, Appendix 6].

SUMMARY

In summary, the quality assurance requirements of the international quality system standards and the quality control requirements of the federal aviation regulations are complementary. Both require the establishment of a quality control system that ensures the quality of the product. Additionally, the FARs also include the requirements for a system that will assure the safe operation of the approved product. These systems shall be documented in a quality assurance manual, written in English, and extrinsic audits will be performed to substantiate conformance. However, the requirements of the international quality standards also place emphasis on prevention of nonconformances though the implementation of internal audits, whereas internal audits are only a desired element of the FAA quality system and are found in AC 21-39 and FAA Order 8100.7. Further reading of this book will display the comparisons of the international quality standards to the various FAA quality system requirements and will provide examples of methods of compliance. It must be stressed that the examples displayed in this book are not the only method of compliance, but are only examples of proven methods.

NOTES

1. On 2 March 1994 the RAB released a letter to all RAB-certified auditors and applicants, registrars, and training course providers notifying them of the recent agreements of the certification bodies.

2. ANSI/ASQC Q9001-1994. *Quality Systems—Model for Quality Assurance in Design, Development, Production, Installation, and Servicing* (Milwaukee, Wis.: American Society for Quality Control, 1994), 2, para. 4.2.2, Quality System Procedures.

3. Ibid., 2–3, para. 4.2.3, Quality Planning.

4. DOT/FAA, Advisory Circular 21-39, *The Aircraft Certification Systems Evaluation Program* (Washington, D.C.: DOT/FAA, 31 August 1994), 2, para. (4)(f), Standardized Evaluation Criteria.

5. Ibid., para. (5)(c), Objective of ACSEP.

6. DOT/FAA, Federal Aviation Order 8100.7, *Aircraft Certification Systems Evaluation Program* (Washington D.C.: DOT/FAA, 30 March 1994), 3, para. (4)(m).

Chapter 3

MANAGEMENT RESPONSIBILITY

Experience has shown that most quality system failures can be directly attributable to a lack of management commitment. This lack of commitment can come in various forms, such as management not understanding the requirements, not delegating authority and responsibility, being only bottom-line oriented, overriding quality inspection, not providing funds for preventive measures, and not supporting training. This type of management is short-term results oriented. The lack of commitment toward the prevention of discrepancies in products and processes, as well as employee development, will strongly affect the long-term viability of such an organization.

On the other hand, many managers are becoming ever more aware of the consequences of not having an effective quality assurance system. With the implementation of team building and total quality management (TQM), organizations are becoming more focused on objectives and are finding that through continued process improvement they can do more with less. In today's global economy, it is no longer "What is the competition on the other side of town doing?" Now it is "What is the competition on the other side of the world doing?" Aviation is not immune to the global influences of competition. Many U.S. aviation manufacturers have already lost much of their workload to countries outside of the United States because of lower labor and overhead expenses. If American companies cannot get a good firm grasp on the costs, schedules, and quality of their products and services, the trend to manufacture where it is cheaper will continue.

All three levels of the international quality standards have recognized the need for management commitment and responsibility for ensuring the implementation of an effective quality assurance system. The three levels have the responsibilities of management outlined into five subsections:

- Quality policy
- Responsibility and authority
- Resources

- Management representative
- Management review

The FAA also has recognized the importance of management commitment, though to a lesser degree. Within the various sections of the FARs, the FAA has established the requirements for a quality control system, but not a quality assurance system. This is because the FAA is not primarily concerned with the productivity of an organization, but rather with the conformance of the product. The quality control system will only ensure product conformance and the quality assurance system will place emphasis on prevention of nonconformance and the improvement of processes. Each of the regulations for manufacturing approvals has similar requirements for the responsibility of management. FAR section 21.165, under the responsibilities of a Production Certificate holder, states that "the holder of a Production Certificate shall maintain the quality control system in conformity with the data and procedures approved for the Production Certificate."[1] Because management is the holder of the approval, it is ultimately responsible for the conformance of the quality control system. However, the FARs will not state the methodology for management to use for such control, whereas the international quality standards provide solid direction. As stated in the previous chapter, ACSEP does provide evaluation criteria that go beyond the requirements of the FARs, including the need for management involvement.

As will be common throughout this book with the various quality elements, the five subsections of management responsibility will be discussed individually and compared to the FAA requirements. This should provide a clear understanding of the international quality standards and how the individual elements can be implemented in conformance with the requirements of a commercial aviation manufacturer.

QUALITY POLICY

The three international quality standards state that "the supplier's management with executive responsibility shall define and document its policy for quality, including objectives for quality and its commitment to quality. The quality policy shall be relevant to the supplier's organizational goals and the expectations and needs of its customers." They also state that "the supplier shall ensure that this policy is understood, implemented, and maintained at all levels of the organization."[2]

These policies and objectives are to be outlined in a policy statement, typically a stand-alone document. The document should be an honest statement of the management's commitment, and should be implementable throughout the organization. To enhance the possibility of adherence of the documented policies and objectives, the document should be jointly signed by the highest level executive and the head of quality assurance. This will give the document the backing it needs to be enforced.

It is very important that this document does not just sit in the front office; it must be distributed throughout the entire organization. Ideally, this quality policy document would be the first page of the corporate manual, training manuals, quality manuals, and departmental procedure manuals. Additionally, new employees should be introduced to the management's commitment during their indoctrination training. As changes to the document occur, these too should be distributed throughout the organization, so that all employees are aware of the changes to the management's philosophy and commitment. This change distribution process would fall under the requirements of document control and are further discussed in chapter 6.

Though the FAA does not make any mention of the creation of a quality policy document in the FARs, it is a part of the ACSEP evaluation criteria.[3] The author has found that during FAA evaluations, if such a policy document is published, it is recognized and appreciated by the FAA auditor. When developing such a policy, be careful not to overcommit. Quality system auditors, both of the FAA and the registrar, will ensure, through audit, that the organization does practice what it preaches.

Though not yet discussed, quality assurance should place this element on a recurring internal audit schedule (reference chapter 18). Audit characteristics, such as the presence of the document, distribution of the document, and understanding of the document, can be checked. Additionally, the quality policy document should be treated as a quality record. This is because if changes have occurred in the policies of management, the practices under one policy may not be appropriate under another. Maintaining the previous revisions of the policy statement (even signature changes) on file will provide a traceable audit trail when needed.

RESPONSIBILITY AND AUTHORITY

Responsibility and authority and interrelation of personnel and departments who manage, perform, and verify work affecting quality must be clearly defined, documented, and understood, to ensure processes and operations are performed as specified. The FAA makes exacting requirements for the responsibility and authority of personnel who directly affect quality, as do the international quality standards.

The FAA holds management primarily responsible for all actions of the manufacturer, but provides direction for delegation of that responsibility. In FAR section 21.143, under the quality control data requirements for a prime manufacturer authorized under a Production Certificate, the requirement for documenting responsibility and authority is stated.

> *Each applicant [manufacturer] must submit, for approval, . . . a statement describing assigned responsibilities and delegated authority of the quality control organization, together with a chart indicating the functional relationship of the quality control organization to management and to other organizational components, and indicating the chain of authority and responsibility within the quality control organization.[4]*

In review of this requirement, the only requirement for the manufacturer is to document the authority and responsibility of the quality control organization. This requirement also implies that the quality control organization should be autonymous.

Through further clarification in Advisory Circular 21-1B, the FAA's requirement for quality assurance to have an unobstructed flow to the top of the organizational management is made clear. Additionally, the quality control organization shall be delegated the responsibility and authority for ensuring the conformity of the product. Advisory Circular 21-1B states,

> *The manufacturer's organizational structure would ensure that any decisions with regard to workmanship, quality, conformity, safety, materials review, and corrective action are not unduly influenced by other considerations. This can be achieved by having the quality control organization report directly to top management.[5]*

The international quality standards have a similar requirement for the delegation of responsibility and authority. ANSI/ASQC Q9003 has a lesser degree of direction for this delegation. It requires manufacturers to define the responsibility, authority, and interrelation of all personnel who manage, perform, and verify final inspections and/or tests. It also requires that these personnel are delegated the organizational freedom and authority to ensure this final conformance. As will be discussed in later chapters, the FAA requires that in-process inspection is performed, making ANSI/ASQC Q9003 not stringent enough for aviation applications.

ANSI/ASQC Q9001 and ANSI/ASQC Q9002 are identical in their requirements for delegation of authority and responsibility. They require manufacturers to define and document the responsibility, authority, and interrelation of all personnel who manage, perform, and verify work affecting quality. These two standards place special emphasis for this delegation for personnel who need the organizational freedom and authority to "initiate action to prevent the occurrence of any nonconformities relating to product, process, and quality system; identify and record any problems relating to the product, process, and quality system; initiate, recommend, or provide solutions through designated channels; verify the implementation of solutions; and control further processing, delivery, or installation of nonconforming product until the deficiency or unsatisfactory condition has been corrected."[6] All of these are basic quality assurance functions.

In comparison of the international quality standards with the requirements of the FAA, the requirement for documenting the authority and responsibility of the quality assurance organization is clear. Furthermore, it is clear that the quality assurance organization shall have a direct reporting structure to the top management. The international quality standards require that the delegation of authority and responsibility be documented and that this process flows down to all personnel that manage, perform, and verify work affecting quality. This includes engineering, manufacturing, procurement, and any other organizational discipline whose actions affect the quality system. In essence, TQM is being implied.

RESOURCES

The resources subsection within the international quality standards is directed to the verification of processes, operations, tests, designs, and personnel ability. This is the core inspection and audit requirement, placing the responsibility upon management for the effective implementation of controls.

All three of the international quality standards are identical in their basic requirements. "The supplier shall identify resource requirements and provide adequate resources, including assignment of trained personnel, for management, performance of work, and for verification activities, including internal quality audits."[7]

The various FAR sections place considerable emphasis on verification of processes and operations that affect product quality, as well as the training of personnel that perform these verifications or those operations that directly affect the quality of the product. FAR section 21.143 requires Production Certificate manufacturers to provide a description of the methods used for production inspection of individual parts and complete assemblies; inspection procedures for raw materials and procured parts and components; performing in-process inspections; identification and control of special processes; performance of final tests; and the establishment of a materials review board. Using other phraseology, but providing the same requirements, PMA manufacturers have these requirements outlined in FAR section 21.303 (h), designated alteration stations are referred back to their base approval requirements, and TSO manufacturers are referred back, in FAR section 21.605 (a)(3), to the requirements for a quality system for a Production Certificate holder. Repair stations have their requirements for verification outlined in FAR Part 145, along with other special requirements and stringent personnel qualifications. The ACSEP evaluation criteria also addresses the control of processes.[8]

The training of personnel is discussed within each of the FAA requirements for manufacturing approvals; but these discussions are directed primarily at inspection personnel and, in the case of design organizations, engineers. The personnel training requirements of the repair station are the most exacting, in some cases requiring FAA certifications. However, with regard to the international quality standards, all personnel that directly affect quality shall be trained. This includes personnel in such functions as purchasing, human relations, sales, finance, contracts, engineering, and manufacturing.

Verification of resources also is discussed in the individual sections of the FARs. The FAA requires manufacturers to provide the resources needed to verify the conformity of a product and to ensure safe operation. If a manufacturer states, within an approved test procedure, that a final test shall be performed with a certain piece of equipment, management must ensure that that equipment is provided to the test personnel. Otherwise, the manufacturer is not in compliance with the FAA-approved data.

The requirement for design verification (also an ANSI/ASQC Q9001 requirement) will be under the requirements for Type Certificate (TC), Supplemental Type Certificate (STC), or Technical Standard Order (TSO) approvals. Additionally, the requirements for a repair station to verify its repair designs are under FAR Part 145, and designated alteration stations have their requirements for modification design approval under FAR section 21.463. The verification of designs for repair stations and designated alteration stations are somewhat different than that of production manufacturers. Some repair stations and all designated alteration stations will have their designs verified by a delegated representative of the FAA who is called a *designated engineering representative* (DER), who, for repair stations may be and for designated alteration stations is, a member of the company's organization. This person will not only verify the design, he or she may also issue the final FAA approval for that design.

These are often referred to as *field approvals*. Production manufacturers under TC and STC approvals may or may not have a DER on staff. If not, the final design verification is performed by an FAA engineer or by an independent DER. All TSO designs have their final design verification performed by an FAA engineer. However, these are all final external verifications and not internal, as required by the international quality standards.

Other than in the ACSEP evaluation criteria,[9] the FAA makes no requirements upon manufacturers to perform internal audits. However, the author has found that the establishment of an internal auditing system will enhance the confidence that the FAA has in the manufacturer.

When coupling the international quality standards with the FARs, manufacturers will find that they are required to establish procedures that will ensure conformity verification of products, services, processes, and operations. Internal audits will verify the conformity of the testing and training activities. Each verification, whether that of product conformance or system compliance, shall be documented and the results shall be considered quality records. Additionally, the requirements for training are expanded under the international quality standards. Any individual who can even remotely affect quality shall be trained to ensure an ability to perform and maintain an understanding of the requirements, and shall have the necessary resources to perform his or her verifications.

MANAGEMENT REPRESENTATIVE

The appointment of a management representative should not be made without much consideration. This is the person who will be the organization's focal point with regard to implementation and maintenance of the systems to comply with the international quality standards.

> *The supplier's management with executive responsibility shall appoint a member of the supplier's own management who, irrespective of other responsibilities, shall have defined authority for:*
>
> > *(a) ensuring that a quality system is established, implemented, and maintained in accordance with [the international quality standard]; and*
> >
> > *(b) reporting on the performance of the quality system to the supplier's management for review and as a basis for improvement of the quality system.[10]*

The responsibility of the management representative may also include liaison with external parties on matters relating to the manufacturer's quality system. Such interfacing would be typical during the quality system registration process and could also be an everyday occurrence with the FAA. In interpretation of the international quality standards this does not necessarily have to be a quality assurance responsibility. This is because the international quality standards are written generically, to accommodate various commodities, not just aviation. However, because of FAR requirements, aviation manufacturers should delegate this position to the head of quality assurance. Otherwise, it may be perceived as management placing a link between the quality assurance organization and top management, which is not allowed under the FARs [reference FAR section 21.143 (a)(1)]. During the ISO 9000 quality system registration process, the management representative will be the liaison between the manufacturer and the registrar.

MANAGEMENT REVIEW

Each of the international quality standards has the identical requirement for the manufacturer's executive management to review the quality system. "The supplier's management with executive responsibility shall review the quality system at defined intervals sufficient to ensure its continuing suitability and effectiveness in satisfying the requirements of the [international quality standards] and the supplier's stated quality policy and objectives. Records of such reviews shall be maintained [as quality records]."[11] The FARs covering manufacturers have similar requirements placing the responsibility of system compliance upon management. As stated earlier, FAR section 21.165 requires PC holders to maintain the quality control system in conformity with the data and procedures approved for the PC approval. Each of the other manufacturing approvals has similar requirements for the compliance of the quality control system. However, none of the FAR sections require management to perform periodic reviews of the system, but periodic reviews are part of the ACSEP evaluation criteria.[12]

   As will be discussed later, the internal audit is a useful tool in assessing the conformity of a quality system. The results of these audits should be presented periodically to the executive management for its review. This should be presented by the management representative on at least a monthly schedule to ensure that problems are addressed quickly. Normally such reviews are incorporated into other topic meetings. The emphasis is on management's awareness of the system and the assurance of its involvement and commitment. During an audit, compliance with this requirement can be demonstrated only through the presentation of documentation. However the reviews are to be developed, they must be documented and performed at intervals that will ensure the effectiveness of the quality system.

The management review itself should be formalized in a procedure, identifying and controlling the structure and desired results of these reviews. This could be sufficiently addressed within the quality assurance manual; however, it would be more appropriately located in a standalone procedure, such as the corporate procedure. In defining the procedural requirements, there are a number of ways to structure such a review; however, the basics of the procedure should cover

- Frequency of the reviews
- Provisions for urgent reviews
- Method of notification to attendees
- Detailed characteristics of such a review
- Documentation of the results
- Implementation of any changes

The noted structure is self-explanatory; however, the individual characteristics of the actual review may require additional outlining. During the actual review, the results of the internal audits are presented to top management. In addition to the internal audits, management also should review the present procedures and policies for currency. This portion of the review may not be as frequent as the review of internal audit results, and may only occur when there have been substantial changes in regulation or technology. Such elements of change would include FAR changes, environmental legislation, safety issues, advances in material or process technology, market changes, and feedback from customers. However, at a minimum, such a currency review should be performed at least on an annual cycle.

The minutes of the review (record of discussion), including associated documents, shall be considered quality records and retained in appropriate file. Additionally, the quality assurance group should include the performance of management review on the annual internal audit schedule (as will be seen in Figure 18.1). The internal audit should ensure that the process is performed as described in the applicable control procedure.

SUMMARY

Ultimately, management is responsible for the success of the quality system. If there is no commitment, there will be no implemented system. If there is no policy, there will be no guidance. Where there is no delegation, there is stagnation. A quality system does not just happen; it is planned, molded, and implemented, then checked and rechecked. The process is never ending.

Executive management must take the first step by pledging its commitment to quality in the form of a quality policy. This policy must be distributed throughout the organization and understood by all.

The responsibility and authority of the quality assurance organization must be clearly defined, with reporting to the executive management. Furthermore, the responsibility, authority, and interactions of the organization also should be clearly defined, and the reporting structure documented.

The resource requirements for each individual project shall be identified. This includes providing training of personnel in the new processes performed, as well as providing the necessary equipment for the performance of work and the verification of the activities. This would include the planning and performance of internal audits.

A management representative shall be selected who will be responsible for ensuring that the requirements of the international quality standards are implemented and effective. Because of FAR requirements, this representative should be the head of the quality assurance organization.

Management reviews shall be performed periodically by executive management to address the results of internal audits and review changes in regulation, technology, and the market. These reviews also will address the suitability and effectiveness of the quality system. The results of these reviews shall be considered quality records.

NOTES

1. DOT/FAA, Federal Aviation Regulation Section 21.165 (a), *Certification Procedures for Products and Parts—Responsibility of Holder* (Washington, D.C.: DOT/FAA, March 1991).

2. American Society for Quality Control, ANSI/ASQC Q9001-1994, *Quality Systems—Model for Quality Assurance in Design, Development, Production, Installation, and Servicing* (Milwaukee, Wis.: American Society for Quality Control, 1994), 1, para. 4.1.1., Quality Policy.

3. DOT/FAA, Federal Aviation Order 8100.7, *Aircraft Certification Systems Evaluation Program* (Washington D.C.: DOT/FAA, 30 March 1994), Appendix 6, Section 1.

4. Federal Aviation Regulation Section 21.143 (a)(1), *Certification Procedures for Products and Parts—Quality Control Data Requirements; Prime Manufacturer* (Washington, D.C.: DOT/FAA, March 1991).

5. FAA, Advisory Circular 21-1B , *Production Certificates* (Washington, D.C.: FAA, 10 May 1976), 3, para. (9)(b)(1), Quality Control Data Requirements.

6. ANSI/ASQC Q9001-1994, 1–2, para. 4.1.2.1., Responsibility and Authority.

7. Ibid., 1, para. 4.1.2.1., Resources.

8. Federal Aviation Order 8100.7, Appendix 6, Section 4.

9. Ibid., Appendix 6, Section 15.

10. ANSI/ASQC Q9001-1994, 2, para. 4.1.2.3., Management Representative.

11. Ibid., 1, para. 4.1.3., Management Review.

12. Federal Aviation Order 8100.7, Appendix 6, Section 15.

Chapter 4

CONTRACT REVIEW

A complete and thorough review of the contract and its associated documents must be performed at the earliest possible phase of customer interface. A concise review will highlight any grey areas and clear up any misunderstandings before they become damaging. Besides, it can be easy for a manufacturer to get itself into a contract that it really does not want to be in in the first place. The various FARs place no requirement for the performance of a contract review. However, companies that have been operating under the quality standards of the military standards, as well as those who have been exposed to ACSEP evaluations, have been aware of the requirement. Whether or not these companies have been in compliance can be determined only through audit.

Much like the military standards that have been predominant in the aviation industry for decades, the international quality standards require contract review. The international quality standards require manufacturers to establish and maintain procedures for contract review and for the coordination of the activities involved with contract review.

The basic description of the company's contract review system should be documented within the contents of the quality assurance manual. However, the step-by-step elaboration of the process should be contained within either a corporate/company policy or a program management procedure. Either way, it should have applicability throughout the organization and be signed by a member of management that can ensure its enforcement.

The international quality standards require that

before submission of a tender, or at the acceptance of a contract or order [statement of requirement], the tender, contract or order shall be reviewed by the supplier to ensure that:

(a) the requirements are adequately defined and documented; where no written statement of requirements is available for an order received by verbal means, the supplier shall ensure that the order requirements are agreed before their acceptance;

(b) any differences between the contract or accepted order requirement and those in tender are resolved; and

(c) the supplier has the capability to meet contract or other accepted order requirements [for ANSI/ASQC Q9003, this capability assessment shall be applied to finished product].[1]

Additionally, the records of contract reviews shall be maintained as quality records. These usually take the form of minutes of meetings (record of discussion).

The contract review process, once established, should be carried out regardless of the size or nature of the contract. Even the smallest of companies probably already accomplishes some form of contract review, perhaps without even realizing it as such. By reading the order and determining what actions, materials, equipment, and other resources are required to fulfill the order, a basic contract review is accomplished. However, in many cases these review cycles are not documented. Objective evidence can be established by the development and implementation of a simple checklist and, depending on the size of the company, a distribution cycle. However, in the larger organizations, the contract review process is much more detailed.

It is very important, before any work is initiated, that all concerned are aware of their responsibilities and that the appropriate tools and equipment are available. To determine this, a multifunctional review team should be established. These teams should comprise project managers, lead discipline engineers, manufacturing managers, and a quality assurance representative. Additionally, if representatives from other functions are required, because of contract content, such as product support, purchasing, or scheduling, they too should be part of the review team. These teams can be made up from contract to contract, depending on the organizational structure, or remain as a consistent, permanent team. The program manager should be the chairperson of such a team. Though quality assurance personnel should play a supporting and auditing role, they should also sign off on the contract or order prior to issuance.

Though the manufacturer has little control over the customer's schedule, it is important that the customer is part of the contract review cycle. It is recommended to have internal meetings prior to those with the customer. This will allow individual departments time to research topics and inventory capabilities and capacities. Performing internal reviews prior to meeting with the customer will present an informed appearance to the customer. Additionally, if a supplier is to play a participating role within the program, it may prove beneficial to include it in the review process.

Within the control procedure for the contract review process, the manufacturer must develop the controls to govern the amendment of contracts. The international quality standards state that "the supplier shall identify how an amendment to a contract is made and correctly transferred to the functions concerned within the supplier's organization."[2] This document change process is discussed in more detail in chapter 6, "Document and Data Control."

THE REVIEW PROCESS

As later discussed in "Design Control," chapter 5, a design development plan (DDP) matrix can be useful in developing a better understanding of the process. As will be seen in Figure 5.4, contract review (CR) is the first item to be given attention in developing a new design. To elaborate even more, a contract review matrix can be developed. Figure 4.1 is an example of such a CR matrix.[3] Though generic in nature, this example will fit most organizations and commodities with little or no modification.

As displayed, the matrix should be divided into 20 activities, but should also reflect the unique requirements of the individual organization. Each of the activities should be evaluated for the scope, and responsible departmental activities identified. Additionally, the assurance and auditing actions of quality assurance personnel can be identified to provide more transparency of the quality assurance process.

CONTRACT REVIEW

The first activity that should be addressed in the contract review process is the actual review of the contract. Within this activity the review team is created and the basics are accomplished.

WORK SCOPE

A work scope is a detailed review of the scope of work. It is very important that all concerned understand exactly what is required.

SPECIFICATIONS AND STANDARDS

It should be established that all applicable standards and specifications are available at their latest revision. This can include customer specifications, FAA requirements, Environmental Protection Agency (EPA) regulations, Occupational Safety and Health Administration (OSHA) standards, and U.S. Public Health standards, as well as various others. The distribution of updates also should be considered.

MATERIAL REQUIREMENTS

It should be ensured that the correct materials are available. This includes the appropriate sizes and quantities. Organizations that do business with

Activity	Performance scope	Responsible departments	Actions by QA*
1. Contract review	Review work scope. Review standards and specifications. Review material requirements. Review inspection and test requirements (FAI). Review manufacturing processes.	Management Program management Manufacturing Engineering Procurement Scheduling QC/QA*	Verify, through audit, that all open points are closed and that all uncertainties are clarified, as specified within the review process.
2. Document preparation and control	Ensure that all required documentation is available. Develop special procedures and plans, as required. Develop supplier documentation packages, as required. Determine certification documentation requirements. Identify turnover/shipping documentation requirements.	Program management Manufacturing Planning QC/QA	Audit the process to ensure that all documentation requirements are addressed.
3. Control of inspection, measuring, and test equipment	Review for additional equipment requirements. Ensure facilities are appropriate for testing. Review for any special calibration requirements. Evaluate special requirements for suppliers.	Program management Manufacturing QC/QA	Audit compliance to applicable procedures and verify that appropriate calibration cycles are utilized.

*QA, quality assurance; QC, quality control.

FIGURE 4.1. *Contract review matrix.*

4. Control of purchased items and equipment	Review capabilities of suppliers. Evaluate need for source inspection. Review supplier training requirements. Evaluate delivery schedule requirements.	Program management Procurement Manufacturing QC/QA	Audit compliance to applicable procedures and plans, and verify performance of supplier training, as required.
5. Incoming inspection	Identify special inspection requirements. Determine if additional inspection/test equipment is needed. Identify additional training needs. Develop receiving plans.	Program management QC/QA	Audit compliance to procedures and inspection/test plans. Audit performance of training, as required. Verify special equipment.
6. Purchaser-supplied items (Buyer-furnished equipment)	Identify special handling and storage requirements. Establish special identification and inventory control methods. Establish reporting requirements. Determine delivery schedule. Ensure drawings and material safety data sheets are supplied, as required.	Program management Manufacturing Engineering Scheduling QC/QA	Audit compliance to procedures and plans.
7. In-process inspection	Identify special in-process inspection/test requirements. Develop inspection planning, as required. Evaluate inspection/test equipment. Verify applicability to suppliers.	QC/QA	Audit compliance to procedures and plans. Verify flow-down of requirements to suppliers.

FIGURE 4.1.   (continued)

Activity	Performance scope	Responsible departments	Actions by QA
8. Final inspection	Identify special inspection/test requirements. Review for additional equipment requirements. Ensure facilities are appropriate for inspection/testing. Evaluate training requirements.	QC/QA	Audit compliance to procedures and plans. Verify performance of training, as required.
9. Sampling (Statistical process control)	Evaluate for applicability. Select appropriate sampling plans. Develop inspection planning. Determine approval requirements. (Evaluate processes; ensure personnel are qualified, and plans are developed. Flow requirements down to suppliers.)	Quality assurance (Program management Procurement Manufacturing Engineering QC/QA)	Audit compliance to applicable procedures and inspection plans. (Audit compliance to applicable procedures and plans. Verify requirements flow down to suppliers.)
10. Inspection and test status	Identify special customer identification requirements. Evaluate marking equipment needs. Determine FAA requirements (FAR Part 45). Determine planning requirements.	Program management Manufacturing Planning QC/QA	Audit compliance to applicable procedures and plans.
11. Identification and traceability	Review for special identification and traceability requirements. Verify marking equipment is available. Review training requirements. Determine FAA requirements.	Program management Manufacturing Engineering Planning QC/QA	Audit compliance to applicable procedures and plans.

FIGURE 4.1.   (continued)

12. Handling and storage	Verify special handling and storage equipment. Ensure facilities are appropriate for the requirements. Calculate additional protection material costs.	Program management Manufacturing QC/QA	Audit compliance to applicable procedures and plans.
13. Special processes	Identify special requirements. Identify certification requirements (second- and third-party). Evaluate internal capacity and capabilities. Evaluate supplier capacity and capabilities, as required. Review training requirements. Evaluate need for additional procedures and plans for inspection/testing.	Program management Manufacturing Planning Scheduling Engineering QC/QA	Audit compliance to applicable procedures and plans. Verify supplier compliance.
14. Preservation, packaging, and shipping	Identify special customer requirements. Evaluate route and mode of transport. Evaluate shipping schedules. Identify shipping material needs. Calculate related costs.	Program management Manufacturing Procurement Scheduling QC/QA	Audit compliance to applicable procedures and inspection plans.
15. Nonconforming materials	Establish appropriate reporting methods. Determine material review board authority. Evaluate need for additional procedures and plans.	Program management QC/QA	Audit compliance to applicable procedures and plans.

FIGURE 4.1.   (continued)

Activity	Performance scope	Responsible departments	Actions by QA
16. Records	Identify special record retention requirements. Establish special distribution methods.	Program management QA records Quality assurance	Audit compliance to applicable procedures and plans.
17. Training	Evaluate the need for training in an overall scope of the project. Include manufacturing processes, inspection and testing techniques, and supplier training. Budget and schedule training, as required.	Management All departmental heads	Audit compliance to applicable procedures and plans.
18. Audit and corrective action	Identify special requirements. Review documentation requirements. Establish reporting methods.	Program management Quality assurance	Audit compliance to applicable procedures and plans. Verify supplier compliance.
19. Product support	Evaluate for special requirements. Identify logistic requirements. Determine spares requirements. Evaluate FAA certification requirements (FAR Part 43 and 145).	Program management Manufacturing Product support Quality assurance	Audit compliance to applicable procedures and inspection plans.
20. Warranty	Identify special contract requirements. Establish reporting methods. Establish invoicing process. Identify logistics for replacement parts. Evaluate FAA certification requirements for replacement parts (possibly the need for an FAA-PMA). Evaluate drop-shipment requirements and possibilities.	Program management Product support Quality assurance	Audit compliance to applicable procedures and plans.

FIGURE 4.1.   (continued)

overseas customers may find that the customer may require that the product be made with a specific material that is not known in the United States. In such cases, look for material cross-reference documents. The same material in the United States may have a different identity elsewhere. For example 6061-T6 Aluminum Sheet is the identifier for an aluminum sheet alloy in the United States; the same alloy is known in Germany as 3214.T6 Aluplatte. One source for obtaining this information could be the customer, but it is recommended to use the customer as a last source. Asking questions that may seem elementary to the customer may affect the light in which the customer views the manufacturer. Finding this information on your own will reflect the company's ability and desire to research and be knowledgeable in the global market. The American National Standards Institute (ANSI) can be a source for such information.

INSPECTION AND TEST REQUIREMENTS

For aviation, inspection and test requirements is one of the more complex parts of the contract review cycle. This includes evaluation of the testing and inspection requirements of the product, as well as the certification process. The team must determine what method of certification will be pursued and how it will be accomplished. This will normally require the establishment of a separate certification team. This certification team should report directly with the head of engineering for design issues and to the head of quality for manufacturing certification issues, and should be represented in each of the contract and design review meetings.

As will be discussed in chapter 5, "Design Control," first article inspection also should be discussed and incorporated into schedules.

MANUFACTURING PROCESSES

As in the inspection and test requirements, if the processes required by a new project are the same as those performed in earlier projects, then there probably will be no problems, and no new procurement or changes will be needed. However, the process also should be considered for volume. If the additional project overloads the internal capacities, other options must be considered. The possibility of adding additional shifts or going to outside sources may be considered.

If there are new processes that have not yet been performed, consideration must be given whether to develop these processes in-house or to give them to an outside source. In either option, training should be considered. Personnel who perform the processes must be competent and inspection personnel must be qualified. Outside sources also must be qualified and approved for the processes they are performing.

ORGANIZATION

As for each characteristic of the CR matrix, the structure of each project organization should be documented in an organizational matrix. Consideration should be given to the qualifications of each member of the review team, and to the required number of staff needed to complete the contract on time.

ACTIONS BY QUALITY ASSURANCE

In addition to the supportive actions in certification, inspection, and testing, quality assurance (QA) personnel shall perform auditing functions to ensure activities have been completed per procedural requirements and documented accordingly. The minutes of the review will be a good source to determine whether or not all of the items of the contract have been identified within the review process.

In smaller companies, where such a formal review cycle is impractical, a checklist is used to identify contract requirements. This checklist can be used as objective evidence of a review and should be maintained as a quality record (reference chapter 17).

DOCUMENTATION PREPARATION AND CONTROL

Documentation will be discussed in more detail in chapter 6, "Document and Data Control"; however, for contract review purposes special documentation requirements must be considered. Especially in aviation, it is very common to have large influxes of documentation requirements in the beginning of new programs. This is mostly attributable to the certification requirements of the governmental agencies. Some of these documents include

- The creation of manufacturing work instructions
- Special departmental procedures
- Supplier instruction packages
- Internal inspection and test planning
- Certification document packages, including test proposals and results

As will be discussed later, the document control system must be established and documented within a procedure.

ACTIONS BY QA

In many cases, the test plans and inspection documents will be created by the quality assurance department. Certification documents that are substantiating a design through engineering analysis are often created by a disciplined engineering department, with assistance from quality assurance, through the certification team.

CONTROL OF INSPECTION, MEASURING, AND TEST EQUIPMENT

At the beginning of each new program, the contract must be evaluated to determine whether or not there is sufficient inspection and test equipment available to substantiate the design. If there are new procurement requirements, decisions must be made about whether to lease or buy equipment or use outside sources. Where the procurement of inspection tools, such as micrometers and calipers, may not be required for the new contract/design because of earlier procurement on other projects, the need for special equipment and facilities such as burn labs and stress jigs may be a first-time requirement. The cost and uses of each procurement should be evaluated to determine a lease, buy, or subcontract decision.

Additionally, tooling used to manufacture the product must be evaluated. If existing tooling is to be used, the frequency of inspection or calibration must be evaluated. If new tooling is required, its procurement or manufacture must be planned into the schedule and the budget must be planned accordingly. This will include the appropriate first article inspections.

ACTIONS BY QA

Quality assurance shall ensure through audit that all applicable tooling is calibrated, and that appropriate calibration intervals are being used. For high-use tooling, unit-cycle inspection may be considered as an option (reference chapter 12).

CONTROL OF PURCHASED ITEMS AND SERVICES

For new projects, the review team must determine whether or not its suppliers are capable of supplying the materials it needs. This determination is to be based upon the supplier's quality system, and its special process capabilities. If the supplier is registered as having a complying ISO 9000 quality system, the manufacturer may rely on the registration as proof of a conforming quality system. However, if special processing is involved, the manufacturer should verify the supplier's capabilities to perform those processes required. This is normally accomplished through process audits.

ACTIONS BY QA

Through audit, quality assurance personnel should verify the supplier's ability to perform special processing. The supplier's quality system also shall be evaluated. If the supplier has an approved ISO 9000 quality system, QA should accept the supplier's system, with proof of current registration. If the supplier does not have an approved ISO 9000 quality system, QA shall substantiate the quality system through audit. In some instances, the development of quality plans may be required to control the product or service quality of suppliers.

INCOMING INSPECTION

During the contract review process, requirements that would require special or additional actions at incoming inspection should be identified. Special documentation requirements also should be evaluated, and suppliers should be informed about documentation requirements for what they supply. Additionally, capabilities and capacities should be considered to ensure that both the additional volume and inspection requirements can be met at the manufacturer's receiving area.

ACTIONS BY QA

Incoming inspection plans are to be created for new or changed materials and parts. If special inspection techniques are required, inspection tooling is evaluated. Statistical inspection processes also are evaluated for applicability. QA should verify, through audit, that all special incoming inspection characteristics have been considered and that all open items are closed.

PURCHASER-SUPPLIED ITEMS

The control of purchaser-supplied items should be described in the contract. However, the manufacturer also should have internal procedures that describe the generic control of such items. The creation of a procedure is not necessary if the manufacturer never receives purchaser-supplied items.

The method of receipt, handling, and storage should be considered for each contract. Materials that must be stored in environmentally stable areas or frozen, or that have a shelf life, must be given additional consideration. Disposition systems of discrepant materials must be established, to include names and telephone numbers of customer representatives responsible for the disposition. Delivery schedules must be established to ensure a continuously flowing production schedule, as well as to ensure that life-limited materials are not supplied too early.

Drawings of purchaser-supplied items or material specifications should be coordinated for receipt, to assist in the incoming inspection. Material safety data sheets for raw materials should be procured and supplied to the manufacturer's safety department.

ACTIONS BY QA

Quality assurance personnel should prepare special instructions for the handling of purchaser-supplied items, when necessary. They also shall verify compliance, through audit, to contract requirements and internal procedures, ensuring the proper receipt, handling, storage, and disposition of purchaser-supplied items.

IN-PROCESS INSPECTION

At the contract review phase, the manufacturing process is evaluated for any special in-process inspection requirements, including testing. These requirements shall flow down to the supplier, but may be delegated, providing the supplier has an acceptable quality system. The complexity of in-process inspections should be evaluated for possible impact on contract price and schedule. The requirement for customer in-process inspections also should be considered. Such customer inspections can affect (and have affected) production and certification schedules.

ACTIONS BY QA

Quality assurance shall evaluate the design/contract to determine in-process inspection requirements. Any inspection activities that may add substantial cost or time to the project should be identified, and the project manager should be informed.

FINAL INSPECTION

Much like the in-process inspection, inspection requirements for the final acceptance of the product should be evaluated to determine required resources and costs. This also should include final testing. The need for new test equipment or additional software should be evaluated early in the review process, in order to accurately project cost and schedule. Customer source inspection requirements should be considered and coordination processes developed.

ACTIONS BY QA
Like the actions for in-process inspection, quality assurance shall determine inspection needs and inform project management of any cost or schedule issues.

SAMPLING

Sampling inspection is a responsibility of the quality assurance activity. In the contract review phases of a project, quality assurance should evaluate the product, and its details, to determine whether or not sampling inspection or statistical process control can be implemented. Statistical process control may be implemented where appropriate and economically feasible, and will require the involvement of various activities. It also may require the approval of the customer prior to implementation. All statistical techniques used for acceptance of products or processes must be documented within a procedure and approved by the FAA prior to implementation. The status of FAA approvals should be considered early in the review process.

INSPECTION AND TEST STATUS

Though the manufacturer already should have a set procedure on how to identify products that are in manufacture, any special customer requirements should be evaluated. In the case of a company acting as a subcontractor, it is common to perform in-process identification according to the customer's procedures. Additionally, any special FAA requirements should be considered, such as FAA-PMA or TSO identification. Plans can be created to control program-specific requirements.

ACTIONS BY QA
Customer in-process identification requirements, as well as FAA requirements, should be verified by quality assurance through audit and review.

IDENTIFICATION AND TRACEABILITY

Customer identification requirements should be reviewed to determine the requirement for creating new procedures or procuring new identification marking equipment. This can include special marking requirements for electrical wires, such as laser or ink marking that is resistant to ultraviolet rays. Additionally, traceability should be considered, including to what extent it is required to be incorporated into a project. Some products that are fracture-critical have traceability requirements that require a traceable trail throughout product life.

ACTIONS BY QA

Quality assurance shall verify, through audit, that an effective identification system has been established and ensure that all of the contract requirements are fulfilled.

HANDLING AND STORAGE

Above and beyond the handling and storage requirements of purchaser-supplied items, the review team must evaluate all the materials required for the project to determine any special handling and storage requirements. These requirements not only flow to the stores department, but also to the shop floor departments. When these materials are released for use, they must be correctly identified, stored, and handled throughout their useful life.

ACTIONS BY QA

Quality assurance shall ensure, through audit and review, that all items that require special handling and storage receive such according to applicable requirements/specifications. Additionally, quality assurance shall include special handling and storage requirements in the internal audit schedule.

SPECIAL PROCESSES

Special processes, such as anodizing, shot peening, welding, and nondestructive testing must be considered during the contract review process to ensure that there are no hidden surprises. The contract itself may not specify any special processing, so the design specifications and drawings also must be reviewed.

Internal capabilities and schedules must be considered to determine whether or not the special processes can be accomplished in-house. If the special processes are to be subcontracted to a service supplier, the supplier's capabilities, internal scheduling, and desire to accomplish the job must be considered. Regardless of what the special process is and who performs it, training requirements should be considered. Chapter 10 discusses special processes in more detail.

ACTIONS BY QA

Quality assurance should ensure that there are procedures that control the special processes. In cases where the special process is to be performed in accordance with customer specifications, quality assurance shall ensure there are internal work instructions that encompass the scope of the customer's specification. If new special processes are introduced into the manufacturing cycle, quality assurance shall determine compliance of its performance to applicable specifications, as well as its incorporation into the internal audit schedule.

PRESERVATION, PACKAGING, AND SHIPPING

The customer's requirements for preservation, packaging, and shipping shall be considered. Often the customer will define what type of packaging shall be used. This is done to ensure the packaged product is compatible with the customer's stores. For items that may spend some time on a spares rack, or for longer lead-time production lines, the customer may specify that the product is to be preserved in a special manner. The mode of shipping also may be a concern to the customer, or even the quantity to be shipped at one time, which may include just-in-time methodologies. These types of customer concerns vary widely, depending on the product and the geographical distances involved. If the customer has not noted any special preservation, packaging, and shipping requirements in the contract, ask during the coordination meetings. In order to prevent later disagreements, make sure the inquiry is documented in the minutes of meeting (record of discussion).

Even if the customer has stated no special concerns, it is still the manufacturer's responsibility to ensure the product is properly packaged and preserved to prevent any possible damage along the entire route of the product's shipping process. Additionally, the manufacturer should consider the mode of transport. If the product is to be shipped via air transport, then the product's size and weight may be an issue. Some airfreight companies can handle larger shipments better than others can. Because of this, it may be necessary to ground transport the product to an airport further than your local one, because it is serviced by higher-capacity aircraft.

ACTIONS BY QA

Quality assurance shall ensure, through audit, that inspection plans contain the required preservation, packaging, and shipping instructions. Additionally, through audit, adherence to the applicable inspection plans should be verified.

NONCONFORMING MATERIALS

Because there are so many variables involved in nonconformance documentation and disposition in the aviation industry, and because it is influenced by the regulations of the FAA, each contract shall be reviewed to define the appropriate material review system. Once the appropriate material review system is defined, it must be documented. If the customer has special requirements, these also shall be documented. Appropriately, the documentation of such special requirements should be contained in a quality plan, specific to the individual project.

Corrective action of the discrepancy also may be a requirement of the contract. Like the nonconformance documentation, appropriate corrective action systems shall be established, if different than those established in the company's procedures.

ACTIONS BY QA

Quality assurance shall ensure that the contractual agreements and internal plans are in accordance with applicable federal aviation regulations or other civil air agency requirements. Quality assurance also is responsible to ensure that the effective implementation of the material review system is achieved and maintained. The material review system shall be verified, through internal audit, for compliance.

RECORDS

Though the FAA requires that records be retained for only two years, many customers will require a manufacturer to retain them longer. Customers also may have specific quality record requirements that must be supplied with each product shipment. All special record requirements should be documented in a quality plan, or outlined in detail in a customer's specification or contract.

ACTIONS BY QA

Special records requirements should be reviewed by quality assurance. Where there is a conflict between the customer's requirements and FARs, the FARs must take precedence. The exception would be for products that are not certified by the FAA and are intended for foreign use only. In such cases, the applicable requirements of that civil airworthiness authority should be met. Such special requirements should be clearly addressed early in the contract review process. Quality assurance should ensure that special requirements are documented in applicable quality plans. Through audit, conformance to the requirements should be verified.

TRAINING

One of the most neglected areas of a quality system is training. Often companies will buckle under the pressures of budget constraints and schedule pushes and forego necessary training. If correctly planned and budgeted, in the earliest phases of the project, training can be an integral part of the project. In some cases, where the customer is requiring a process that is totally foreign to the manufacturer, it may be necessary to send selected employees or entire teams to special training centers, or even to the customer's facilities. During the evaluation for training, consideration must be given throughout the organization. It is not sufficient to send only a technician to training, when a company does not have an inspector who can capably inspect the part or process.

ACTIONS BY QA

Quality assurance should ensure, through audit and review, that special or additional training requirements are identified and met.

AUDIT AND CORRECTIVE ACTION

The results of internal audits and the corrective actions of associated discrepancies are rarely contract requirements that require customer review and approval. However, under the concept of third-party quality system registration, this internal auditing process is monitored through audit by the quality registrar with whom the manufacturer is registered. However, if it is required per contract, it should be established during the review process how the reporting activities are to be accomplished. If the new project brings with it new processes or procedures, these new characteristics should be considered for incorporation into the internal auditing schedule.

ACTIONS BY QA

If reporting is a contractual requirement, quality assurance shall ensure that there are appropriate plans or procedures documenting the process. Quality assurance shall also ensure that all of the special items of the contract review are incorporated into the internal audit schedule.

SUMMARY

Though it is an element of the ACSEP evaluation criteria, the various FARs concerning the quality systems of approved commercial aviation manufacturers make no requirement for the review of a contract. This system requirement is derived from the international quality standards. Its purpose is to create transparency of the individual project, assess the present capabilities and capacities, and identify the needs of the organization to meet the requirements of the specific contract and its associated documents. This process should be performed as early in the project as possible to prevent any misunderstandings, and should include any departmental activity that plays a role in the performance of the contract requirements. The process also should include suppliers, when appropriate. Additionally, prior to any contract reviews with the customer, the organization, internal to itself, should perform a "dry run" to ensure that everything is in order prior to the customer's presence.

The development of a contract review matrix will assist an organization by guiding it through the contract review process. At each review, minutes of the meeting (record of discussion) shall be maintained as quality records and will provide the needed objective evidence during audit. The review process should be a team effort, led by the program management, with the goal of identifying any uncertainties and comparing capabilities and capacities. If effectively performed, a successful and mutually beneficial program should evolve.

NOTES

1. ANSI/ASQC Q9001-1994, *Quality Systems—Model for Quality Assurance in Design, Development, Production, Installation, and Servicing* (Milwaukee, Wis.: American Society for Quality Control, 1994), 3, para. 4.3.2., Review.

2. Ibid., para. 4.3.3., Amendment to Contract.

3. Lionel Stebbing, *Quality Assurance: The Route to Efficiency and Competitiveness* (Chichester, West Sussex, England: Ellis Horwood, 1993). The contract review matrix displayed in this chapter was derived from Mr. Stebbing's book and adapted for aviation purposes.

Chapter 5

DESIGN CONTROL

Because there are various methods to achieve FAA design approval, design control may be the most complex function of your organization. Because of this complexity and diversity, the various types of FAA design approval should first be discussed. Within FAR 21 there are primarily three methods of design approval, which are Type Certificates (Subpart B), Supplemental Type Certificates (Subpart E), and Technical Standard Orders (Subpart O).

Type Certificates (TC) are issued for new approved designs of entire aircraft, engines, and propellers (Figure 5.1). TCs are not issued for components or parts, like radios, wind screens, and galleys. Typically, for new aircraft, parts and components that are installed prior to delivery are design approved under the TC of the aircraft in which they are installed. The TC data sheet will list the equipment that shall be installed, as well as the equipment that may be installed as an option.

If the TC holder desires to change the TC, an amendment can be requested (Subpart D, "Changes to Type Certificates," and Subpart C, "Provisional Type Certificates"); or a Supplemental Type Certificate (STC) may be applied for (Figure 5.2). The STC is much like the TC except it will also allow for a part's or component's design to be approved. Many manufacturers of aircraft components that are sold in aftermarket sales—such as lighting installations, stowage units, onboard telecommunications, and galley installations—will pursue an STC as their design approval. Modification companies that provide services and kits like cockpit revisions, cargo loading systems, and passenger entertainment systems also will apply for STCs as design approvals. Application for both the TC and STC are made on FAA Form 8110-12, as displayed in Figure 5.3.

Technical Standard Order (TSO) authorizations are design approvals of aircraft appliances designed within the parameters of an existing engineering design specification of the FAA. What this means is the FAA created design specifications for a particular appliance and the manufacturer is free to design the product as it sees fit as long as the product remains within the parameters of the TSO specification. However, all designs and test data must be submitted to the FAA for approval. The TSO approval is either a "TSO authorization" for approved designs of manufacturers within the United States, or a "letter of TSO design approval"

The United State of America

Department of Transportation
Federal Aviation Administration

Type Certificate
Number A 920CE

This certificate issued to Aviation Company X, Inc.
certifies that the type design for the following product with the operating limitations and conditions therefor as specified in the Federal Aviation Regulations and the Type Certificate Data Sheet, meets the airworthiness requirements of Part 121 *of the Federal Aviation Regulations.*

This certificate, and the Type Certificate Data Sheet which is a part hereof, shall remain in effect until surrendered, suspended, revoked, or a termination date is otherwise established by the Administrator of the Federal Aviation Administration.

Date of application: 15 July 1994

Date of issuance: 05 August 1994

By direction of the Administrator.

(Signature) _____

(Title) ___ Engineering Manager _____

This certificate may be transferred if endorsed as provided on the reverse hereof.

Any alteration of this certificate and/or the Type Certificate Data Sheet is punishable by a fine of not exceeding $1,000, or imprisonment not exceeding 3 years, or both.

FAA FORM 8110-9 (2-82)

FIGURE 5.1. *Sample FAA Form 8110-9, Type Certificate.*

United States of America
Department of Transportation — Federal Aviation Administration

Supplemental Type Certificate

Number A 3541BA

This certificate, issued to Aviation Company X, Inc.

certifies that the change in the type design for the following product with the limitations and conditions therefor as specified hereon meets the airworthiness requirements of Part 121 *of the Regulations.*

Original Product — Type Certificate Number: A 920CE
Make: ACXI Propeller
Model: 5678901-205

Description of Type Design Change:

      Pitch of blade changed, increasing by 1 degree.

Limitations and Conditions:

      Remain as noted on Type Certificate Data Sheets.

This certificate and the supporting data which is the basis for approval shall remain in effect until surrendered, suspended, revoked, or a termination date is otherwise established by the Administrator of the Federal Aviation Administration.

Date of application: 15 July 1994   *Date reissued:* 07 August 1994

Date of issuance: 05 August 1994   *Date amended:* 12 August 1994

                                       By direction of the Administrator

                                     (Signature)

                             Engineering Manager

                                       (Title)

Any alteration of this certificate is punishable by a fine of not exceeding $1,000, or imprisonment not exceeding 3 years, or both.

This certificate may be transferred in accordance with FAR 21.47.

FAA Form 8110-2 (10-68)

FIGURE 5.2. *Sample FAA Form 8110-2, Supplemental Type Certificate.*

72 *Aviation Industry Quality Systems*

No certificate may be issued unless a completed application
form has been received (14 C.F.R. 21)

U.S. DEPARTMENT OF TRANSPORTATION FEDERAL AVIATION ADMINISTRATION **APPLICATION FOR TYPE CERTIFICATE, PRODUCTION CERTIFICATE, OR SUPPLEMENTAL TYPE CERTIFICATE**	*FORM APPROVED* O.M.B. No. 04-R0078

1. Name and address of applicant Aviation Company X, Inc. 1234 W. Main Street Wichita, Kansas, 67213	2. Application made for — [X] Type Certificate [ ] Production Certificate [ ] Supplemental Type Certificate	3. Product involved [ ] Aircraft [ ] Engine [X] Propeller

4. **TYPE CERTIFICATE** *(Complete item 4a below)*

a. Model designation(s) *(All models listed are to be completely described in the required technical data, including drawings representing the design, material, specifications, construction, and performance of the aircraft, aircraft engine, propeller which is the subject of this application.)*

ACXI Propeller Part Number 5678901-205.
Top assembly drawing 5678901-205, Rev. "K".
Qualification Test Report 5678901-205, Rev. "B".

5. **PRODUCTION CERTIFICATE** *(Complete items 5a–c below. Submit with this form, in manual form, one copy of quality control data or changes thereto covering new products, as required by applicable FAR.)*

a. Factory address *(If different from 1 above)*	b. Application is for — [ ] New Production Certificate [ ] Additions to Production Certificate *(Give P.C. No.)*	P.C. No.

c. Applicant is holder of or a licensee under a Type Certificate or a Supplemental Type Certificate *(Attach evidence of licensing agreement and give certificate number)* ⟶ | T.C./S.T.C. No.

6. **SUPPLEMENTAL TYPE CERTIFICATE** *(Complete items 6a–d below)*

a. Make and model designation of product to be modified

b. Description of modification

c. Will data be available for sale or release to other persons? [ ] YES [ ] NO	d. Will parts be manufactured for sale? *(Ref. FAR 21.303)* [ ] YES [ ] NO

7. **CERTIFICATION** – I certify that the above statements are true.

Signature of certifying official R.W. Plane	Title Engineering Manager	Date 15 July 1994

FAA Form 8110-12 (3-80) SUPERSEDES PREVIOUS EDITION

FIGURE 5.3. *Sample FAA Form 8110-12, Application for Type Certificate, Production Certificate, or Supplemental Type Certificate (displayed as a type certificate application).*

for approved designs of manufacturers located outside of the United States. Appliances that usually fall under a TSO are seats, seat belts, tires, radios, and various other standard-type equipment. Advisory Circular 20-36 provides a listing of the various products controlled by a TSO.

Making the process a little more complicated, to determine what FAA requirements apply to an individual manufacturer, the requirements for the design (TC, STC, TSO) and those for the production system (APIS, PC, PMA, repair station, DAS) must be coupled. If a manufacturer possesses more than one production or design approval, then systems must be developed to control the individual product under its specific approval requirements. In reality, this should not be too difficult. This is because most of the requirements have the same basic core characteristics, with differences in approval and identification methods. These differences could be controlled by creating one core procedure, the quality assurance manual, that addresses the core requirements, and then by creating individual procedures to control the differences.

This also would be acceptable for the quality system that operates under the international quality system standards. When selecting the appropriate level of the international quality system standards, manufacturers need to look at their design system. If they are in control of design activities, then ANSI/ASQC Q9001 would be applicable. Even if under some projects the design is not controlled by the manufacturer, the manufacturer will still maintain its system in accordance with ANSI/ASQC Q9001, providing there are other programs that are design controlled. However those characteristics of the standard regarding the design control process would not be applicable for those projects.

LICENSING AGREEMENTS

In the case of a licensing agreement, the manufacturer has received written authorization from the holder of the design approval allowing the manufacturer to produce the articles in accordance with the applicable drawings and specifications. It must be made clear that the drawings are not the only documents that are required to be complied with. Various process specifications and federal and industry standards that must be adhered to may be called out within the drawings or contract. In some cases, there may be requirements that are not called out in the design and contract documents, but are still mandatory compliance items. Regardless, in the case of licensing agreements, the manufacturer does not have design control. However, the quality system still shall have procedures for incorporating design changes that come from the design approval holder. These changes must be incorporated into the manufacturing processes, as required. Provisions for the reverse shall be true also. If for any reason the licensed manufacturer determines a design change is needed, there shall be internal procedures for the upstream notification/approval cycle. Organizations without engineering design control should develop their quality systems to the requirements of ANSI/ASQC Q9002. The majority recipients of licensing agreements are PMA manufacturers.

REPAIR STATIONS AND DESIGNATED ALTERATION STATIONS

Repair stations and designated alteration stations do not always work to type-certificated design. Other methods of design approvals exist for such operations, but mainly fall under individual cases of material review that have been approved by the FAA. Usually the design approval responsibility has been delegated to a designated engineering representative (DER), who may be a company employee. A DER is a qualified person who has been authorized by the FAA as its field engineering representative and may approve certain designs and test data.

APPROVED DATA

It must be stressed that designs and data are only recognized by the FAA after they have been approved. This so called "approved data" is often a confused issue. Documents such as a manufacturer's service bulletin and service manuals are not normally approved data. If a document has been approved by a foreign airworthiness authority, it may or may not be viewed as FAA-approved data. The individual bilateral agreements are documented in Advisory Circular 21-18, and export airworthiness approval procedures are outlined in Advisory Circular 21-2F. The language of each individual bilateral agreement must be reviewed to determine acceptability. But as a rule, the FAA usually will require that all such data be approved by an FAA engineering office or a DER. Only after the document has either a stamp or letter of FAA approval is it "approved data."

DESIGN CONTROL ACTIVITIES

As ANSI/ASQC Q9002 and ANSI/ASQC Q9003 do not require procedures for design control, we will concentrate on the requirements of ANSI/ASQC Q9001. However, because each of the FAA manufacturing approvals does require some sort of design interaction by the manufacturers and the design owner, it is required to have procedures to outline how design changes will be integrated into the product, as well as how design problems are transmitted back up the design change/approval cycle.

The individual elements of ANSI/ASQC Q9001's design control are

- General
- Design and development planning
- Organizational and technical interfaces
- Design input
- Design output
- Design review
- Design verification
- Design validation
- Design changes

GENERAL

In general, the manufacturer is required to establish and maintain procedures to control and verify the design of the product in order to ensure that the specified requirements are met. This can overlap into various other sections of the quality system, such as contract review and inspection and testing, but there is absolutely no harm in restating the requirements within the different sections of the quality assurance manual. The primary system requirements should be clearly defined within the quality assurance manual, but should be broken down step-by-step into individual procedures. These procedures should fall primarily under the jurisdiction of engineering personnel as engineering procedures, with an overlap in quality assurance procedures for verification and auditing purposes.

DESIGN AND DEVELOPMENT PLANNING

The requirements of design and development planning, activity assignment, and organizational and technical interfaces can be incorporated easily into one section of the quality assurance manual or one stand-alone engineering procedure.

In the quality assurance manual, the design and development planning section should be outlined, identifying the responsibilities of each department within the design process. ANSI/ASQC Q9001 states that "the supplier shall prepare plans for each design and development activity. The plans shall describe or reference these activities, and define responsibility for their implementation. These design and development activities shall be assigned to qualified personnel equipped with adequate resources."[1] This documentation is most easily accomplished with the use of a matrix describing the cycle. The structure of program management also should be described within the quality assurance manual.

If needed, individual engineering procedures should elaborate in more detail on the process. To ensure continued accuracy, the plans shall be updated as the design evolves.

What ANSI/ASQC Q9001 is really looking for under design and development planning is a documented control plan for the design or development endeavor. Like flowcharts, a matrix can simplify such a plan into one page. A matrix divided into four sections to show the design control activity to be performed, the performance scope of the activity, the responsible department(s) to complete the action, and the action by QA will provide quick reference. We will call this the *DDP matrix*. As displayed in Figure 5.4,[2] the DDP matrix maps the design cycle through its various phases.

- Contract review
- Document preparation, control, and retention
- Discipline check
- Interdiscipline check
- Internal design review
- Critical design review
- Change control
- First article inspection and certification qualifications
- Audit and corrective action

Typically, the DDP matrix can be a standard document, to be used on all program developments without change. However, it can be changed or modified, as needed, for particular programs where special requirements are present. It is up to the individual organization to develop its own DDP matrix to accommodate the organization's own commodities and infrastructure. In doing so, keep in mind that all of the noted characteristics of the DDP are elements of either ANSI/ASQC Q9001 or the applicable FARs.

The function of activity assignment also can be addressed in the DDP matrix. The assignments for both the design and verification activities shall be assigned to qualified personnel equipped with adequate resources. Such assignments should be made to individuals and not to departments. The international quality standards require that all "personnel performing specific tasks [in activities affecting quality] shall be qualified on the basis of appropriate education, training, and/or experience, as required."[3]

To demonstrate competency levels of the staff, it is recommended that the manufacturer create a standard form that documents employee

Design control activity	Performance scope	Responsible departments	Actions by QA
1. Contract review	Review: Work scope Specifications and standards Philosophies Design criteria Regulatory requirements Organization	Program management Discipline engineers Manufacturing Quality assurance	Verify that missing or ambiguous information has been followed up and satisfactorily closed out by the responsible person.
2. Document preparation, control, and retention	Ensure correct and uniform presentation of documentation. Ensure formal preparation, identification, checking, approval, and distribution, including revisions. Verify retention, retrieval, storage, and turnover requirements.	Project management Discipline engineers Quality assurance (Customer)	Audit adherence to procedure.
3. Discipline check	Verify content and accuracy of documents originating from own discipline.	Relevant discipline engineers	Audit adherence to applicable procedures.
4. Interdiscipline check	Assure compatibility of design between design disciplines and accuracy of content.	Project management Discipline engineers	Audit distribution and approval. Verify that action items have been closed out by the originating engineer.

FIGURE 5.4.   *Design and development matrix.*

Design control activity	Performance scope	Responsible departments	Actions by QA
5. Internal design review	Review design activities in progress or completed. Review qualification tests and certification activities.	Project management Discipline engineers Quality assurance	Verify that all action items have been closed out.
6. Critical design review	Check physical interfaces between systems, related installations, and governmental requirements.	Project management Discipline engineers (Subcontractors) Customers	Audit distribution and approval. Verify that action items have been closed out.
7. Change control	Check changes in design criteria.	Project management Discipline engineers	Monitor change control process as required to close out and approval.
8. First article inspection and certification qualification	Conduct detailed audit of design. —Adequacy of design —Adherence to contract Check production processes.	Quality inspection Quality assurance Discipline engineers (Customer)	Audit to verify that any nonconformances have been closed out.
9. Audit and corrective action	Ensure nonconformances are promptly identified and corrective action taken to prevent recurrence.	Project management Discipline engineers Quality assurance	Verify corrective action.

FIGURE 5.4. (continued)

name, title, responsibilities in brief (electrical design, contract review, and so on), internal authorizations, educational levels and certificates, FAA authorizations, and any other applicable professional experience history. This document could be maintained in any one of various areas, and is often an electronic record; but, to protect the employees' privacy, the information should be secured, with access limited to only those who need to know. Who should be responsible for such a document? Whomever the organization determines; but keep in mind that the same information is required for various activities, such as human resources, the material review board, and repair station activities. To prevent redundancy, use the same document for all of the organizational employee data requirements. If the company has a human resources department, this would be the most appropriate location to maintain this data.

Adequate facilities and equipment are self-explanatory. If the organization is going to create new design drawings that must be substantiated, a stress test may be part of the development cycle. Either the facilities must be available to perform the physical test or the software and hardware must be available to develop a computer-based model.

ORGANIZATIONAL AND TECHNICAL INTERFACES

Organizational and technical interfaces can be shown on the DDP matrix. The transmittal of the design from each interfacing department also shall be documented. The simplest method to accomplish this is to create an internal transmittal cover sheet. This cover sheet will serve also as a quality record to later demonstrate compliance during an audit, so retention is an issue. The cover sheet (Figure 5.5) should include, as a minimum, the project name, drawing number(s), responsible project manager and/or lead engineer, routing dates from department to department, remarks area for each department on the routing, and any other information applicable to the individual commodity and manufacturer. Additionally, provisions for documenting the transmittal to outside organizations should be available, to include response dates.

DESIGN INPUT

The ANSI/ASQC Q9001 quality standard states that the "design-input requirements relating to the product, including applicable statutory and regulatory requirements, shall be identified, documented, and their selection reviewed by the supplier for adequacy. Incomplete, ambiguous, or conflicting requirements shall be resolved with those responsible for imposing these requirements" (3, para. 4.4.4., Design Input). For aviation manufacturers these inputs are the various FAA requirements—such as stress, heat release, and noise—and also can include requirements from

Aviation Company X, Inc. Wichita, Kansas	Design Document Review Routing Sheet

Program name	Program number	Program manager

Drawing number	Revision	Responsible engineer	Telephone no.

Reason for routing   New drawing ☐   Change ☐
Describe reason for change:

Routing

Dept. and reviewer's name	Received date	Return date	Remarks

FAA design approval required   Yes ☐   No ☐   FAA reviewer _____
Date submitted _____ Estimated return _____ Date returned _____
Remarks:

Other Outside Routing

Organization name	Address

Reviewer's name	Telephone no.	Date submitted	Return due	Date returned

Remarks

Signature

ACXI Form 350 (05 Aug 94)

FIGURE 5.5. *Sample design document review routing sheet.*

other regulatory agencies such as the United States Public Health Service (USPHS) for areas of the aircraft that come in contact with food preparation, or the Environmental Protection Agency for manufacturing processes or designs that have an impact on the environment. Customer requirements are also a very important part of the design-input process. Without a customer you will have no need for a design. These customer requirements should be of prime importance during the contract review process.

In the event that a conflict does arise within the design-input process, the issue must be taken to the agency/company responsible for the requirement. Usually either a compromise can be met or an alternative method can be found to accomplish the same output. In any event, all such activities must be documented. When a governmental agency makes a concession within the commercial aviation industry, it will normally be in the form of a letter. Customer concessions to design should be in the form of either a design change or design amendment document. If such changes to the basic requirements are not documented, the customer's quality inspection department will not be able to accept the product at first article inspection or receiving inspection.

DESIGN OUTPUT

According to ANSI/ASQC Q9001, "Design Output shall be documented and expressed in terms that can be verified against design-input requirements and validated." Furthermore, design output shall

(a) meet the design-input requirements;

(b) contain or make reference to acceptance criteria; and

(c) identify those characteristics of the design that are crucial to the safe and proper functioning of the product (e.g., operating, storage, handling, maintenance, and disposal requirements).

Design output documents shall be reviewed before release. (3, para. 4.4.5., Design Output)

Because of the nature of the aviation industry, the design output also should conform to appropriate regulatory requirements [FAA, European Joint Airworthiness Authority (JAA), USPHS, or EPA], whether or not these have been stated in the design input.

At this stage of the design control process, all of the design output requirements just described are still basically only theory; they have not yet been tested or applied. However, from these outputs the product can be produced and the design verified.

DESIGN REVIEW

ANSI/ASQC Q9001 states, "At appropriate stages of design, formal documented reviews of the design results shall be planned and conducted" (4, para. 4.4.6., Design Review). At the beginning of the program such a review would normally be called a *preliminary design review*. This review should clarify any questions regarding the design-input requirements. Toward the end of the design process a *critical design review* will normally take place. This review is normally the last design review prior to first article inspection and may be based on the results of the design verification process. The number of reviews and their intervals will vary from project to project, depending on their complexity. The "participants at each design review shall include representatives of all functions concerned with the design stage being reviewed, as well as other specialist personnel, as required. Records of such reviews shall be maintained as quality records" (4, para. 4.4.6., Design Review). This documentation usually takes the form of minutes of meeting (record of discussion).

DESIGN VERIFICATION

The design verification process is different for aviation manufacturers than it is for many other industries because here quality assurance/inspection departments must be involved with testing and demonstrations. Testing can range from the flammability chamber to the destructive and nondestructive laboratories, and the demonstrations range from in-process inspections and first articles to functional testing of completed units. All of these quality actions are performed after the design has gone through the development and internal approval cycle and may be before the regulatory/customer approval. ANSI/ASQC Q9001 states that "at appropriate stages of design, design verification shall be performed to ensure that the design-stage output meets the design-stage input requirements" (4, para. 4.4.7., Design Verification). This activity goes hand in hand with the design review process. Some of the characteristics that may be used as a means of design verification measurement include, but are not limited to,

> —*Performing alternative calculations, such as computer based models;*
> —*Comparing the new design with a similar proven design [statement of similarity], if available; and*
> —*Undertaking tests and demonstrations (lab test and physical inspections);*
> —*Reviewing the design-stage documents before release. (4, para. 4.4.7., Design Verification)*

FIRST ARTICLE INSPECTION AND DESIGN VALIDATION

Though first article inspection is discussed here in design control, many would argue that it belongs under the category of final inspection and testing. It is up to the individual organization where this requirement is defined, but it is most important that it is defined and the step-by-step operations are outlined. ANSI/ASQC Q9001 requires the validation of designs to "be performed to ensure that product conforms to defined user needs and/or requirements" (4, para. 4.4.8., Design Validation). Because of this requirement within the design control element of the standard, it may be advisable to at least briefly address it within the design chapter of the quality assurance manual.

First article inspections (FAI) are the final steps in the design verification process. The purpose of the FAI is to validate the manufacturing processes, as well as the overall systems in general, that produced the product. It could be viewed as the link between the manufacturing approval and the design approval. A carefully planned and executed FAI will most definitely save the organization both time and money in the long run. By identifying and documenting design and/or manufacturing errors at the beginning of a program, and investigating the root cause and achieving corrective action, the organization can realize a clean-flowing production cycle. Additionally, by analyzing the documented defects, the organization can learn to prevent recurrences.

The department within the quality organization that is responsible for planning the FAI (normally quality planning or quality engineering) should review the applicable drawings for important design characteristics. Special customer interface dimensions and governmental agency requirements also should be noted as inspection/verification points. The following characteristics should be verified during an FAI [reference FAR 21.33 (b)].

- Critical drawing dimensions and compliance with notes
- Special contract requirements not noted on the drawings
- Governmental agency requirements not specified in the drawings
- Tooling used to produce the part
- Successful completion of applicable testing
- Quality of work and processing
- Manufacturing work instructions
- Any other characteristic that may have an adverse effect on the design or finished product if discrepant

Each individual part number that has an FAI performed on it should have an individual FAI report documenting the process. Normally this

ACXI Aviation Company X, Inc. Wichita, Kansas	First Article Inspection Report (FAIR)	1. FAI serial number
		2. Page of

3. Supplier	4. P.O. number	5. Ship, advice no./Work order no.
6. Drawing no. and revision	7. Part number	8. Serial number

9. Part nomenclature	10. Project	11. Reason for FAI ☐ New part ☐ New supplier
12. Material test report no.	13. Supplier's FAI report no.	☐ Changed part ☐ Changed process ☐ Tooling change ☐ Other

14. Deviation reports/Enclosures/Remarks

15. Article   ☐ Accepted   ☐ Conditionally accepted   ☐ Rejected

16. Inspector's name (printed or typed)	17. Inspectors stamp and signature	18. Date
19. Customer acceptance		20. Date

ACXI Form 1 01 (05 Aug. 94)

FIGURE 5.6.   *Sample first article inspection report.*

report is structured with a cover sheet (Figure 5.6) and various applicable attachments. The cover sheet should include, at a minimum, report control number, total number of pages in the report (counting all attachments), part number being inspected, nomenclature of the part number being inspected, applicable drawing number with revision, serial number of the part (when applicable), reason for the FAI, remarks section, acceptance status, and name and signature of the verifying quality representative. Additionally, if provisions are made on this cover sheet for documenting supplier information, it could be used for both internal and external production. This could cut down on the number of forms the quality organization needs to maintain. Taking it one step further, customer acceptance can be documented on the same form by adding an additional block.

The FAI report attachments can, and should, include test reports, material certificates from suppliers, dimensional inspection results, and any other document that can substantiate conformance. For any dimensional report data, the "should be" and "actual" results should be recorded (Figure 5.7). For instance, if a part has a dimensional characteristic that

First Article Inspection Characteristics
Page 2 of 11

Drawing: 5678901-205   Revision "D," Part name: panel assembly
Serial number: A9408-0001   Part number: 5678901-205

Line no.	Zone	Note	Should be	Actual	Stamp
1.	G-16	1994 – 38 mm	1956 mm	1956 mm	
2.	D-13		1625.5 mm	1624.2 mm	
3.	D-8	955.2 + 24 mm	979.2 mm	979.3 mm	
4.	D-6		2292 mm	2293.8 mm	
5.	D-12		965.2 mm	965.2 mm	
6.	F-1	225.0 – 201.5 mm	23.5 mm	23.5 mm	
7.	F-1	227 – 201.5 mm	25.5 mm	25.5 mm	
8.	K-15		311 mm	311 mm	
9.	K-14		286.5 mm	286.5 mm	
10.	K-13		367.5 mm	367.5 mm	
11.	K-16		286.5 mm	286.5 mm	
12.	H-16		286.5 mm	286.0 mm	
13.	K-6	301.5 + 5 mm	306.5 mm	307.0 mm	
14.	H-5		286.5 mm	286.5 mm	
15.	H-10	43 + 30 mm	73.0 mm	73.0 mm	
16.	H-11		65.6 mm	65.5 mm	
17.	H-12	50 + 11 mm	66.0 mm	65.8 mm	
18.	J-4		72.5 mm	72.0 mm	
19.	K-2		72.5 mm	72.0 mm	
20.	L-5	980 + 12 mm	992.0 mm	991.5 mm	

FIGURE 5.7.   *Sample first article inspection characteristics sheet.*

should be 35.000 mm and in actuality it measures 34.500 mm, both dimensions should be noted on the report. Typically, all of the "should be" measurements are already entered onto the dimensional inspection report, along with applicable drawing zone locations, by quality planning/quality engineering personnel. This requires quality inspection personnel only to measure/test the characteristic and document the results. By accurately documenting the inspection results, the manufacturer is obtaining objective evidence of the actual conditions. It may seem redundant at the verification time to measure so many characteristics, but this type of report has proven to be a powerful tool in resolving later differences.

FAIs are only effective if they are performed on real production parts and assemblies. Performing an FAI on a prototype part or assembly that was manufactured under special conditions and processes only checks a prototype cycle. The goal is to assure the production cycle, as it is to be run. This means all tooling to be used and processes to be performed shall be in place. If for any reason parts of the production cycle are not yet ready when production begins, the FAI can be performed in sections through deferral. This will depend on the part or assembly and is acceptable providing the characteristics to be deferred do not affect any other characteristics of the design. For instance, a product requires an anodized surface treatment and the organization plans to do it in-house; however, the tanks are not yet ready. The process can be performed at a subcontractor and that characteristic of the FAI can be rechecked when the in-house process is qualified. Another example would be if tooling was not yet available for a subassembly. Depending on the design interface impact, the subassembly may have the FAI deferred until the tooling is available. However, all deferrals shall be reasonable with regard to time frames and quantities. If production is to run for a great length of time with the initial provisions, the FAI should be performed as a full-compliance verification. When the longer lead-time processes are ready, the FAI can then be updated. Deferring an FAI characteristic does not relieve the manufacturer of any other inspection and test responsibilities. The product must be verified for conformance.

As a rule, FAIs shall be required

- On the first production installation of a new design part or assembly
- On a new production process
- On new designed tools and all new manufactured tools
- When a tool has been moved
- When the production has moved to new facilities
- On any new supplier-furnished parts

- After any major changes to design are incorporated (including material changes)

CHANGE CONTROL

Drawing changes occur when customer requirements change, when regulatory requirements are changed, when required under a FAR Part 39 Airworthiness Directive, when design discrepancies are discovered during design verification, or when a design improvement is desired. Both the FARs and ANSI/ASQC Q9001 require that "all design changes and modifications shall be identified, documented, reviewed, and approved by authorized personnel before their implementation" (4, para. 4.4.9., Design Changes). FAR 21 continues by stating that "in the case of a major change in type design, the [manufacturer] must submit substantiating data and necessary descriptive data for inclusion in the type design."[4]

There are basically two levels of design changes—minor and major. "A minor change is one that has no appreciable effect on the weight, balance, structural strength, reliability, operational characteristics, or other characteristics affecting the airworthiness of the product."[5] Anything that cannot be called a minor change is a major change. However, within FAR 21.93 (b) there are additional rules covering the acoustical changes to aircraft engines. Basically, if the acoustical noise levels are changed in a engine/aircraft application, with numerous exceptions, it will be considered a major change.

The FARs require that minor changes are approved under a method acceptable to the FAA.[6] In most applications this means that the FAA will never see a minor change because it is handled within the manufacturer's approved change system or material review board (MRB) system. Even ANSI/ASQC Q9001 does not state how this process is to be structured, other than that the identification, documentation, and review and approval steps are to be established and completed.

So it is up to each individual company to develop its own design change process. Typically, this will be the same as the initial design approval process, but possibly with a couple of additional functional stops, depending on the size and structure of the organization. If properly developed, the existing routing cover sheet, used to transmit the initial design, could also be used for design changes. Within the quality manual, under Design Change, the basic functions and responsibilities should be outlined. Then under the stand-alone design control procedure, which should be an engineering procedure, a step-by-step account of how the process is to be conducted and controlled should be outlined. If the organization is small, it may be possible to document all these features within the quality assurance manual. In any case, keep it simple, controllable, and concise.

For whatever reason the design change is required, the change requirement flows from the initiator to engineering. Engineering reviews the change requirement and compares it to design input requirements, such as interface, flammability, structural substantiation, and special customer requirements. After reviewing the change requirement, engineering creates the change vehicle. This vehicle can be a complete new drawing, a revised drawing, or an attachment to the drawing documenting the change. These attachments are often called drawing change notices (DCN), changes in design (CID), and engineering orders (EO). There are also design changes that only affect a part of the production run and are sometimes termed serialized engineering order (SEO), as well as other internal descriptions. The actual term is usually unique to the organization itself. These temporary changes are handled in the same way as permanent changes, except they will note the block of product serial numbers that are affected, normally in very small, sandwiched groups. The change vehicle is then distributed through the functional groups within the organization, for review of their disciplines. This means the quality assurance group (QA) will review for inspection items and manufacturing will review for potential to produce. Departments such as procurement and scheduling may also need to be involved, to procure new materials and schedule the change. Communication is critical to ensure a smooth change process. If required by contract, the design changes must be sent to the customer for review and approval.

After the reviews are complete and documented, engineering incorporates the minor change, as authorized by the FAA. This authorization is in the form of an approved control procedure. Major changes are forwarded to the FAA engineering function. Normally, the FAA will not accept attachment documents (DCNs, CIDs, and EOs) and will require the manufacturer to have the change documented in either a new or revised drawing. Exceptions are rarely made. FAA engineering personnel then review the change vehicle and return the vehicle and the review results to the manufacturer. If the change is approved, it is incorporated into the production. If the change is not approved, the manufacturer must act on the rejections from the FAA and repeat the cycle.

When the design change is incorporated into production, all applicable plans and associated documents must be adjusted to include the change. Documents that can be affected by a design change are

- Manufacturing work instructions
- Stockroom inventory control sheets
- Contract documents
- Inspection and test plans

- Shipping documents
- Certificates of conformance
- Various others, depending on the organization and product

CHANGE NOTIFICATION

For FAA-approved products, the customers must receive any applicable information regarding the product they operate. This data transmission is accomplished in various ways depending on the type and severity of the change. If the change is a minor one that does not affect operation or safety, action is optional and a service bulletin (SB) is usually created. This document, as well as other manufacturer service documents, is discussed in FAA Advisory Circular 20-114. When a service bulletin is created it shall include the scope of the work, what part numbers are applicable, serial numbers affected, and step-by-step instructions guiding the performance of work.

Another method that can be used to transmit and document minor design improvement changes is by simply updating the manufacturer's maintenance manual and parts list. If a part or component has been changed but is still interchangeable with the previous design(s), it can be noted within the maintenance manual and parts list as optional. However, if the changed part or component is not interchangeable, that must be noted. If the changed product is not interchangeable but can be installed inadvertently and may affect operation, strength, weight, balance, or reliability, it could be classified as a major change. In such a case, a warning should be inserted within the maintenance manual. Additionally, the part should be placarded, noting the potential hazardous situation. If at all possible, such potentially dangerous design changes should be avoided. They are, in actuality, very rare because, as a rule, the FAA will not accept such conditions. Major changes also can be transmitted to the customer, after FAA Type Certificate approval, via a service bulletin and drawing attachments. These would normally be of a design improvement nature and would not affect safety of flight.

Airworthiness directives (ADs) are usually issued to transmit critical (major) design changes or errors to the owners/operators of aircraft, aircraft engines, propellers, or appliances when

- An unsafe condition exists in a product, and
- That condition is likely to exist or develop in other products of the same design.

The AD is issued by the FAA, based on manufacturers' data. It shall include the part number, nomenclature, affected serial numbers, manufacturer's name, description of the problem, activity to undertake to resolve the problem, and operation restrictions (including the deadline for compliance).

When ADs have been complied with, an authorized individual shall note this in the historical documentation of the end item. For example, for an engine, a bolt has been determined to be failing in tests, resulting in an AD. After the bolt has been replaced, as instructed in the AD, the compliance will be documented in the applicable engine logbook and signed off by an authorized individual. The authorization of individuals varies depending on how the aircraft, engine, propeller, or component is certified for operation. In most aviation applications, ADs will be signed off by an FAA-authorized inspector or a repairer (reference FAR Part 65). Sometimes they will be signed off by an FAA-designated airworthiness representative when in conjunction with a major repair or modification, or if the AD in itself is extensive. Compliance with an AD is not optional unless it is specifically noted as such in the AD.

SERVICE BULLETINS

Only those documents that have FAA approval are approved data. Service bulletins are not normally approved data; TCs, STCs and their approved changes are.

If instructions within a service bulletin have been approved by the FAA, only those applicable paragraphs shall be noted as such. Manufacturers shall never indicate that an entire document has been FAA approved, FAA/DER approved, or DER approved, or use any other statement that implies that the service bulletin has been reviewed, evaluated, and approved by the FAA, unless this is, in fact, the case and total FAA approval is required by regulation and has been conferred in accordance with prescribed procedures.

If a service bulletin is recommended by the manufacturer, and design change approval is required by the FAA, the service bulletin shall indicate the scope of the FAA approval within the document. The following are examples of how such approval statements are made.

The resultant alteration (or repair) to the affected (product type, e.g. aircraft, engine, propeller, appliance, etc.) described by paragraph XX has been shown to comply with the applicable Federal Aviation Regulations and is Approved.

The retirement life limits of paragraph XX have been shown to comply with the applicable Federal Aviation Regulations and are FAA approved. [This entry can be used only when life limits have been previously approved and are considered part of the type certificate.][7]

Manufacturers shall not indicate FAA approval of:

(a) Compliance times recommended in Service Bulletins, unless they are retirement times or continuous operation till a structural repair is completed;

(b) Background information on the reasons why the recommendations are being made;

(c) Maintenance action recommendations, including inspections, that do not require FAA approval in the type certificate process; or

(d) Step-by-step detailed instructions on how to accomplish a manufacturer's recommended and FAA-approved alteration, repair, rework, etc., when these instructions have no effect on type design.[8]

If a service document does have FAA approval, it should read "FAA Approved." This also applies if a designee of the FAA approves the data. Using the one term will eliminate considerable confusion when referring to approved data.

SUMMARY

The international quality standard that provides the requirements of design control is ANSI/ASQC Q9001. This quality standard requires that the manufacturer identifies the responsibilities and interface methods of the departments and individuals involved in the design and development activities. Additionally, it requires that the manufacturer establishes controls that ensure there are checks and balances in place to verify the design input and design output. Such checks and balances would include design reviews, secondary checks in performance (audits), and first article inspections.

The control of design changes is also a requirement of ANSI/ASQC Q9001. Within this requirement, the manufacturer is required to establish and maintain procedures for the identification, documentation, and appropriate review and approval of all changes and modifications.

There are three prime FAA approvals for design—the Type Certificate (TC), the Supplemental Type Certificate (STC), and the Technical Standard Order (TSO). These design approvals are issued to a part number and its associated drawing sets. Changes to these documents can occur through amendment or supplement. However, no changes may be incorporated until the data have been approved by the FAA. Minor changes are approved by the FAA through an approved control procedure. Major changes are physically reviewed by the FAA engineering function.

In addition to these three, the FAA also provides guidelines for field approvals of designs. These field approvals are the typical methods of design approval a repair station or designated alteration station would use. These field approvals are normally for individual aircraft, component, or product, and have very limited effectivity, normally one unit.

NOTES

1. ANSI/ASQC Q9001-1994, *Quality Systems—Model for Quality Assurance in Design, Development, Production, Installation, and Servicing* (Milwaukee, Wis.: American Society for Quality Control, 1994), 3, para. 4.4.2., Design and Development Planning.

2. Lionel Stebbing, *Quality Assurance: The Route to Efficiency and Competitiveness* (Chichester, West Sussex, England: Ellis Horwood, 1993). The design and development matrix displayed in this chapter was derived from Mr. Stebbing's book and adopted for aviation purposes.

3. ANSI/ASQC Q9001-1994, 9, para. 4.18., Training.

4. DOT/FAA, Federal Aviation Regulation Section 21.97, *Certification Procedures for Products and Parts—Approval of Major Changes in Type Design* (Washington, D.C.: DOT/FAA, March 1993).

5. DOT/FAA, Federal Aviation Regulation Section 21.93, *Certification Procedures for Products and Parts—Classification of Changes in Type Design* (Washington, D.C.: DOT/FAA, March 1993).

6. DOT/FAA, Federal Aviation Regulation Section 21.95, *Certification Procedures for Products and Parts—Approval of Minor Changes in Type Design* (Washington, D.C.: DOT/FAA, March 1993).

7. DOT/FAA, Advisory Circular 20-114, *Manufacturers' Service Documents* (Washington, D.C.: DOT/FAA, 22 October 1981), 4, para. (5)(b)(1)(a)(b), Discussion.

8. Ibid., para. (5)(b)(3), Discussion.

Chapter 6

DOCUMENT AND DATA CONTROL

Much like design control, document control also has an approval and change flow cycle. The various parts of the FARs make little reference to the methodology of document control, other than if a document is required as part of the type design approval process (maintenance manual with replacement and retirement times), or manufacturing process approval (quality assurance manual or process specification). Such a document, and its changes, are to be approved prior to implementation and must be in English. This also can include test reports and plans, checklists, tags, and placards.

In many aviation companies, document control systems can become very complex and cumbersome. Each department—manufacturing, engineering, scheduling, quality, procurement, and so on—usually has its own way of identifying documents. Ideally, if the entire company can standardize its procedures into one corporate methodology, the documentation system can become generic, and departments will no longer have to learn how to interpret another department's documents. If kept simple, this will result in enhanced communication.

The international quality standards require manufacturers to establish and maintain documented procedures to control all documents and data that relate to the requirements of the applicable international quality standard, including, to the extent applicable, documents of external origin such as standards and customer drawings. This would also include applicable FAA forms. This documentation can be in the format of any type of media, such as hard copy or electronic media.

> *The documents and data shall be reviewed and approved for adequacy by authorized personnel prior to issue. A master list or equivalent document-control procedure identifying the current revision status of documents shall be established and be readily available to preclude the use of invalid and/or obsolete documents.*

This control shall also ensure that:

(a) the pertinent issues of appropriate documents are available at all locations where operations essential to the effective functioning of the quality system are performed.

(b) Invalid and/or obsolete documents shall be promptly removed from all points of issue or use, or otherwise assured against unintentional use.

(c) Any obsolete documents retained for legal and/or knowledge preservation purposes shall be suitably identified.[1]

This does not mean that only the latest revisions of documents should be available. If an earlier revision of a document is required to perform an activity, per the work instructions, which is common for manufacturers' repair activities, it too must be available, but controlled. However, if these earlier revisions are not needed, the standard requires that they are removed from all points of issue and use.

Though it may be necessary to have individual departmental procedures outlining the method of completion and distribution of specific documents, it is recommended to have one basic corporate methodology that standardizes the format. This standardization should include the structure for issuing procedure numbers and use of approval blocks, and should define the basic structure of the procedure.

IDENTIFICATION

The international quality standards require document identification, but do not provide any direction on how to structure it. It is up to the individual organizations to develop their own methods and systems. This following document identification section is a model of an identification system, and offers an organization the flexibility to expand or abbreviate, as it determines necessary. It is not the only method of compliance; it is only one method.

The responsibility for developing the method for identification should lie at the top of the organizational ladder. Corporate management should be responsible for issuing identifying numbers to organizational groups, for procedural identification. For example,

100 series: Quality assurance

200 series: Manufacturing

300 series: Scheduling

400 series: Planning

500 series: Engineering

600 series: Administration

700 series: Facilities

800 series: Procurement

900 series: Sales and marketing

Thus, a quality assurance procedure defining the in-process inspection process could be titled as QAP 105, In-Process Inspections.

All of the company procedures should have a consistent structure, and at a minimum, should include approvals, identification, applicability within the organization, scope of the procedure, any necessary definitions, a statement of requirements, and a step-by-step outline of actions to accomplish the requirements. Once the format has been defined, there should be no compromises. For instance, the planning department is creating a simple procedure that has no special terminology; definitions may not be required. So, instead of deleting the "Definitions" title, simply note "Not applicable," maintaining the set structure. Continuity in structure can be very important in preventing an "us and them" atmosphere.

DEPARTMENTAL PLANS AND DOCUMENTS

Departmental plans and documents can work the same way, by adding a serial number to the issued organization number. The serial number can be made up of a combination of the date of issuance and the consecutive number of the plan. For instance, the quality department is creating a test plan for a certain product. This plan was created in 1994 and in the first month (9401), and is a quality assurance plan (100), and the seventh one of the month (7), so the plan number would be 9401-100-7. The same method can be used for any of the departments within the organization.

PROGRAM-SPECIFIC DOCUMENTS

Many quality consultants argue that the contract number should be a part of the document's identification; however, this could only be true for program-specific documents. Such documents can include design specifications, critical design review minutes, telephone conference (telecon) minutes, and cover sheets for customer data transmittals, or any other document that is program specific. However, contract numbers should not be used for identification of standard procedures or documents that can be used in various programs.

If the contract number is a part of the document identification, it should include, at a minimum, the following:

- Contract number
- Type of document (CDR, critical design review; TM, telecon minutes; and so on)
- Serial number (use progressive number)
- Revision status (should be defined if letters or numbers are to be used, and if new documents are to be identified as "new" or "N/C," for no change)

Figure 6.1 displays an example of how this identification system would look.

INSPECTION DOCUMENTS

Test and inspection documents, which could include manufacturing work instructions, that document inspection status and/or test results, should have a method of traceability to the contract number, and shall have traceability to the end item serial number. This can be achieved through various methods. Most aerospace manufacturers use a cost charge number or program number that is located in the heading of the particular document. This number relates to the end item serial number and provides positive recall abilities within the system (reference "Inspection and Testing," chapter 11).

MEMORANDUMS AND FACSIMILE MESSAGES

Though not a requirement, memorandums and facsimile messages (fax) also should have identification. Again, this can be achieved through various methods. One such method is by incorporating the date, department, and consecutive serial number. Figure 6.2 displays such an identification method. Though not mandatory, it may prove to be a beneficial tool.

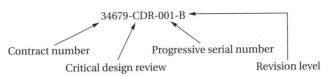

FIGURE 6.1. *Sample document identification method for contract-specific documents.*

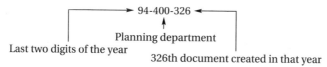

FIGURE 6.2. *Sample document identification method for memorandums and facsimile messages.*

To maintain consistency, these numbers should be controlled at one point within the applicable department. Caution is advised; it can be tempting to quickly fax a document without applying the control number. However, when this is done, the traceable reference to that transmission is lost. It might as well have never happened.

For smaller companies that only use one fax machine, the department number could be omitted. This would leave only the year and the consecutive serial number for the fax document (for example, 94-326). The same is true for memorandums, if the company is small enough to manage the control of all memorandums from one location.

The identification of the memorandum should be controlled by a control log. The control log for the memorandums should include the document serial number, to whom the memorandum was sent, name of the memorandum initiator, the subject title, and date of the memorandum.

The fax control log should be similar to that of the memorandum control log; but instead of a subject entry, the target phone number and number of pages sent should be documented. What has also proven helpful is when the person who sent the fax initials the log. This will allow for a point of contact when messages have not been received or have been received incomplete.

For both logs, if a copy of the applicable document is maintained in a centrally located control book, it can be recalled quickly. This will prevent the need of trying to track down the initiator for a copy. This will also make the communication trail open for the entire organization. The exception should be for those documents that are considered confidential.

These identification actions should be documented within the corporate policies and consistency should be required throughout the organization. The responsibility for managing this process should lie with the individual department managers using it. The quality assurance function can easily include this process into the internal auditing schedule.

DRAWING IDENTIFICATION

With regard to identification and type design, the only FAR requirements are for the primary language on the drawings and other type-certificated data to be in English, and that an effective revision system be established.

Keep in mind, with regard to information on the drawings, that FAR Parts 23 and 25 have additional requirements. These requirements are mostly specific in nature to the product and are normally required to substantiate airworthiness of type design.

In general, the system for identification of drawings shall be so established that it can be controlled effectively. With regard to the international quality system standards, the requirements for drawing/design control fall under the design requirements of ANSI/ASQC Q9001. Typically, aviation drawing numbers are made up of a core design project number and a dash number, depicting the subassembly level. But, of course, there are exceptions. Some manufacturers will use a mix of alphanumeric combinations in developing their drawing identification systems. As long as there are provisions for identifying the revision level of the drawing and an identification control system is established, the manufacturer can develop the system in any way it sees fit.

REPAIR STATIONS

Repair stations have an additional document identification requirement than other aviation organizations. As required by FAR Section 145.25, whenever the advertising of a certified repair station indicates that it is certified, it must clearly state its certificate number. This applies to documents such as, but not limited to,

- Business letterheads
- Billheads and statements
- Customer estimates and inspection forms
- Hangar or shop signs
- Magazines, periodicals, or trade journals
- Any form of promotional media

The simplest method of complying with this identification requirement is to identify all documents within the organization with the applicable certificate number. This may seem redundant, but in view of the volatile nature of the legal system, it may be the safest method of protecting the organization from potential claims of nonconformance. The quality assurance department should ensure that this special document identification requirement is part of the internal auditing cycle.

APPROVAL CYCLE

ANSI/ASQC Q9001-1994 states that all documents that relate to the requirements of the international quality standards "shall be reviewed and approved for adequacy by authorized personnel prior to issue" (4, para. 4.5.2., Document and Data Approval and Issue). The various FARs only require that those documents that relate to type design, the approved quality system, or the DAS procedure manual, need to be approved by the FAA. This approval cycle must be established and documented, with applicability throughout the organization.

First, it should be established which documents are required to be approved; then the cycle should be mapped. This is most easily accomplished through the use of flowcharts showing the document's initiation point and its end approval. Additionally, the flowchart should show a document distribution cycle after the approval, for issuance and replacing obsolete documents.

Document approval cycles can remain within one department, go through various departments, and even go outside of the company. Documents that do not affect any other group or organization can be approved internal to the department, providing the data is not FAA approved. However, any time a document affects multiple departments, it must go through each departmental management for review. The same holds true for documents that affect customer and government agencies.

Once the correct approval flow is determined, the approval process may begin. This process must be documented. To achieve this, the document should be accompanied by a routing cover sheet, much like that used in design control (as was shown in Figure 5.5). This cover sheet should provide documentation, at a minimum, of the document number, name of the initiator, date of initiation, and routing flow, and should provide room for comments. Ideally, this form will have the routing of departments already printed on it, only requiring the initiator to place a check in the applicable distribution box. This routing cover sheet could take the form of an electronic file in a paperless network system.

After the reviewers have approved the document, their signatures should be applied on the routing cover sheet. For electronic files this can be entry of a password. Once completed, this cover sheet is maintained, in file, as a quality record. It is recommended that this cover sheet is maintained as long as the document is active, and disposed of after it has become obsolete. A buffer time after obsolescence may be desirable. Prior to issuing the document, the master copy should be signed by an appropriate level of management that can ensure its compliance.

Another method some companies use is making the routing cover sheet part of the document. By placing signature blocks of all of the approvers on the document, the document itself is proof of the review and approval processes. This method will provide for stand-alone verification, but when many approvals are required, the paper document may become messy or illegible. This same method could be implemented in a paperless network system without the risk of creating an illegible document.

Either way, the review and approval process must be documented within a control procedure. The method chosen to accomplish this requirement is up to the manufacturer, but it must remain consistent. The quality assurance department shall verify the process through audit.

The manufacturer should be careful in selecting which documents are to be approved and by whom. It is easy to say that all purchase orders are to be reviewed by the purchasing manager, but at the end of the day the manager may have a stack of purchase orders on his or her desk and no time to make orders. The potential for rubber-stamp approval becomes great. The manager may resort to signing the documents without the appropriate review, just to get them off the desk. The same can be true for engineering with drawings, or any other department for that matter.

The following are types of documents that shall be found within the approval cycle

- Policies and procedures
- Engineering drawings
- Purchase orders
- Production schedules
- Manufacturing work instructions
- Contracts and proposals
- Inspection plans and reports

By selecting only those documents that have an effect on quality, measuring them for severity impact, then identifying personnel within the organization that are qualified to perform a checking function, the responsibility can be distributed among qualified members of the organization. However, personnel qualifications must be carefully reviewed, and selections distributed relative to experience. For instance, if a structural engineer designs a structural component, the design should not be checked by an electrical engineer who has no structural experience. However, if that same electrical engineer has a structural background that qualifies him or her to check structural designs, then that background should be documented as such. The same can be applied in any other departmental discipline.

When documenting authorized checkers, the following information, at a minimum, should be available: name of checker, title, description of authority, sample of checker's initials and signature, and, when applicable, a sample of checker's stamp. This will aid in later verification of the process, even after personnel have left the organization.

FAA APPROVAL

In the case where an FAA approval is required for documentation approval, this too should be identified within the documentation flowchart. It is not necessary to attach letters of FAA authorization [designated airworthiness representatives (DARs), designated manufacturing inspection representatives (DMIRs), and DERs] or other certification of personnel to the authorization rosters, but copies should be available in the employee files (reference "Training," chapter 19). Documents that require FAA approval include, but are not limited to,

- Maintenance manuals with life limitations of components
- Operational checklists
- Type design documents, including
  — Design drawings
  — Flammability test plans and results
  — Acoustical test plans and results
  — Structural substantiation documents
  — Identification and placarding data
- DAS procedure manual
- Quality system documents
- Quality assurance manuals

As noted in chapter 5, "Design Control," the FAA approval can be obtained either from the FAA directly or through one of its authorized representatives, depending on the type of document. In either case, the document always should be submitted with a cover sheet stating the document's characteristics and providing room for applicable remarks. The following document characteristics should be on the cover sheet.

- Type of document (PMA request, STC request, and so on)
- Document number(s) (entire document packages can be sent under one cover)
- Names and phone numbers of persons to contact for questions
- Reference documents
- Program information
- Remarks

This cover sheet also can be used as a valuable tool, in case of document rejections. The reason for rejection can be noted on the submitted cover sheet, and from that a corrective action can be established. This corrective action can be used in preventing any future discrepancies as well as in correcting the present problem. It is highly recommended for manufacturers to reverse this process with their suppliers. If suppliers are not supplying documents with a cover sheet, they probably should. Even more important is ensuring that suppliers establish corrective action for any discrepant documents. By reducing and even eliminating supplier documentation rejections, lead times for data transmittals can be greatly reduced and can even accelerate a program and reduce cost.

DOCUMENT DISTRIBUTION

As far as the international quality system standards are concerned, as stated in ANSI/ASQC Q9001-1994, the only requirement for document distribution is for the established system to ensure "that pertinent issues of appropriate documents are available at all locations where operations essential to the effective functioning of the quality system are performed" (4, para. 4.5.2.a., Document and Data Approval and Issue).

The FARs are quite similar in their requirements for ensuring that current design drawings must be readily available to manufacturing and inspection personnel and used when necessary [reference FAR Section 21.125 (b) (6)]. The various FARs have their own requirements for the distribution cycle, depending on their applicability. However, to define the distribution cycles of each type of FAA form or approved document would be in excess of the intent of this book. To generalize the distribution of FAA forms and approved documents, any document that affects the core quality system, affects type design, or documents discrepancies that are reportable shall be forwarded to the appropriate FAA office, as described in the applicable FARs. When changes are made or new procedures are developed, these shall be approved by the FAA prior to implementation.

It is quite simple to send someone a copy of a document; however, unless records are kept of all recipients of that document, it is impossible to notify recipients when revisions to the document are made. There must be an established control over revision-controlled documents. For documents requiring approvals, such as procedures, drawing sets, and specifications, there should be a central issuing point. At the issuing point, the original copies and distribution lists should be maintained. Each individual revision-controlled document should have its own distribution list. This distribution list will document the names and addresses of the recipients, number of copies sent, and in which format the document is to be sent (paper standard, microfiche, or electronic file). Additionally, the list should note what revisions were sent and when. The distribution list also should have a means to document an acknowledge-ment of receipt from the recipient. In the case when documents are sent outside the company (customers, governmental agencies, and so on), it is recommended that an acknowledgement form be sent with the docu-ment, with a self-addressed postage-paid envelope. The easier it is for the outside source to return a form, the more probable the return is.

For the internal paperless network system, the control of documents can be simplified. When changes are approved they can be released in real time and made available to all who have access to the system. At the same time, obsolete documents are automatically removed from the system. However, a control system must be in place to ensure that obso-lete documents outside of the network are recalled and replaced. Exam-ples of such include copies of documents that are sent to the FAA, customer, and registrar for approval or informational purposes.

If a controlled document is to be sent for informational purposes only, it should be identified as such. The first page of the document should have a stamp noting "For reference only—Will not be updated." Such documents are not allowed to be used in any process that affects quality.

Memorandums usually have a distribution cycle built into the docu-ment under the title line Copies. On this line, the names and depart-ments of the distribution recipient are typically noted. As mentioned in the identification section of this chapter, copies of memorandums should be maintained at a central point and controlled by the identifica-tion log. So, if there is a central repository for the memorandums, each memorandum should note "File" on its Copies line, sending one copy to the control file. Memorandums that are confidential in nature would probably not have "File" on the Copies line. If acknowledgement of re-ceipt is required, each recipient can initial by his or her name on the Copies line, and the initialed copy may be placed in the file. Another method would be the use of a routing sheet or through some sort of elec-tronic acknowledgement.

Though not a quality requirement, uncontrolled documents should be included when establishing a distribution procedure. Again, there are various methods of establishing a distribution cycle. One proven method is by using a distribution stamp. When this stamp is applied to a master copy, all of the department identifiers are noted on the docu-ment. By simply checking off the applicable department identifiers, the distribution is established. If the box is not checked off, the department (individual) will not be included in the distribution. Recommended is a stamp design that complements your company document format. The distribution intent is defeated if the stamp impression obscures the con-tent of the document. Additionally, a few empty lines should be left on the stamp to allow for special distribution. However such a system is developed, it must be unique to the organization and functional. In some cases a distribution system for noncontrolled documents would require more effort than the resulting benefit. This noted methodology is only a recommendation and not a requirement.

CHANGE CONTROL

The requirements for the change control of documents are almost identical to those of change control of design (chapter 5), except that in this section of ANSI/ASQC Q9001 it clearly specifies that all "changes to documents and data shall be reviewed and approved by the same functions/organizations that performed the original review and approval, unless specifically specified otherwise" (4, para. 4.5.3., Document and Data Changes). This includes design documents, such as drawings and specifications.

The changed or modified document must go through the same cycle it went through during its initial approval cycle. A routing cover sheet could be used to document these review and approval actions. When the review and approval cycle is complete, the routing sheet should be maintained in the same individual document file as the initial document and applicable changes. This will provide evidence of conformance and a clear trail to follow during an audit, to include one point of reference. Instead of making a new form for the change routing control, it may be preferred to add a box on the same type of form used in the initial review/approval cycle, identifying the reason for routing as a changed document.

The exception that the standard does allow is for the organization that determines that it is not necessary to go through the same review and approval cycle as it originally did. However, if the change and approval cycles are different for a changed document than for a new document, those cycles must be clearly defined in a control procedure or plan.

When the changed or modified document is in the change review process, all of the reviewers "shall have access to all of the pertinent background information upon which to base their review and approval." Furthermore, with relation to the background information, the standards do require, "where practical, the nature of the change shall be identified in the document or the appropriate attachments" (4, para. 4.5.3., Document and Data Changes). The most common method for complying with this requirement is through the use of a change cover sheet. This sheet can provide additional information that does not necessarily need to be in the document itself. Making the change cover sheet a different color than the document will further identify and draw attention to the change. Keeping this change cover sheet with the document will make it easier to reference the changed data later.

If documents have been changed through the use of attachments that supersede paragraphs within a document, these should be limited. The 1987 revision of the international quality standards required that the documents be reissued after a practical number of changes have been made. The 1994 revision omitted this requirement. However, the practice of limiting the number of attachment revisions is a good one. Such limitations promote maintaining clean documents. In reality, few companies allow more than five changes to be attached prior to a reissue.

The one type of document that is usually the most susceptible to such attachment changes is the engineering document. These are commonly referred to as drawing change notices (DCNs), changes in design (CIDs), and engineering orders (EOs). For engineering documents, such as new drawings, it is recommended to note in the engineering control procedure that attachment changes will be incorporated into the applicable drawings, as a reissue, in consolidation at the completion of the first article inspection. This is because it is typical for a new design to have numerous changes in the early design phases. Incorporating the changes in one large consolidation will provide a broader view of the changes, and the risk of incorporating conflicting changes is lessened.

The FARs are exacting in their requirements for changing of individual approved documents (reference "FAA Approval," page 101). As more thoroughly described in chapter 5, "Design Control," any controlled document that is approved by the FAA and changed or modified shall not be issued or incorporated until after FAA approval of the change or modification has been issued. It is the manufacturer's responsibility to ensure that this FAA approval is in writing prior to implementation.

OBSOLETE DOCUMENTS

After a document has been changed, the previous revision, if now obsolete, must be removed from all points of issue. As stated earlier in this chapter, there are some cases in which older revisions are needed in the performance of a manufacturer's repair. These earlier revisions should be maintained at one controlled point of issue and released to individual work orders as required. This will prevent inadvertent use within the manufacturing process.

However, in most manufacturing cases, older revisions are not required. Because the control of obsolete documents is extremely cross-functional in nature, it is recommended that is defined in a corporate policy. Individual departments can elaborate in more detail with regard to their particular documents in departmental procedures. However, in the development of the departmental procedures, caution should be used to ensure that a consistent method throughout the entire organization is maintained.

Developing the policy/procedure within a cross-functional team will provide the best results in developing a methodology that is functional throughout the entire organization. This may even prevent the need for individual departmental procedures, if one standard policy/procedure can be created.

MASTER LIST

In order to provide clarification and direction in determining the appropriate revision level for a document, a point of reference must be maintained. ANSI/ASQC Q9001 states, "A master list or its equivalent document-control procedure identifying the current revision of documents shall be established and be readily accessible to preclude the use of invalid and/or obsolete documents" (4, para. 4.5.2., Document and Data Approval and Issue).

Depending on the size of the organization, the master list can be maintained either on computer database or on hard copy issues, or both. Regardless of which method is used, the master list must be accessible to anybody in the organization that uses any of the applicable documents on the list. As this is usually everyone in the company, it will probably be required to be accessible to everyone in the organization.

Though computer network systems are convenient for updating and real-time capabilities can be achieved, computer networks are not always accessible to everyone in the organization and are prone to failures. So it is recommended to maintain at least a copy of the master list at locations where access is available to everyone. For a smaller company this could possibly be one location for the entire organization; however, for larger companies, this could mean many locations.

Any time a document that is listed on the master list is changed in revision status, the master list must reflect the change and be reissued accordingly. Primarily, this should be the responsibility of the document control department. But the managers of all the individual functions should share in the responsibility. By taking an active role in checking the issued documents, including the master list, the individual functional managers are becoming participative in a quality role. Additionally, the master list should be included in the internal audit schedule.

Keep in mind that this master list does not need to be anything fancy. A simple computer printout in a three-ring binder would suffice. In many smaller companies, this list could be one page posted on an information bulletin board. But it must be revision controlled, and usable. In creating a revision system for a master list, instead of using a letter or number, an issue date may work best.

SUMMARY

The requirements for document control are derived primarily from the international quality standards and relate to all documents required as part of the quality system. This would include purchase orders, contract proposals, minutes of meetings (records of discussion), critical design reviews, procedures, work instructions, inspection/test plans, as well as various others. However, as discussed in chapter 5, any data that require FAA approval (design data, quality procedures, flight manuals, and so on) must also be subjected to approval and change controls.

Document standardization within the organization is very important. If documents are standardized in one common format, the methodology as well as the data therein can be more easily interpreted and used. This should include the standardization of document identification.

The international quality standards require that procedures are created that control the various processes of a document, which include the approval cycle, distribution cycle, change cycle, and control of obsolete documents. Additionally, through the implementation of a controlled master list, transparency will be created of the document status. It also will provide a one-source location for this information.

To ensure that the document control process is conforming, and remains capable, the elements of document control should be included in the internal audit schedule.

NOTES

1. ANSI/ASQC Q9001-1994, *Quality Systems—Model for Quality Assurance in Design, Development, Production, Installation, and Servicing* (Milwaukee, Wis.: American Society for Quality Control, 1994), 4, para. 4.5.2., Document and Data Approval and Issue.

Chapter 7

PURCHASING

Purchasing, more commonly referred to as "procurement" in the aviation industry, envelops all interactions with supplying organizations outside of the company. These interactions would include the procurement of human services (engineering and accounting), processing services (surface treatments), material procurement (raw stock and off-the-shelf components), and manufacturing subcontracting. Typically, most organizations will have a department dedicated to the management of these activities.

Within the scope of the international quality systems standards, only ANSI/ASQC Q9001 and ANSI/ASQC Q9002 require control within purchasing, and the requirements for both are identical. Under the title of Purchasing, there are three main subtitles.

- Evaluation of Subcontractors
- Purchasing Data
- Verification of Purchased Products

Federal Aviation Regulation (FAR) Part 21, Subparts F, G, K, and O require the establishment of an inspection/quality control system as a prerequisite to issuance of an FAA production approval, and maintenance of such system after the approval has been issued. One of the criteria for approval of an inspection/quality control system is the establishment by the applicant of requirements and procedures for ensuring that parts and components produced by suppliers conform to the approved design data and are in condition for safe operation. These same requirements are applicable for repair stations operating under FAR Part 145. Up until the early 1980s, the FAA's policy for monitoring supplier activity has been to conduct regularly scheduled audits of selected domestic suppliers, and, in the case of foreign suppliers, allow the use of only those in countries with which the United States has bilateral airworthiness agreements, and only when each component produced has been issued a conformity certificate (export certificate) by the Foreign Civil Air Authority (FCAA).

Though now superseded by revision A, Advisory Circular 21-20 best describes the FAA's rationale for placing the responsibility of supplier control on the manufacturers.

> *The FAA had reassessed its past policies concerning supplier surveillance, and with the need to reduce government operating costs, and the problems experienced with the surveillance procedures with respect to foreign suppliers. Also considered was the ultimate responsibility of the production (manufacturing) approval holder, for ensuring that each completed product, including supplier furnished articles, that leaves the holder's domestic production facility conforms to the approved design data and is in condition for safe operation.[1]*

Thus, the requirement of supplier control was placed on the holder of the manufacturing approval. This responsibility is to be enforced without regard to where suppliers may be located, whether suppliers have been under FAA surveillance, or whether procured components have been certified under a bilateral airworthiness agreement. The ACSEP evaluation criteria also requires the control of suppliers by the manufacturer.[2]

The FAA also concluded

> *that the safety objectives of the FAA will be met, without regularly scheduled audits of the suppliers, by concentrating FAA resources at the manufacturing approval holder's main domestic facilities, with emphasis on supplier controls and receiving inspection. The FAA will not, however, relinquish the authority or responsibility for reinspection of suppliers, either foreign or domestic, at any time for cause, using either FAA inspectors or FAA designees. The use of Foreign Civil Air Authorities to certify components produced in countries with which the U.S. has bilateral airworthiness agreements will be retained as an option, dependent upon individual circumstances.[3]*

Under the FAA's present policy, the holder of the manufacturing approval is responsible for ensuring that the supplier control is effective. Though the FAA may sound strict when it comes to supplier management, other than requiring procedures for the assurance of conforming product, it does not offer a system to control it. The system methodology should be, and is, the responsibility of the individual aviation manufacturer to develop and control. Using the international quality standards, and coupling the FAA requirements, a company can achieve an effective and conforming supplier management system. These controls and requirements must be documented in procedures or policies. Like all major quality system characteristics, the procurement system should be described within the quality assurance manual (QAM). Depending on the size of the organization, the individual characteristics of the procurement system should be broken down into individual procedures, to allow for more detailed description. The smaller the company, the fewer the procedures needed to control the system. It is also recommended to use the evaluation criteria of ACSEP as a reference in the development of control procedures.

Revision A of AC 21-20 provides more definition of a conforming supplier control system and less background information. AC 21-20A states that

> *the PAH (production approval holder) shall have established and documented in its FAA-approved Quality Assurance Manual or other FAA-approved procedures the method by which suppliers, including sub-tier suppliers, are qualified, controlled, and monitored. These procedures should also describe the quality control or inspection system the PAH has in place to ensure conformity to FAA-approved design data and condition for safe operation of parts produced by supplier. The quality control system or inspection system and its implementation at a supplier facility are subject to evaluation by the FAA at any time.[4]*

This system "should include procedures whereby first production-run parts [reference chapter 5, discussion on first article inspections, pages 83–87] are subjected to inspection and testing, as necessary, to verify that the articles conform to FAA-approved design data and are in condition for safe operation" [2, para. (6)(b)(3), Procedure]. Sometimes during a development program it will be required to perform first article inspections (FAI) on more than one article, until the production consistency of the supplier is verified.

To substantiate the effective control of the supplier's quality system, AC 21-20A also addressees the necessity of evaluations. "The procedures should also provide for the PAH to plan and conduct on-site quality control or inspection system and product evaluations of the supplier, including sub-tier suppliers. The evaluations, conducted at established intervals, should include all parts" [2, para. (6)(b)(3), Procedure]. The results of such evaluations shall be considered quality records (reference chapter 17). Some of these on-site evaluations may be performed by third parties. However, these third parties must be experienced in the applicable applications and familiar with the applicable methods of control.

The manufacturer must be cautious not to use a supplier in a foreign country whose authorities would prohibit the entry into the country of FAA personnel or FAA representatives, or inhibit in any manner a proposed audit by the FAA of a manufacturer's system to oversee the performance of a supplier in that country. However, when the FAA does perform an audit of a foreign supplier, it will not audit the supplier's entire quality control system. It will only audit the control system established by the U.S. manufacturer that assures the FAA-approved product. Furthermore, the foreign civil air authority of the country in which the supplier is located would be invited to either participate in such audits, or, as mutually agreed upon when a bilateral agreement exists, conduct the audit and submit findings to the FAA for approval. With regard to any data submitted to the FAA for review and/or approval, it must be in the English language.

Advisory Circular 21-20A dictates that,

> *When a PAH intends to use a supplier in a non-bilaterial airworthiness agreement [BAA] country, the cognizant FAA office having certificate management responsibility should be contacted for appropriate guidance. There are two acceptable methods for a PAH to utilize the services of a supplier from a non-BAA country.*
>
> > *(1) Inspection upon receipt. The part being purchased is completely inspectable upon receipt at the PAH's facility located in the United States. This may include periodic verification of material and processes.*
> >
> > *(2) Under specific procedures acceptable to the FAA. The PAH may use a supplier from a non-BAA country when it has established and documented in its quality control or inspection system the procedures that specifically identify how suppliers from a non-BAA country are qualified, approved, and controlled. The system established must ensure conformity and condition for safe operation of all parts and/or services provided by the suppliers. This system would be approved by the FAA only after a determination has been made that no undue burden (e.g. insufficent resources) would be placed on the United States in administering the applicable requirements of the Federal Aviation Act of 1958 or the Federal Aviation Regulations. Implementation at the supplier facility is subject to evaluation by the FAA. [3, para. (6)(c), Procedure]*

EVALUATION OF SUBCONTRACTORS

The international quality standards require the manufacturer to "evaluate and select subcontractors on the basis of their ability to meet subcontract requirements, including quality requirements and any specific quality assurance requirements." Additionally, the manufacturer shall "define the type and extent of control exercised over the subcontractors. This shall be dependant upon the type of product, the impact of subcontracted product on the quality of final product, and, where applicable, on the quality audit reports and/or quality records of previously demonstrated capability and performance of subcontractors." Furthermore, the manufacturer shall "establish and maintain quality records of acceptable subcontractors."[5] This record would include an approved suppliers list.

When using ISO 9000 registered suppliers as the sole sources for procurement, the manufacturer should be assured that the supplier has a conforming quality system. But a conforming quality system does not necessarily mean that the supplier can meet other contract requirements. Placing a contract with a supplier just because it has ISO 9000 registration could be a reckless act. The individual capabilities of the subcontractor must also be given attention. For example, if a subcontractor was to manufacture a composite structure in an autoclave bonding process, but has never used an autoclave, there should be reason for concern. Individual process audits should be performed to ensure capabilities. The same holds true for capacity evaluation and financial strength. It does little good to give a contract out to a company who might not have the time or space to perform the work, or worse, may not be around next month.

In determination of a supplier's engineering capabilities, an audit should be performed by qualified personnel. These qualified personnel should come from the manufacturer's engineering departments and have been trained in the skills of auditing. This will ensure that the auditors are familiar with activities being audited. Studying the supplier's past history in such engineering projects will help establish a track record. Additionally, engineering equipment should be evaluated. There should be sufficient equipment to perform the job. Interfacing of engineering software should be considered also. If the manufacturer is running its engineering system in CATIA and the supplier in CAD, an interfacing software program will be required.

The capacity of the supplier also should be reviewed to prevent surprises when the delivery date rolls around. This will require auditors from the manufacturer's scheduling and program management departments. Again training is a prerequisite for such auditors, to ensure the audit process is carried out correctly. Looking at the supplier's track record for on-time shipping, as well as a detailed review of the supplier's internal production schedule will provide the best insight to the suppliers' capacity. Additionally, when using a foreign supplier it is helpful to find out if that country has mandatory military participation. For example, in

Switzerland all able-bodied males between the ages of 18 and retirement must participate in military training for at least two weeks a year. Because the country is small, many of the men in a company will be in the same military units. So, when it is time to participate in military training the company is often forced to shut down or perform at reduced staff. This has become a problem in numerous instances for U.S. manufacturers who have stringent delivery needs during these typical time frames of military training. In other countries, the daily work day is broken into two parts, allowing for a siesta. Germany is also a good example; the IG Metal, the largest technical union in Germany, is so strong it has shut companies down for weeks. It has also negotiated for a nationwide 37.5-hour work week and limited overtime for its members. So, when evaluating the company's capacity, it may prove beneficial to be acquainted with the local social habits, union interactions, and governmental requirements.

The financial stability of a company is important as well. The personnel of the manufacturer's finance and contracts departments are the most appropriate to make this evaluation. Particularly when a contract is going to be of high value and long term, it is important to ensure that the supplier will be around to deliver the product. The concern is even more complex when the product has a long lead time. This means if the supplier goes into receivership, the manufacturer may not be able to procure the product from other sources in time to maintain the schedule. Many larger manufacturers will maintain a second source for a product procurement, to ensure its availability in the event that the prime supplier goes under. Two of the best sources of determining a supplier's financial status are an examination of the supplier's published accounts and a report from an accredited agency.

The manufacturing abilities of the supplier also must be evaluated. A trained team, consisting of representatives from the manufacturer's tooling, manufacturing, and quality inspection and assurance departments, would be the best qualified to perform such an evaluation. The manufacturer should ensure that the supplier is capable of performing the labor that is being subcontracted. This includes the actual manufacturing labor force, tooling production, and inspection capability. Reviewing the supplier's past performance in similar contracts would provide the track record, but looking at the equipment will provide additional insight. If the subcontracted project is heavy with machining processes, the question must be asked if the supplier has sufficient machining capabilities. The same is true for special inspection techniques. Is the inspection department trained in the proper techniques of the process required and are the instruments and equipment available for such? Training is very important. For instance, for a project that has a lot of composite bonding and aluminum brazing—two processes that are complex—the supplier's personnel must be capable of performing the required processes correctly. A review of the supplier's training records, as well as the list of certificates and licenses its personnel hold, will provide additional insight into this area.

There are areas of special interest that may require additional audit. They should be performed by personnel that are both trained in auditing methods and competent in the area of evaluation.

The quality assurance system is the most frequented area of evaluation. Where most of the other areas would most likely be evaluated once at the beginning of the project, the quality assurance system should be audited on a recurring schedule. The quality system audit should go deep enough into the supplier's system that, if any of the other disciplines are out of control, it would be obvious in the quality audit. First, the standard and level to which the audit is to be performed must be determined. There are various quality standards available upon which suppliers can develop their quality systems. In the U.S. commercial aviation industry, MIL-Q-9858A and MIL-I-45208 are probably the most common of the quality standards used. However, the rest of the world has adopted the international quality standards, and since this book is based on the coupling of those standards we will concentrate on the international quality system standards.

If a prospective supplier is registered under one of the two upper-level international quality standards (ANSI/ASQC Q9001 or ANSI/ASQC Q9002), then the manufacturer could accept that registration as proof of a conforming quality system. However, objective evidence of that registration should be required. A copy of the registration certificate would suffice. If there are questions regarding the validity of the registration certificate, the manufacturer should contact the supplier's registrar. The manufacturer should repeat this process annually to ensure the supplier's registration is current. It must be stressed that though the supplier may have a third-party quality registration, the manufacturer is still responsible for the quality system of its suppliers per the FARs. The registration to one of the two upper-level international quality standards does not include the applicable FAA or CAA requirements. It also does not certify special processing—all the more reason for having registrars certified for aviation evaluations. With such special certification, a higher level of confidence may be achieved in quality system registration.

Special process audits also should be placed on a regular schedule for reevaluation, and may be performed by third-party evaluation firms. However, process evaluations may not be as frequent as quality audits and may be spaced as far as five years apart. Whatever method the manufacturer determines appropriate to ensure process conformity, it must be documented within a procedure (reference chapter 10) and the evaluation intervals must be established to assure continuous conformance.

If there are additional quality requirements that may not be covered under the scheme of the international quality standards, the manufacturer should perform an addendum audit covering only those extra areas of concern. This will be typical for aviation companies that have additional FAR requirements. It will be a fact of business that not every supplier will obtain ISO 9000 quality system registration right away, if ever. If a supplier is not registered to an international quality system standard and the manufacturer desires or requires the services or product of that supplier, then the manufacturer must perform an audit of the quality system itself or contract a third party. This evaluation does not necessarily have to be to one of the international quality system standards. The supplier's quality system shall be dependent on the product and the level of control required. In some cases the supplier will not be evaluated to a quality system standard, but rather to a quality plan that was developed specifically for that supplier and its product or service.

AUDIT PLANS

Prior to performing the audits of the various aspects of the supplier's systems, audit plans should be developed. These audit plans will guide the auditing team through the various phases of the audit and will keep the team on course. Without such an audit plan it is simple to get off course during the audit and never accomplish the desired objective.

Preceding the audit plan is normally a cover sheet (Figure 7.1). This cover sheet is the one-stop source for the overall audit information. It should be a serial number–controlled document and should include the name of the organization being audited, address, telephone number and other communicative numbers (for example, fax, modem, telex), name of the contact person, project/purchase order/contract number, name of the product or service supplied, type of audit, date of audit, audit criteria (ANSI/ASQC Q9001 or ANSI/ASQC Q9002 and FAR subpart, when applicable), names of the individuals on the audit team, date of last audit, control number of last audit, summary of the audit, and signatures of both the lead auditor and the audited quality manager and date. When completed, this cover sheet can be used as the objective evidence that the audit was performed. The cover sheet serial number and status can be controlled by a log sheet, as displayed in Figure 7.2.

Most aviation companies have their own preformatted audit checklists for evaluation of suppliers' quality systems. These checklists have standardized questions and are based on the level of quality desired by the manufacturer, normally one of the military standards or one of its

```
+-----------------------------------------------------------------------+
|        ACXI            Supplier Quality                               |
| Aviation Company X, Inc.  System Audit Report                         |
| 1234 W. Main St.                              Audit S/N _____       |
| Wichita, Kansas                                                       |
|                                                                       |
| Preassessment [ ]   Other _____         Audit date _____        |
|                                                                       |
| Supplier _____   Address _____           |
|                                                                       |
| City _____  State _____  Zip _____  Area code _____       |
|                                                                       |
| Head of QA _____  Title _____  Phone _____             |
|                                                                       |
| Reports to _____  Title _____  Phone _____             |
|                                                                       |
| Other _____  Title _____  Phone _____                  |
| contacts                                                              |
|                  _____  Title _____  Phone _____       |
|                                                                       |
| Fax _____  Telex _____  Other _____            |
|                                                                       |
| Products manufactured _____                        |
| Special processing (Attach additional sheets when necessary)          |
|                                                                       |
| Briefly                                                               |
| describe: _____                                    |
| Quality system approvals (attach additional sheets when necessary)    |
|                                                                       |
| ISO  [ ]    ISO  [ ]    ISO  [ ]    Other [ ]    (Note on             |
| 9001        9002        9003                     attachment)          |
|                                                                       |
| Total no. of   Number in       Number                Shifts          |
| employees ___  manufacturing ___ in QA/QC ___ Ratio ___ worked ___    |
|                                                                       |
| Comments/recommendations: _____                    |
|                                                                       |
| Audit conducted by: _____  Title _____           |
+-----------------------------------------------------------------------+
|                          Audit results                                |
+-----------------------------------------------------------------------+
| Approved [ ]   Disapproved [ ]   For the following commodities: ____  |
|                                                                       |
| At quality level (Note quality standard and revision): _____        |
|                                                                       |
| CAR required              [ ]    CAR number and date _____          |
| Follow-up audit required  [ ]    Approximate follow-up date _____    |
| Distribution:                                                         |
|                                  Concurrence: _____         |
|                                  Title _____                |
|                                  Date _____                 |
+-----------------------------------------------------------------------+
```

ACXI Form 118 (05 Aug. 94)

FIGURE 7.1. *Sample supplier quality system audit report.*

ACXI Wichita, Kansas	Supplier Quality System Audit Report Status Log							
Audit report serial no.	Supplier's name	Type of audit	Audit date	Audit team leader	Procedures/criteria audited	Contract/ purchase order no.	Date audit report issued	CARs issued

ACXI Form 156 (05 Aug. 94)

FIGURE 7.2. *Sample supplier quality system audit report status log.*

own design. Through experience, these audit checklists have been proven to be too narrow and not adaptive to the commodity or the demographics. The other option is to create an individual audit plan for each supplier audited. This audit plan should be developed after review of the supplier's quality manual, procedures, and other departmental procedures, and compared to the standard of control desired, in this case ANSI/ASQC Q9001 or ANSI/ASQC Q9002, and the applicable FARs. The audit plan questions should be structured to ensure that each of the requirements of the applicable standard are addressed (Figure 7.3). This type of audit plan can be developed for all applicable discipline audits, and would provide the best overall results.

When the audit plan is being developed, the questions should be structured around what the activity should produce. Then ask, Is it produced? Is it available? Is it complete? The audit plan should record the specific details of the objective evidence that has been examined. This documentation will assist in later discussions regarding the audit and substantiate how the findings were made.

AUDIT DISCREPANCIES

Any discrepancies found during these audits shall be documented and the supplier informed in writing. This notification should be made on a corrective action request (CAR) form (Figure 7.4). A separate CAR should be initiated for each individual discrepancy. When the CARs are presented to the supplier, they should be covered by a form letter addressing the audit findings, documenting the serial numbers of the CARs issued, and stating what further actions are expected to be taken by the supplier. When presenting such documents, the manufacturer should refrain from making recommendations or suggestions. As will be discussed in chapter 15, corrective action must be documented to prevent recurrence.

The form used to document corrective action on quality systems may be somewhat different in appearance than that used to document nonconformances in products. However, the basic differences are in the heading. Otherwise the process is the same. The nonconformance is documented, the action taken to correct the nonconformance is documented, the action taken to prevent recurrence is documented, and a means is provided to document follow-up audit results. Controlling the issue of CARs should be a log, as displayed in Figure 7.5.

It is important to provide the supplier with a due return (suspense) date for achievement of the corrective action. This will ensure that the expectations of both parties are understood. Extensions may be granted, but not as a rule. The procedure that controls the auditing process

| | | | Aerospace Company X, Inc.
Wichita, Kansas | Audit Plan | Report no. WA94-023 | Page 1 of 6 |

Audit Plan

Aerospace Company X, Inc.
Wichita, Kansas

Report no. WA94-023   Page 1 of 6

Item no.	Requirement	Compliance status	Comments/Remarks/Evidence
	Quality Assurance Procedure 101, Rev. C		
1.	Is a controlled copy of QAP 101, Rev. C, available?	Acceptable	A controlled copy, number 048, of QAP 101, Rev. C, was found to be available and complete.
2.	References		
2.1.	Are controlled copies of the following documents available and current? Quality Assurance Procedure 105, Rev. D Quality Assurance Procedure 109, Rev. C Engineering Procedure 350, Rev. E Manufacturing Procedure 220, Rev. G Corporate Policy 905, Rev. L	Acceptable Acceptable Acceptable Acceptable Unacceptable	Available and current Available and current Available and current Available and current Available but not current. Revision D was available. Documented on CAR no. 1
3.	Definitions		
3.1	Are all definitions fully understood by applicable employees?	Acceptable	Found that all available personnel had an understanding of the definitions.
4.	Actions		
4.1	Has the authority been defined for document control activities?	Acceptable	Memo W94-321, dated 5 August 1994, defines and delegates authority.

ACXI Form 129 (05 Aug. 94)

FIGURE 7.3. *Sample of an audit plan.*

Corrective Action Request (CAR)			
Aviation Company X, Inc.	Audit report number	CAR no.	Date

Name and address of supplier

Auditor	Type of audit	Area audited
Supplier representative	Title	Telephone and/or fax number

Description of nonconformance and suspected cause

Additional sheets attached?   ☐ Yes   ☐ No

Requester's signature	Reviewer's signature

Determined root cause   Additional sheets attached?   ☐ Yes   ☐ No

Corrective action and effectivity   Additional sheets attached?   ☐ Yes ☐ No

Follow-up and closeout results   Proposed follow-up date

Remarks   Signed when complete and closed

_____   _____
Auditor signature   Date

ACXI Form 147 (05 Aug. 94)

FIGURE 7.4.   *Sample corrective action request.*

ACXI
Wichita, Kansas

Corrective Action Request Status Log

CAR serial no.	CAR issued to	Discrepancy	Issue date	Name of auditor	Response due date	Response received date	Proposed follow-up date	Date CAR closed

ACXI Form 153 (05 Aug. 94)

FIGURE 7.5. *Sample corrective action request status log.*

should outline the process for responding to supplier's requests for extensions and outline the allowed extension intervals. For many manufacturers it used to be acceptable practice to provide a foreign supplier with a longer suspense date than a domestic supplier, mainly because of the distances involved and language barriers. However, with the evolution of electronic communications, it really does not matter if you are next door or on the other side of the world. The only thing that may still require leniency for foreign suppliers is language barriers. This may require up to a week longer for a corrective action response, but it should not be forgotten that the FAA requires all of the documentation to be in English. So the excuse that nobody in the company understands English may require another investigation in itself. As a rule all suppliers should have a standard suspense time. Most companies have found that 10 working days works well and is fair to both parties.

When documenting the discrepancy, it should be grouped into one of three categories.

- Category 1 nonconformances are major or unacceptable discrepancies and alone are cause to reject a supplier's approval. Such nonconformances would include the supplier not addressing an element of the applicable international quality system standard or FAR requirements, an activity which is in direct contravention of the standard, or an activity which is in direct contravention of a procedure and will have consequential effect on the quality of the product or the service.

- Category 2 nonconformances are also called minor or conditional discrepancies. Category 2 nonconformances also should be documented on corrective action requests; however, they do not necessarily preclude a supplier from approval. As long as there are not more than three incidents of the same discrepancy encountered in the audit, the supplier should be conditionally approved. However, if more than three discrepancies of the same type exist, they should be upgraded to a major (category 1) nonconformance. Category 2 nonconformances are isolated incidents of nonconformance with a system or procedural requirement which has no direct consequential effect on the quality of the product or service.

- Category 3 nonconformances are not nonconformances at all. Rather, they are observations or comments on the supplier's quality system. This comment is not a requirement for change, but should provide a view to improvement.

As noted earlier, the corrective action request will document the follow-up audit results. This should be scheduled upon receipt of both the corrective action and the preventive action, and should be scheduled long enough after the preventive action is implemented to ensure effectiveness. The corrective actions and preventive actions shall be reviewed and, when found acceptable, signed off by the initiating auditor. If, upon further evaluation, it is found that the condition still exists or the discrepancy is only partially rectified, a new corrective action request should be initiated. The old CAR should be closed out by referencing the new control number of the corrective action request. If a supplier is unwilling or unable to comply with the requirements, then the subcontract should not be placed with that supplier, unless other means are provided to compensate for the discrepancy (for example, source inspection).

APPROVED SUPPLIER LIST

After a supplier has been approved to supply services or products, or as a subcontractor, the supplier should be added to the manufacturer's approved suppliers list. This list should be maintained by the activity that performs and approves suppliers, and should include the supplier's name, address, telephone and fax numbers, name of contact person, list of the products or services the supplier is allowed to supply, and dates of the last and next quality audits. The quality level to which the supplier was approved also should be noted. For suppliers that are registered to one of the international quality system standards, the audit dates would actually be the dates of registration certificate review. This list shall be treated as a revision-controlled quality document and distributed to all personnel who require its information. Normally, this would include the purchasing, quality, and program management departments. It is also good practice to send copies to approved suppliers. This will promote approved suppliers using approved suppliers.

It is very important that the accuracy of this document is maintained. If a supplier was disqualified for any reason, the supplier should be removed from this list to preclude further use. A company would look rather silly if its purchasing department was to ask a supplier to provide a bid for a product or service only days after the supplier was disqualified for a quality reason. The list shall be revision controlled and updated as major changes occur, but at least annually. Minor changes can be distributed through addenda to the document and can be issued as often as needed. However, the company should take precautions to ensure that the addenda do not become overwhelming in quantity. A maximum number prior to total revision should be set within the applicable procedure (reference chapter 6).

PURCHASING DATA

The individual FARs make little reference to the contents of the purchase order or contract. However, within the FARs the FAA does make strong mention of product conformity in accordance with applicable specifications, so in essence the control of output data (purchase orders) is implied. Advisory Circular 21-1B clarifies the FAA's position as it states that purchase orders should provide specifications or other design data in the detail necessary to ensure procurement of articles or services that meet the requirements of the approved type design. As it is the manufacturers' responsibility to control their suppliers, it is also their responsibility to keep them informed. The first step in doing so is providing a complete and concise data package with the appropriate purchase order or contract.

In aviation companies, it has been the traditional responsibility of the quality assurance department (hereafter referred to in this chapter as QA) to review all outgoing purchase orders and contracts to ensure that the applicable quality clauses are applied and special data are provided. Within the concept of the ANSI/ASQC Q9000 (ISO 9000) series, this action is no longer necessarily the responsibility of QA, but that of whoever is responsible for the process, in this case the purchasing or program management departments. Providing that personnel in these departments were trained in the various certification requirements, they should be capable of fulfilling this responsibility. One person from purchasing or program management would create the purchasing documents and ensure that all of the appropriate data required are applied or supplied with the purchasing document; and another qualified person from the same department would check the document and data package to ensure its conformity to company procedures, quality standards, and FAA requirements. QA would perform auditing and training roles, ensuring that the process is capable and the personnel knowledgeable. The qualified checking personnel should be identified within an authorization list. This will enhance visibility of authority within the organization and assist auditors to substantiate conformity during an audit.

It is not a requirement to give these responsibilities to the purchasing and program management departments. It is only the global philosophy surrounding the international quality standards and of total quality management that everyone should be responsible for their own actions and properly trained and qualified to perform the responsibilities they are assigned. If this philosophy is true, then these departments would be capable of checking their own work. However, many larger aviation companies may find it almost impossible to do so with their constant turnover rates in these departments. The most appropriate place for this responsibility is where it can be accomplished the most effectively and still conform to the requirements. Because of the complex variety of requirements in aviation, and the fast pace of change, it may be most practical and effective to keep this responsibility within the QA organization.

The recommended method for this process is to give purchasing or program management the responsibility for ensuring that the appropriate data is supplied and the quality clauses applied to the purchasing document. Then a department within QA would review the document for correctness, with regard to quality requirements. This process could be further assured through later internal audit. As the process became more capable, the possibility of responsibility shift may become more realistic, but only after the process is capable, and keeping in consideration that personnel changes may affect the process, requiring additional safeguarding.

ANSI/ASQC Q9001 and ANSI/ASQC Q9002 state that the "purchasing documents shall contain data clearly describing the product ordered (ANSI/ASQC Q9001, 5, para. 4.6.3., Purchasing Data). All guesswork should be removed. When describing the desired product or service, its precise identification shall be used, to include the type, class, style, or grade. This is very important, especially when a supplier may manufacture a variety of products that are similar in appearance and function and only have very slight differences. Additionally, when reference is made to design control documents or other specification documents (such as specifications, drawings, process requirements, inspection instructions/plans, and other relevant technical data), the document's title, revision designation, number, or other positive identification shall be used to describe the document. This would include requirements for approval or qualification of product, procedures, process equipment, and personnel.

The level of the required quality system also shall be noted on the purchase document. The applicable quality system standard shall be described by its title, number, and revision level. For many aviation products this will most likely be a combination of both the applicable international quality standard and the applicable FAR subpart. Attention should be given to the identification requirements of FAR 45, that may be in addition to the applicable FAA manufacturing approval.

A proven method in application of the data to the purchase document is through the use of quality clauses. These clauses are normally alphanumeric identifiers for prewritten clauses. For example, if there is a requirement for source inspection to be carried out, a reference number that identifies the source inspection requirement would be applied to the purchase document (Figure 7.6). Applicable clauses should be supplied to

SQ62XX *Inspection*

SQ6210 *Aviation Company X, Inc. Source Inspection*

Source inspection by Aviation Company X, Inc. (ACXI) is required at seller's facility after seller inspection and prior to packaging and shipment from your plant. Evidence of such inspection must be indicated on the packing sheet and ACXI-supplied documentation accompanying each shipment. Notify ACXI source inspection department at least ninety-six (96) hours in advance of time product is to be inspected.

FIGURE 7.6. *Sample quality clause.*

the supplier as an attachment to the purchase document. This method cuts down the bulk of the purchase document and standardizes the requirement instructions. This streamlines the process all the way from the document's initiation to the time it is received. Personnel that receive the product and compare it with the purchase requirements would only need the purchase document sheet that lists the quality clauses and special instructions and would be familiar with the standardized system.

VERIFICATION OF PURCHASED PRODUCT

All of the FAA manufacturing approval regulations require that the manufacturer inspect all parts in process for conformity with the design data at points in production where accurate determination can be made. So, if the conformity of the product cannot be substantiated at receiving inspection, source inspection may be required. To ensure the contractual right to perform source inspection, it must be noted in the purchase document. ANSI/ASQC Q9001 and ANSI/ASQC Q9002 also state this requirement for source inspection as a purchase document requirement. However, when creating the quality clause for the source inspection requirement, it shall be noted that when it is elected to carry out verification at the supplier's facility, such verification shall not be used by the supplier as evidence of effective control of quality by the supplier. The supplier must be held accountable continually for its own performance and adherence to contract requirements.

ANSI/ASQC Q9001 and ANSI/ASQC Q9002 also require, "where specified in the contract, the supplier's customer or its customer's representative shall be afforded the right to verify at the subcontractor's premises and at its supplier's premises that subcontracted product conforms to specified requirement (ANSI/ASQC Q9001, 5, para. 4.6.4.1., Supplier Verification at Subcontractor's Premises). So during the contract review process, it would be wise to verify any source inspection requirements and flow these requirements to the suppliers, as required.

Like in the manufacturer–supplier relationship, when a customer performs such a source inspection it does not absolve the manufacturer of the responsibility to provide acceptable product, nor shall it preclude subsequent rejection by the customer. Applying this one tier lower, when the customer performs a source inspection at the manufacturer's supplier, such verification shall not be used by the manufacturer as evidence of effective control of quality by the supplier. The manufacturer remains ultimately responsible for the quality of its suppliers.

The FAA also shall be provided access to the supplier's subcontractor's facility to verify the conformity of a product. This too should be a quality clause, and should be applied to all purchase orders. As mentioned earlier, caution must be taken when using foreign suppliers. Even though the idea behind ISO 9000 quality system registration is to create a level global playing field, the requirements of the FAA will limit the global participation of aviation manufacturers—in the name of safety. The manufacturer may not use a supplier in a foreign country whose authorities would prohibit in any manner a proposed audit by the FAA. Again, bilateral agreements will play a role in the interactions of the FAA in other countries. Basically, if the country does not have a bilateral agreement with the FAA, then business in that country would be greatly restricted. Advisory Circular 21-18 documents the actual contents of each of the individual bilateral agreements. Prior to doing business in a particular country, it is recommended that this document is reviewed.

When a supplier is located in a country with which the United States has a bilateral airworthiness agreement, the manufacturer has the option of either meeting the supplier control requirements, as described earlier, or using the bilateral agreement provisions for the conformity certificates issued by the foreign civil air authority for each component. Notification of the intention to use bilateral agreement procedures should be made by the manufacturer to the FAA office that has jurisdiction over the manufacturer's domestic facilities. The FAA will arrange for appropriate notification to the foreign civil air authority. This will normally mean that the component that is being processed under the provisions of the bilateral agreement will be certified to type design by the foreign civil air authority and will be delivered with an export certificate. These bilateral provisions apply only to components that are to be installed in civil aircraft, propellers, engines, or appliances, and do not include these finished items. Paragraph three of the bilateral agreement with the United Kingdom describes this type of agreement quite clearly.

> *In the case of components which are produced in the exporting State for export and use on products which are or may be certified or approved in the importing State, if the competent aeronautical*

authorities of the exporting State certify that the component con-
forms to the applicable design data and meets the applicable test
and quality control requirements which have been notified by the
importing State to the exporting State, the importing State shall
give the same validity to the certification as if the certification had
been made by its own competent aeronautical authorities. This
provision shall only apply to those components which are pro-
duced by a manufacturer in the exporting State pursuant to an
agreement between that manufacturer and the product manu-
facturer in the importing State. Furthermore, it shall only apply in
those instances where, in the judgement of the importing State,
the component is of such complexity that determination of con-
formity and quality control cannot readily be made at the time
the component is assembled with the product.[6]

Though this is the agreement with one foreign civil air authority, it is
consistent with most of the others. It should not be forgotten that these
agreements are subject to revision, though this rarely occurs.

DIRECT SHIPMENT FROM A SUPPLIER

Advisory Circular 21-20A provides additional clarification for manufacturers who wish to have their suppliers ship directly to a user. It is possible to ship components directly to a user from a foreign supplier,
without the components first being processed through the production
approval holder's (manufacturer's) facilities; however, prerequisites
must be met.

The PAH may authorize suppliers to direct ship parts to a user
(e.g., air carrier, commercial operator, repair station, or desig-
nated alteration station) if the PAH has established a system for
the approval and release of supplier-produced parts. This may in-
clude supplier facilities located in BAA countries. Without a BAA,
there are no reciprocal agreements with a country for the U.S. ac-
ceptance of imported products or parts. This situation creates a
possible undue burden for the FAA in administering applicable
airworthiness requirements abroad. Therefore, in most cases, the
FAA would not allow direct shipment from a non-BAA country.[7]

First, the manufacturer must authorize such a shipment in writing
and accept full responsibility for conformity to the FAA-approved design
data and for condition for safe operation of the components so shipped.
Normally, a manufacturer would not accept this responsibility unless its

own quality personnel had performed a source inspection or the supplier had demonstrated acceptable performance over a specified period of time. Either way, it is not normal to allow direct shipment at the beginning of a program, and the FAA probably would not allow it.

Second, the manufacturer must ensure that each part shipped is accompanied by a shipping ticket, invoice, or other document containing a declaration that the individual part was produced under the production approval and is authorized for direct shipment.

Third, the manufacturer must advise the FAA office that has jurisdiction over the manufacturer's domestic facilities for each authorization. This is one area that is still wide open for interpretation. Some FAA field offices may allow such an authorization to remain effective for a specified time span and others will require that such notification be given for each shipment. However, typically it will be required to advise the appropriate FAA office for each individual delivery.[8]

The requirements and actions for a supplier to ship directly to an end user (drop shipment) must be outlined in a company procedure or policy and is commonly referred to as a 21-20 plan. This plan must be approved by the FAA prior to implementation. Though these requirements are for both domestic and foreign suppliers, foreign suppliers may not issue export airworthiness approvals for new engines, propellers, or class II or class III products. So the direct shipment of these parts will be restricted.

SUMMARY

Both the requirements of the international quality standards and the individual manufacturing approvals under the FARs require the control over purchased parts and materials. The specific requirements are more pronouncedly stated within the international quality standards, whereas within the FARs they are more implied. The extent of control exercised over suppliers shall be dependent on the type of product, on the impact of subcontracted product on the quality of final product, and, where applicable, on records of the previously demonstrated capability and performance of the suppliers. In analysis of a supplier's capability and performance, characteristics such as its manufacturing abilities, processing capabilities, financial status, and quality system should be considered. Though an ISO 9000 quality system registration certificate may certify a supplier to the international quality system standards, it does not necessarily mean that the supplier is in compliance with the FAA requirements. It may be necessary to ensure FAR compliance through addendum audit.

When purchase orders are to be released to a supplier, it should be assured that that supplier is approved to supply the specific commodity. The purchase order shall be reviewed prior to release to ensure that all applicable data are applied. This could include specifications, drawings, and quality clauses. Quality clauses are codes that coordinate to specific quality requirements.

Regardless of the supplier's capabilities, the manufacturer remains ultimately responsible for all materials, processes, and services it receives. In order to substantiate conformance, it is at times necessary to perform source inspections at the supplier's facility. Foreign suppliers are subject to the bilateral agreements of the United States and their own government. Manufacturers should be aware of the requirements of the FAA when procuring materials from foreign sources. To increase awareness of the FAA's interpretation it is advisable for manufacturers to be familiar with advisory circulars.

NOTES

1. DOT/FAA, Advisory Circular 21-20, *Supplier Surveillance Procedures* (Washington, D.C.: DOT/FAA, 22 July 1982), 1, para. (2)(b), Information.

2. DOT/FAA, Federal Aviation Order 8100.7, *Aircraft Certification Systems Evaluation Program* (Washington D.C.: DOT/FAA, 30 March 1994), appendix 6, section 10.

3. DOT/FAA, Advisory Circular 21-20, *Supplier Surveillance Procedures* (Washington, D.C.: DOT/FAA, 22 July 1982), 1, para. (2)(c), Information.

4. DOT/FAA, Advisory Circular 21-20A, *Supplier Surveillance Procedures* (Washington, D.C.: DOT/FAA, 25 July 1994), 2, para. (6)(b)(1), Procedure.

5. ANSI/ASQC Q9001-1994, *Quality Systems—Model for Quality Assurance in Design, Development, Production, Installation, and Servicing* (Milwaukee, Wis.: American Society for Quality Control, 1994), 4–5, para. 4.6.2., Evaluation of Subcontractors.

6. DOT/FAA, Advisory Circular 21-18, *Bilateral Airworthiness Agreements* (Washington, D.C.: DOT/FAA, 20 August 1982), 166, para. 3.

7. DOT/FAA, Advisory Circular 21-20A, 4, para. (6)(e), Procedure.

8. Ibid.

Chapter 8

CONTROL OF CUSTOMER-SUPPLIED PRODUCT

Customer-supplied products, also known as customer-furnished material/equipment (CFM, CFE) or buyer-furnished material/equipment (BFM, BFE), are materials or equipment that the customer supplied for incorporation into a product or process. These materials or equipment can be just about anything. Some customers will supply consumable materials because of proprietary design reasons, and others because they can reduce the manufacturer's cost by procuring the material in bulk. Major components, such as galleys and seats, are often supplied for installation into completed aircraft. Customers also will supply special equipment to perform assembly, processing, and testing operations for various reasons. Regardless of type or design, material or equipment that is supplied by the customer must be given additional attention.

The various FAA manufacturing regulations make no specific designation toward customer-supplied products. The FAA is more concerned on the global scale of product conformity. The FAA requires that each manufacturer ensure that each article produced conforms to the type design and is in condition for safe operation. This includes all materials received, not excluding purchaser-supplied materials. If customer-supplied material is installed on any product approved under a type design, that material must be approved either under that type certificate, either through original issue or amendment, or under a supplemental type certificate. The manufacturer who certifies the finished product is responsible for ensuring conformance to type design. It is often the case that customer-supplied material cannot be certified in time for delivery, requiring installation at a later time after approval. The rule is, if the furnished product is not certified for installation on the finished product, it does not go on. There are no exceptions, unless authorized by the FAA, as outlined in FAR 21 Subparts B, C, D, or E.

With regard to customer-supplied equipment, here too the FAA makes no exceptions. All equipment or tooling that is subject to calibration or condition inspection must be controlled in accordance with established procedures. However, the FAA does not concern itself with materials or equipment that are not to be included in the product or do not have the potential for adversely affecting quality or safe operation.

ANSI/ASQC Q9003 has requirements for the control of customer-supplied materials or equipment, only to the extent that they are incorporated into the final product. The requirements of ANSI/ASQC Q9001 and ANSI/ASQC Q9002 are identical. They state that "the supplier shall establish and maintain documented procedures for verification, storage, and maintenance of customer-supplied product provided for the purpose of incorporation into the supplies or related activities. Any such product that is lost, damaged, or is otherwise unsuitable for use shall be recorded and reported to the customer. The verification by the supplier does not absolve the customer of the responsibility to provide acceptable product."[1] This is placing emphasis on the customer's responsibility to ensure that its suppliers are conforming to the applicable standards and requirements. For many smaller aviation manufacturers this should be like a breath of fresh air. As well, many larger airframe manufacturers have attempted for years to get their customers to take care of their own suppliers and associated problems.

The control of customer-supplied materials and equipment should be described within the contents of the manufacturer's quality assurance manual. Unless there are special concerns or requirements, there is really no need to create individual stand-alone procedures for the control of such materials and equipment. The existing procedures for receiving, tool calibration, equipment storage and handling, special processes, and any other applicable procedure can contain the provisions for the handling of customer-supplied materials and equipment. This would include the instructions for disposition of nonconforming materials and notification to the customer (reference chapter 14). However, if there are special characteristics for an individual program, these can be controlled by a plan and identified within the contract review process.

Customer-supplied materials and equipment should be treated basically the same as other manufacturer-procured/produced materials, except for additional provisions in inventory control, calibration, and disposition when found nonconforming. It is imperative to ensure absolute inventory of customer-supplied materials and equipment. Customer relations have been damaged easily when their supplied materials and equipment are damaged, lost, or stolen. If there is an incident, the manufacturer should be aware of exact quantities, types, and when applicable, serial numbers. It is recommended to have a special field or block in the inventory system that identifies the material as purchaser supplied. Contrary to many beliefs, customer-supplied material does not have to be stored in separate locations from other materials and equipment. The exceptions may be if your customer is the U.S. government, or if the customer has specified special segregated storage in the contract. In either scenario, special storage requirements always should be considered early in the program, during contract review. This would include the creation of special plans or procedures.

As will be discussed in chapter 12, customer-supplied tooling and equipment are also susceptible to calibration and inspection. The customer should provide the manufacturer with the applicable instructions for performing the checks, perform them themselves, or provide other instructions to ensure proper control of these items. However the controls are established, it remains the manufacturer's responsibility to ensure that the equipment that may affect quality or safe operation is in suitable condition for use.

Identifying the potential for the supply of customer-supplied materials and equipment should be performed as soon as possible in the development of a quality system. In the aviation industry it should not be a surprise when the customer drops the articles off at the receiving door. Making customer-supplied materials and equipment a variable of every procedure, where applicable, is the best method of controlling the process. Additionally, as discussed in chapter 4, "Contract Review," any special requirements for the control of customer-supplied materials and products should be addressed early in the program development phases. If there are any special requirements for control or use of these articles, program management should ensure that all data is provided, and, when required, new procedures or plans are developed.

SUMMARY

Customer-supplied product must be controlled by documented procedures. Because customer-supplied product can be just about anything, including equipment and consumables, it is recommended to incorporate control means within the various control procedures of the quality system. These control procedures shall include the documentation and reporting methods to the customer of product that is lost, damaged, or otherwise unsuitable for use.

Though the manufacturer may have an effective means for assuring conformity upon receipt, it is the customer's responsibility to provide acceptable product. The customer should ensure that technical data, such as engineering drawings and specification and material safety data sheets are supplied with the product.

NOTES

1. ANSI/ASQC Q9001-1994, *Quality Systems—Model for Quality Assurance in Design, Development, Production, Installation, and Servicing* (Milwaukee, Wis.: American Society for Quality Control, 1994), 5, para. 4.7., Control of Customer-Supplied Product.

Chapter 9

PRODUCT IDENTIFICATION AND TRACEABILITY

The requirements and development of an identification system for document control were discussed in chapter 6. This chapter, on identification and traceability, concerns itself specifically with the requirements for the identification of the product. This identification is not just the application of a part number, but identification of inspection status, special processing, and origin as well.

All three of the international quality system standards require some sort of product identification control. ANSI/ASQC Q9003 only requires an identification system for the product if contractually required. ANSI/ASQC Q9001 and ANSI/ASQC Q9002 require that "where appropriate, the supplier shall establish and maintain documented procedures for identifying the product by suitable means from receipt and during all stages of production, delivery, and installation."[1] They also require a documented traceability system that will uniquely identify individual product or batches, when and to the extent required by contract. Traceability is not an ANSI/ASQC Q9003 requirement. A problem that many companies may have is determining what "appropriate" is.

Part 45 of the FARs is solely dedicated to the marking and identification of aircraft parts and whole aircraft. However, this FAR deals primarily with finished products, and does not reference in-process identification. FAR Part 21 Subpart K and Subpart O have special identification requirements for parts manufactured under a Parts Manufacturing Approval and Technical Standard Order, respectively, and make vague reference to in-process identification. The quality assurance requirements in FAR Part 21 Subpart G, for Production Certificates, also make vague reference to in-process identification. Only when the related individual advisory circulars are reviewed are the requirements for in-process identification made clear. Regardless of what type of manufacturing approval the manufacturer holds, the FAA requires that the in-process parts are identifiable and their inspection status verifiable.

Though chapter 13 will go into detail with regard to inspection status, because identification and inspection status are so interrelated, this element should be briefly discussed here as well. Advisory Circular 21-303.1A, *Certification Procedures for Products and Parts,* provides insight to the FAA requirements for a conforming identification system. It states that "this system would ensure that appropriate stamps and marks are placed on articles to indicate their inspection status. It would be helpful if these procedures included copies of all inspection forms, checklists, and imprints of the various inspection and process stamps and their meanings."[2] This also indicates a requirement for stamp control. The advisory circular notes that most identification procedures also should call for suitable acceptance, rework, or rejection stamps to be placed on

> *(a) Articles which have been subjected to a process such as heat treatment, welding, bonding, etc., or testing and inspection which may include hardness tests, laboratory analysis, magnetic particle inspection, or similar functions;*
>
> *(b) Articles which have been inspected at the specified point in production and are found in conformity with the approved design; and*
>
> *(c) Articles which are rejected as being unusable or scrap so as to preclude absolutely their installation on the part.*[3]

There are FAA references to traceability, but primarily with regard to special processes. Where the majority of the traceability requirements will be found are within the individual design documents (take for example an O-ring that is manufactured in accordance with an industry specification). The specification that contains the design parameters for the O-ring also will provide the identification and traceability requirements within the context. This will usually require the identification of the O-ring to be the same as the specification number, as well as to make reference to the manufacturer and a lot or batch number. When the end user receives the O-ring, it more than likely will not have an inspection stamp applied to the packaging. This is because the lot/batch number can be traceable to the inspection personnel who accepted the product. Additionally, when the product is presented at receiving inspection, it will be accompanied by a certificate of conformance, bearing either an inspection stamp or a signature.

So, when the international quality standards are compared to the requirements of the FAA, ANSI/ASQC Q9003 does not meet the FAA requirements. If an aviation organization is pursuing ANSI/ASQC Q9003 registration, it will be required to meet the requirements of ANSI/ASQC Q9001 and ANSI/ASQC Q9002 for identification and traceability purposes.

PART NUMBERING SYSTEM

Most established organizations will have a part numbering system already in place, and would feel uncomfortable changing it. Providing that the system meets the requirements of the specific FAA manufacturing approval, as well as those of the international quality standards, there is no reason to change it. However, if the part numbering system does not meet these applicable requirements, the organization's management must take action to change the system. The following system outline will also benefit a new organization in its developmental stages.

The organization must have a procedure controlling the part numbering system. Making this procedure an engineering function will place emphasis on the part number in the design phase. The procedure should identify the various methods of identification as well as the responsibilities of those who apply it.

There are various methods of identification. These include simple ink applications, laser engravings, mechanical engravings, chemical etching, identification plates, and label attachments, as well as many others. Each of these methods should be described in detail within the identification procedure or, preferably, within stand-alone process specifications. Giving the individual detailed instructions within the process specification will allow for simpler updating of the process, without updating the entire procedure.

Additionally, if the customer requires special identification methods, per its process specifications, provisions must be made to incorporate the customer's process specification into the work process. This will normally be accomplished within the manufacturing work instructions. Program management must ensure that either controlled copies of the process specification are available where applicable, or the internal manufacturing work instructions are written adequately to include all of the customer's requirements. As will be discussed in the next chapter, "Process Control," all work instructions shall be reviewed—in the case of the aerospace industry, by quality assurance personnel—for adequacy prior to release. If stipulated within the contract, the customer shall be given the opportunity of reviewing the work instructions that incorporate the customer's special processes and shall have the right to final approval, prior to release.

If the identification application process is complex, such as laser engraving or chemical etching, personnel shall be trained and certified for the special process. As discussed in chapter 19, "Training," evidence of this training and certification shall be readily available.

Like the O-ring example, normally the part number itself will be the same as the design document number. Within the design document (for example, drawing), the identification and traceability requirements should be noted and specific application instructions given. This can be accomplished by either giving the complete instructions within the document (drawing) or noting the application location in the drawing and referencing another document, such as the individual process specification, for the specific details. However, for various reasons, the manufacturer may opt not to place identification requirements on the individual design document.

Identification and traceability requirements can still be met if the requirements are noted within the applicable manufacturing work instructions. Like those for the special process, these work instructions must be clear and complete. In most cases, the identification will be applied by the manufacturing person completing the product. This will be accompanied by a manufacturing buy off on the applicable work instructions. A good test to ensure the adequacy of these instructions would be to verify consistency of the finished products. If the finished products are not identical in their identification then the work instructions may not be adequate. This will require investigation and revision.

IN-PROCESS IDENTIFICATION

The requirements for in-process identification are linked to both the international quality standards and the various FAA manufacturing approvals. As noted earlier, the international quality standards require that, where appropriate, the product shall be identified by suitable means during all stages of production. This identification information normally will be from applicable drawings, specifications, or other documents. The various subparts of FARs are more vague in their requirements for in-process identification. For instance, FAR Part 21 Subpart K states that "parts in process must be inspected for conformity with the design data at points in production where accurate determination can be made."[4] So, if these parts are to be inspected at in-process points, there must be objective evidence that this action was carried out. This is accomplished through some type of quality acceptance identification linked to the applicable parts; for example, part number with revision and quality stamp applied. Similar requirements can be found in all of the FAA manufacturing approval requirements.

As previously mentioned, there are various methods of identification. For in-process identification, there are no real FAA guidelines of what method to use and when, other than for end-item deliverables. It is good practice though to permanently apply the part number and other identification markings, including inspection stamp, directly to a part, when this part can be removed and replaced or sold as a spare part. Other parts that are consumed by larger assemblies and are less likely to be removed can be identified by an attached identification tag. Some organizations may desire to identify parts only on their packaging. Though there are no firm written requirements against this method, it is discouraged. After the part has been removed from its packaging and is waiting on the workbench for installation, it is difficult to demonstrate compliance with identification requirements. This is because identification is lost once the part is removed from its packaging. Some will argue that the same is true for the attached label, which is true if the label is removed prematurely. Manufacturing and stockroom personnel should be instructed in the proper handling methods of such parts, and such methods shall be controlled by a procedure.

INSPECTION STATUS

The inspection status requirements are very clearly outlined in both the international quality standards and in FAR Part 21, and are discussed in more detail in chapter 13, "Inspection and Test Status." To briefly describe the requirement, after a part or a lot/batch of parts is inspected and accepted, quality inspection personnel shall identify the part(s) as such. This can be accomplished in many ways. The most preferred method in the aviation industry is the application of the quality stamp directly to the part. However, applying the inspection stamp to an attached label/tag, or to accompanying manufacturing work instructions or inspection cards that are identifiable to the part or batch/lot, or to any other document that is traceable to the specific item(s) being accepted, will demonstrate acceptance from authorized inspection personnel. The bottom line on inspection status is that if there is no traceable acceptance verification to the products in question, they are not yet acceptable for further use or processing.

TRACEABILITY

Traceability in the aviation industry has numerous definitions, and depending on the product, contract, and application, the need for it will vary. One of the more obvious types of traceability is that of lot and batch identification. Lot and batch numbers trace a specific product, like the O-ring example, back to the manufacturing run that produced it and the quality records that document its acceptance. These are used because thousands can be produced at one time, and the lot or batch will be accepted or rejected as a group. This is not the case for parts that are produced as individual units.

Serial numbers will be assigned to individual units that require traceability to the corresponding quality records. Each manufacturer should develop its own unique serial numbering system. However, in developing such a system, consideration should be given to user friendliness. Internally, if the system designed is too complex, it may be bound for failure. Additionally, control of serial number issuance should be clearly defined and very restricted. Particularly within the commercial aviation industry, when an incident occurs, the applicable government agencies will seize the quality records of the serial numbered part(s)/product(s) involved. If the governmental agencies discover that the serial numbering system is deficient, by either duplication of numbers or through the issuance of erroneous numbers, the manufacturer will be susceptible to legal disputes.

The FAA requires that serial numbers be applied to any product that is limited by time or use (reference FAR Section 45.14). Additionally, any product that is manufactured under the authority of a TSO must be identified with a unique serial number or the date of manufacture or both. This covers many of the items that could be delivered as end items, and the traceability to quality records will be assured if there is a link from the serial number to the records. Other major subassemblies, such as galleys and lighting equipment, that do not have life limitations and are not produced under a TSO will also be identified with a serial number. This is basically for three reasons: (1) to ensure traceability to the quality records, (2) to maintain a record for warranty and maintenance actions, and (3) because the customer requested it per contract or specification. Though it might not be required by either the international quality standards or the FAA manufacturing approval, it would be wise to assign serial numbers to all major products delivered to a customer.

Parts that are delivered as replacements for detail parts within the serial-numbered part do not require serial numbers themselves. Under the requirements of the FAA, they are delivered from the original manufacturer of the end-item assembly and are not life limited. But under the requirements of the international quality standards, all quality records shall be legible and traceable to the product. Because the replacement part required work instructions to be built and shipping documents to be sent to the customer, and all of these are quality records, the replacement parts also must be identified with a traceable link to the quality records. Typically, this will be accomplished by identifying the replacement detail part with either the shipping document number or, preferably, the work instructions control number, in addition to the appropriate part number and inspection stamp. Keep in mind that this can be accomplished either by physical application to the part or by identification of an attached label or packaging.

The FAA requirement for serial number application is that numbers shall be applied permanently and legibly. In many cases, smaller parts will have the serial number applied directly into the part, through etching or engraving. For parts that are too small to be physically identified, an identification tag may be applied to the packaging of the part. However, prior to using the tag method of identification, the process must be approved by the FAA.

Data placards or identification plates are probably the most utilized method of identification of end-item aircraft parts. Even though data placards could be accidentally, or intentionally, removed, the FAA accepts bonded identification plates as an acceptable method of identification. If these data placards are accidently lost, the risk of having to scrap the part may be high. The owner/operator will be required to present objective evidence that he or she can prove the part installed is what it is claimed to be.

The FAA is aware that identification information and identification plates have been altered and switched from one aircraft to another in an apparent effort to avoid the time and expense of establishing that an aircraft conforms to an FAA-approved type design. An example would be removing an identification plate from an aircraft destroyed in an accident and installing it on a similar type aircraft of unknown origin and then applying for an airworthiness certificate on the basis of the data contained on the identification plate. The practice of "building" or "rebuilding" an aircraft and affixing an identification plate which was previously affixed to another aircraft is clearly not in the public interest. Accordingly, the FAA amended FAR Section 45.13 to prohibit the removal, change, or placement of identification information on aircraft, aircraft engines, propellers, propeller blades and hubs, and to prohibit the removal or installation of an identification plate without the approval of the FAA except for authorized persons performing maintenance under FAR Part 43, Maintenance, Preventive Maintenance, Rebuilding and Alteration.[5]

Persons authorized to perform maintenance under the provisions of FAR Part 43 are exempt from the requirement of having to obtain FAA approval when it is necessary, during certain maintenance operations, to remove or change identification information or to remove an identification plate. Removal of an identification plate would be considered necessary during certain maintenance operations such as caustic cleaning, paint removal, or sand blasting, as well as when the structure to which the identification plate is fastened has to be repaired or replaced for maintenance purposes. The changing of identification information would be considered necessary when instructed to do so in compliance with specific maintenance procedures contained in manufacturers' manuals, letters, or bulletins that are incorporated in and made part of an airworthiness directive (AD). An identification plate removed during maintenance operations must be reinstalled in the original location from which it was removed prior to releasing the product to service.[6]

FAR Part 45 allows the manufacturer some flexibility in the location of the identification plates. For aircraft engines, the identification plates must be affixed to the engine at an accessible location, in such a manner that it will not likely be defaced or removed during normal service or lost or destroyed in an accident. If an identification plate is attached to a propeller/rotor and propeller/rotor blades and hubs, it shall be attached in a noncritical surface and will not be likely to be defaced or removed during normal operation, or lost or destroyed in an accident.[7]

On aircraft manufactured after 7 March 1988 the identification plate shall be secured in such a manner that it will not likely be defaced or removed during normal service or lost or destroyed in an accident. The aircraft identification plate must be secured to the aircraft fuselage exterior so that it is legible to a person on the ground, and must be either adjacent to and aft of the rear-most entrance door or on the fuselage surface near the tail surfaces.[8]

On aircraft manufactured before 7 March 1988 the identification plate may be secured at an accessible exterior or interior location near an entrance, if the model designation and builder's serial number are also displayed on the aircraft fuselage exterior. The model designation and builder's serial number must be legible to a person on the ground and must be located either adjacent to and aft of the rear-most entrance door or on the fuselage near the tail surfaces. The model designation and builder's serial number must be displayed in such a manner that they are not likely to be defaced or removed during normal service.[9]

FRACTURE-CRITICAL TRACEABILITY

Traceability of fracture-critical parts has mostly been a requirement of high-performance military aircraft. However, with advancing technology and the introduction of aircraft like the national aerospace plane, commercial aviation will be introduced to this traceability requirement. A fracture-critical part is a part within which even a minor failure is likely to yield catastrophic results. Such parts are typically wing spars and structure beams, machined from castings or forgings. Because of their criticality, even the simplest of repairs are not normally allowed.

The FAA does have some provisions for identification of critical components. In FAR Section 45.14 it states that "each person who produces a part for which a replacement time, inspection interval, or related procedure is specified in the Airworthiness Limitations section of a Manufacturer's Maintenance Manual or Instructions for Continued Airworthiness shall permanently and legibly mark that component with a part number (or equivalent) and a serial number (or equivalent)."[10] The part number/serial number combination is the most common method of traceability.

Traceability of these parts are for the entire product life, and are normally controlled by the end-item manufacturer until the time of delivery. The manufacturer will issue a purchase order to the casting or forging facility with the applicable fracture-critical serial numbers applied. The casting or forging supplier will apply this serial number to all applicable work orders. The casting or forging supplier will create a traceability file containing all the related information of the part, including the raw material information such as where the alloy was obtained; all of the applicable certificates; material properties test results; and anything else that relates to the part. After the casting or forging is complete, it is identified with its appropriate serial number, as outlined within the purchase order/contract. Depending on the instructions of the purchase order/contract the data file may be maintained either at the supplier or the end-item manufacturer. Ideally, the data file should be forwarded to the end-item manufacturer for incorporation into the quality records of the end item. If the machining processes are subcontracted to another supplier, then this data file should be forwarded to the next supplier. When the machining processes are complete, the identification process is repeated and the data file should be forwarded to the next supplier. Normally this would be for heat treatment and stress relieving. As the cycle continues, the data file becomes larger and larger, or the trail of suppliers maintaining the manufacturer's documents becomes longer and longer. Sufficient precautions must be taken to ensure none of the data is lost. If they are lost and copies are not available, scrapping the part is the only option. The final process will most likely be some sort of nondestructive testing (NDT), and in most cases X ray. In reality, the processes usually are not more stringent than those of non-fracture-critical parts, except for the acceptance criteria and NDT processes, but the documentation is by far more stringent.

During the installation process of the fracture-critical part, manufacturing personnel must assert additional caution when handling these critical parts. Industrial engineers may be requested to develop improved handling techniques and devices to prevent accidental damage. When the critical part has been installed into the end item, it should be treated like any other life-limited part would be, with its own logbook card. This card shall include the part number, serial number, and any other applicable information that affects the service or life of the part, and should be maintained with the logbook of the aircraft it is installed upon.

After delivery, the manufacturer shall be able to trace the delivered product, through the use of its serial number, back to the applicable quality records. Additionally, the manufacturer should consider special service and inspection instructions for maintaining the critical product in the field. Special material review procedures also should be created to control internal and field discrepancies. This can be accomplished by adding a section within the quality assurance procedure that controls the material review system (reference chapter 14, "Control of Nonconforming Product").

IDENTIFICATION PLATES

We have already discussed how an identification plate is to be installed and when it is required, but what is required to be on it? The answer may vary depending on the type of manufacturing and design approval the part is approved under.

When the identification plate is required, as it is for finished aircraft, engines, propellers/rotors, propeller/rotor blades, and propeller/rotor hubs, as stated in FAR Section 45.13(a), in addition to the part number and revision, the identification plate will include the following information.[11]

1. Builder's name
2. Model designation
3. Builder's serial number
4. Type Certificate number, if any
5. Production Certificate number, if any
6. The established rating (for aircraft engines)
7. Any other information the FAA finds appropriate

PARTS MANUFACTURER APPROVAL

For products that are manufactured under a PMA, in addition to the part number and revision, they shall be identified with the following information.

1. The letters *FAA-PMA*
2. The name, trademark, or symbol of the holder of the PMA
3. The name and model designation of each Type-Certificated product on which the part is eligible for installation
4. Indication of inspection acceptance

Though it may be typical to attach an identification plate to PMA parts, it is not absolutely required. The part may be identified through any means that will permanently identify the noted characteristics. As noted earlier, if the part is too small for such identification, the FAA may approve the use of an attached identification tag.

TECHNICAL STANDARD ORDER

Like the requirements for the PMA, the requirements for identifying TSO products do not necessarily require the application of an identification plate. FAR Section 21.607(d) notes that the identification shall be permanently and legibly applied. The following information must be applied to the product.

1. The name and address of the manufacturer
2. The name, type, part number, or model designation of the article
3. The serial number or the date of manufacture of the article, or both
4. The applicable TSO number
5. Indication of inspection acceptance

SUPPLEMENTAL TYPE CERTIFICATE

Advisory Circular 21-303.1A notes that when design approval for a part is requested on the basis of its being identical, the applicant may use the same part number used by the Type Certificate or Supplemental Type Certificate holder. In this case, an acceptable method would be to add a letter prefix to the part number to identify the manufacturer. A part that is not identical to the part approved for the Type Certificate or Supplemental Type Certificate holder should carry a different part number. In this case, or in the case where the applicant chooses to use a different part number, the supplement sheet to the FAA-PMA will show the type approved part number with which the manufacturer's part is interchangeable (as was shown in Figure 2.5).

REGISTRATION IDENTIFICATION

Aircraft have additional identification requirements with regard to their registration. Like automobiles, each aircraft has its own individual registration number. In the United States, these registration numbers are known as *N numbers*. This is because all aircraft registered in the United States begin with an *N*, whereas in Germany they are identified with a *D* and in Canada, a *C*. FAR Part 45, Subpart C, Nationality and Registration Marks, outlines the marking requirements for the various types of U.S.

registered aircraft. This section of the FARs also provides guidance on the identification of experimental aircraft.

As far as the quality system is concerned, there must be procedures available that ensure the proper identification of finished aircraft. Such a process should be controlled by a stand-alone process specification or procedure. Quality assurance personnel should include registration identification in the internal audit schedule, if applicable.

SUMMARY

Product identification and traceability is a requirement of both the international quality standards and the various FARs controlling manufacturing approvals. When comparing the international quality standards with the applicable FARs, one would determine quickly that the requirements of ANSI/ASQC Q9003 are not stringent enough to meet the identification requirements of the FAA, whereas the requirements of ANSI/ASQC Q9001 and ANSI/ASQC Q9002, in some instances, exceed the requirements of the FAA. However, the FARs have special identification requirements that also require addressing. ANSI/ASQC Q9001 and ANSI/ASQC Q9002 both require manufacturers to establish and maintain documented procedures for identifying the product during all stages of production, delivery, and installation. This includes in-process identification. The various FARs only imply in-process identification. However, when the associated advisory circulars are reviewed, the FAA's intentions for in-process identification become more clear.

The part numbering system shall be described and controlled by a procedure. This should include the methods of application and the responsibilities of those applying it.

The international quality standards require that traceability be implemented to the extent it is specified as a requirement. This basically means that if it is a design or contract requirement, it shall be controlled by a procedure. The FARs require traceability, under FAR Part 45, to any part or component that is susceptible to replacement times, inspection intervals, or limitation. This traceability is accomplished through the application of controlled serial numbers. Lot and batch numbers are also methods to trace parts and materials back to their acceptance documentation.

Data placards are widely used as a method of identification within the aviation industry, mostly because their use is specified within applicable FARs governing their design or manufacture. Depending on the product's design and production approval status, the data placard will have individual data requirements. Complete aircraft also use data placards and have special location requirements that should be taken into consideration during the design phases. National registration markings are also identification requirements under FAR Part 45.

NOTES

1. ANSI/ASQC Q9001-1994, *Quality Systems—Model for Quality Assurance in Design, Development, Production, Installation, and Servicing* (Milwaukee, Wis.: American Society for Quality Control, 1994), 5, para. 4.8., Product Identification and Traceability.

2. DOT/FAA, Advisory Circular 21-303.1A, *Certification Procedures for Products and Parts* (Washington, D.C.: DOT/FAA, 10 August 1972), 7, para. (10)(e)(2), Inspection Status.

3. Ibid.

4. DOT/FAA, Federal Aviation Regulation Section 21.303(h)(5), *Certification Procedures for Products and Parts—Replacement and Modification Parts* (Washington, D.C.: DOT/FAA, March 1993).

5. DOT/FAA, Advisory Circular 43-17, *Methods, Techniques, and Practices Acceptable to the Administrator Governing the Installation, Removal, or Change of Identification Data and Identification Plates* (Washington, D.C.: DOT/FAA, 5 September 1979), 7, para. (4), Discussion.

6. Ibid.

7. DOT/FAA, Federal Aviation Regulation Section 45.11(a)(b), *Identification and Registration Marking—Identification of Aircraft and Related Products* (Washington, D.C.: DOT/FAA, 8 December 1987).

8. DOT/FAA, Federal Aviation Regulation Section 45.11(a), *Identification and Registration Marking—Identification of Aircraft and Related Products* (Washington, D.C.: DOT/FAA, 8 December 1987).

9. DOT/FAA, Federal Aviation Regulation Section 45.11(d), *Identification and Registration Marking—Identification of Aircraft and Related Products* (Washington, D.C.: DOT/FAA, 8 December 1987).

10. DOT/FAA, Federal Aviation Regulation Section 45.14, *Identification and Registration Marking—Identification of Critical Components* (Washington, D.C.: DOT/FAA, 8 December 1987).

11. DOT/FAA, Federal Aviation Regulation Section 45.13, *Identification and Registration Marking—Identification Data* (Washington, D.C.: DOT/FAA, 8 December 1987).

Chapter 10

PROCESS CONTROL

Processes that directly affect quality must be controlled to ensure their compliance to specified requirements. These processes have a wide range of characteristics and can include special installation methods, chemical processing, drilling operations, heat treatment, and many others. ANSI/ASQC Q9001 and ANSI/ASQC Q9002 both state that "suppliers shall identify and plan the production, installation, and servicing processes which directly affect quality and shall ensure that these processes are be carried out under controlled conditions."[1] This means that there must be documented procedures and/or detailed instructions in the applicable manufacturing work instructions or other internal work document that outline the steps to perform these processes, including any special environmental or equipment requirements, as well as document the acceptance of the completed process.

These two international quality standards also reference the performance of special processes. Special processes are processes whose results cannot be fully verified by subsequent inspection and testing of the product and for which, for example, processing deficiencies may become apparent only after the product is in use. Special processes include methodologies whereby material undergoes a physical, chemical, or metallurgical transformation in which conformance to a specification cannot be readily verified by normal inspection methods. The temperature of a chemical processing tank would be a good example. The tank's temperature cannot be verified after the part is sitting on an inspection table; it must be accomplished while in performance of the process. However, the process of nondestructive testing (NDT) is also a special process, even though the process does not alter a material's structure or properties.

ANSI/ASQC Q9001 and ANSI/ASQC Q9002 both require that "special processing be carried out by qualified operators and/or shall require continuous monitoring and control of process parameters to ensure that the specified requirements are met" (ANSI/ASQC Q9001, 5, para. 4.9., Process Control). Nowhere in these requirements does it say that these actions must be performed by quality inspectors. It is perfectly acceptable for operators to perform the applicable process surveillance and document the obtained results, providing that the operators are trained, qualified, and authorized to perform the individual processes. Quality personnel could follow up either through area surveillance or by audit.

Additionally, these two international quality standards state that "the qualification of process operations, including associated equipment and personnel, shall be specified" (ANSI/ASQC Q9001, 5, para. 4.9., Process Control). When a manufacturer develops a process, that process must be documented and applicable plans created. Prior to releasing the new process for production use, that process also must be qualified. This qualification process is normally performed by qualified personnel within the manufacturer's quality department and assisted by personnel from the applicable processing departments. However, this process qualification may be performed by whatever department the manufacturer feels appropriate, providing the personnel are nonbiased, are qualified in the particular process being evaluated, and have the authority to reject the process when it is found nonconforming.

Additionally, manufacturers are often required to perform special processes in accordance with the customer's specifications. When this occurs, it is common for the manufacturer to transcribe the customer's process to the manufacturer's documentation. Like any other controlled process, the customer process also must be qualified prior to implementation. In most cases the customer will send one of its own qualified personnel to qualify the process. However, the responsibility for process qualification still belongs to the entity who performs the process—the manufacturer or supplier. Prior to the arrival of the customer's representative, the manufacturer should have performed all of the qualification activities, as if there were no further verification required. Then, when the customer arrives the process is capable and customer acceptance is more assured.

Many companies will find it necessary to go outside of the company to accomplish various processing requirements. When a manufacturer goes outside for such processing, it is still responsible for the conformity of that process. Many larger companies will go to the processor's facility and perform a full qualification assessment. Others lack either the expertise or financial ability to perform such audits.

There are a few options open for smaller manufacturers. If a manufacturer is performing as a supplier, use of the customer's approved processors list is an acceptable method of assuring only capable processors are used. However, caution must be used. The activity that approved the processor must be aware that a third party is using that processor under its approval. Additionally, it must be ensured that the manufacturer is on the distribution for changes to the approved processors list, including additions, deletions, or restrictions. This must be a coordinated and documented effort.

Still another method, possibly most preferred by the author, is to ensure processor compliance by contracting for third-party evaluation. This method provides the best results—the processor is approved under the manufacturer's own requirements or under requirements of an industry or international process standard. Within the same context, if a processor is registered for a special process by a third-party registrar, evidence of this registration should be sufficient to justify competency for that registered process. However, other characteristics also should be considered, such as capacity, quality system, and financial status.

As discussed in chapter 7, when outside processors have been approved to perform certain controlled processes, their approval should be documented on a list of approved suppliers. This list should be inclusive enough that it can be used in purchasing functions as well as in quality audits. Normally, this document will be controlled by the auditing agency within the company that qualifies the various processes. It is important that this document remain current and that changes are distributed as they occur. Some companies find an electronic database helpful; however, suppliers welcome hard copies to work from. The functions and controls of this approved supplier/processor list must be documented within the applicable control procedure.

Each individual process must be requalified on a scheduled basis. The manufacturer must determine what time frames and criteria will be used. Changes to a processor's approval status, or any new or changed restrictions, must be noted on the approved suppliers/processors list. These control actions also must be addressed within the applicable procedure controlling special processing.

Most companies briefly describe their requirements for process control within their quality assurance manual and elaborate in individual procedures. This is the ideal method for describing the applicable control processes, particularly when a company performs numerous special processes. However, for smaller companies that require limited or no special processing, control system description may be sufficient within the quality assurance manual. For the larger companies, it may be appropriate to create a procedure for each individual process performed. This will allow for easier updating as techniques and equipment are updated, limit the bulk of the core document, and provide the ability for independent approval of individual processes and procedures. In whichever method the manufacturer designs the control system, it shall be documented and it is subject to review by the FAA.

Each of the FAA manufacturing approval regulations requires control for processes that affect quality and the safety of the finished product. They also require that these processes are accomplished in accordance with acceptable specifications. The FAA requires the manufacturer to ensure that parts in process are inspected for conformity with the design data at points in production where accurate determination can be made. As will be discussed in the next chapter, there is a strong requirement for in-process inspection and, as stated elsewhere in the individual regulations for manufacturers, the requirement for documentation.

The requirements for a PMA manufacturer, in FAR 21 Subpart K, also allow for the use of statistical methods to confirm conformity. Though not specifically stated elsewhere, statistical methods also may be applied within the quality control systems of other FAA manufacturing approvals. When used, procedures must be created, and approved by the FAA, that ensure that a satisfactory level of quality will be maintained where employed. The various methods of statistical process control employed by the manufacturer shall be in accordance with applicable industry standards, and records must be maintained that provide objective evidence of conformance. These statistical methods can be implemented in product fabrication methods, special processing, and inspection acceptance techniques, and are discussed in greater detail in chapter 20.

In essence, process control is basically in-process inspection—of product fabrication, environmental conditions, or special processing—that has been identified and described in detail in applicable work instructions. In the next chapter, in-process inspection is discussed in more detail, as are receiving and final inspection and testing. Additionally, the methods of indication of inspection status, stamp control, and special identification are also discussed, and are applicable to the control of processes and special processing.

The following are considered to be some of the processes that require special control or special processes that require qualification and special verification. These are only examples and are not inclusive of all such processes.

Magnetic particle inspection	X-ray inspection
Penetrant inspection	Tensile and shear strength testing
Radiography	Impact testing
Ultrasonic	Anodizing
Welding	Plastic molding
Salt spray analysis	Heat treating
Brazing	Galvanizing
Shot peening	Forging
Painting	Casting

SUMMARY

Special processes must be controlled by detailed instructions in plans or procedures. The number of processes that would qualify for this type of control is actually immense. ANSI/ASQC Q9001 and ANSI/ASQC Q9002 both require that there are documented work instructions defining the manner of production and installation, where the absence of such instructions would adversely affect quality. They also require that there is control over the equipment and that the environment is suitable for such processing. The work standards for these processes also shall be stipulated within the appropriate control documents.

The various FARs make little mention of the control of processes, other than that procedures must be created that ensure that a satisfactory level of quality will be maintained where employed. They also note that various methods of statistical process control may be employed and shall be in accordance with applicable industry standards. All of these control procedures are to be approved by the FAA prior to implementation.

Suppliers who provide special processing services to a manufacturer shall be approved and subject to surveillance audits. The approval criteria shall include the processes itself, the equipment condition and capability, and the personnel training and abilities. Records shall be maintained as quality records.

The quality assurance function shall place the individual characteristics of process control on the internal audit schedule. This includes the requalification of the process, equipment, and personnel.

NOTES

1. ANSI/ASQC Q9001-1994, *Quality Systems—Model for Quality Assurance in Design, Development, Production, Installation, and Servicing* (Milwaukee, Wis.: American Society for Quality Control, 1994), 5, para. 4.9., Process Control.

Chapter 11

INSPECTION AND TESTING

To verify that a product conforms to the approved design, inspection and testing must be performed. All three of the international quality standards require documented procedures for the control of inspection and testing. ANSI/ASQC Q9003, as designed, concerns itself only with the final inspection and testing of a product. This standard has no requirement for receiving inspection or in-process inspection. Though the standard does require retention of the inspection results as quality records, because of the omission of receiving and in-process controls, it is not sufficient for FAA purposes.

ANSI/ASQC Q9001 and ANSI/ASQC Q9002 are identical in their requirements for inspection and testing of products and services. The standards are broken down into four areas of control.

- Receiving inspection and testing
- In-process inspection and testing
- Final inspection and testing
- Inspection and test records

Every one of the FAA manufacturing approval regulations, as well as those for a repair station (FAR section 145.45), require inspection and testing of products and services at receiving of the articles or services, in-process manufacturing steps, and final completion of the product or service. These inspections and tests shall ensure that the product or service meets the approved type design.

All of the FAA manufacturing approvals also require that the applicant provide a description of the methods used for production inspection of individual parts and complete assemblies, including the identification of any special processes, the final test procedure for the complete product, and, in the case of aircraft, a copy of the manufacturer's production flight test procedures and checkoff list. This description must be contained within the manufacturer's quality assurance manual, but may be broken down into smaller segments of control in the form of quality assurance procedures. These procedures and their changes, like the quality assurance manual, must be approved by the FAA. In addition, these procedures shall outline the materials review system (chapter 14); outline the system for informing company inspectors of current changes in engineering drawings, specifications, and quality control procedures (chapter 6); and for manufacturers who are authorized under FAR 21 Subpart G, Production Certificates, provide a list or chart showing the location and type of inspection stations.[1]

These procedures should document how inspection plans are to be created and who is responsible for what. It is important to keep the procedures as simple as possible, but complete. As for any other procedural requirement, the larger the company, the higher the likelihood of needing more procedures to control its systems. However, the higher the consistency in processes, the lower the need for diversity of control procedures.

Following the issuance of the manufacturing approval, the FAA will maintain periodic surveillance of the production facilities and quality control system. Such surveillance is often in the form of evaluations based on the ACSEP criteria. If an inspection or test performed by the FAA discloses that any part of the data or system which was originally approved does not fully meet the applicable requirements, the FAA will request changes to the quality control system or data as may be required.

RECEIVING INSPECTION

When coupling the requirements of ANSI/ASQC Q9001 or ANSI/ASQC Q9002 with those of the individual FAA manufacturing regulations, the requirements of receiving inspection become clear and exacting. The international quality standards require that "incoming product (or service) is not to be used or processed until it has been inspected or otherwise verified as conforming to specified requirements. Verification of the specified requirements shall be in accordance with the quality plan and/or documented procedures."[2] However, the international quality standards do allow for incoming product to be released for urgent production purposes, prior to verification, when it is positively identified and recorded, in order to permit immediate recall and replacement in the event that the part is determined to be nonconforming to specified requirements. Under the requirements of FAR section 21.125, Materials Review Board of a Production Inspection System, such parts that have not been fully accepted must be processed though the materials review system. If a manufacturer requires the provisions for allowing parts through without being fully accepted, a control procedure must be created and approved by the FAA prior to implementation. Such a process may be typical in new design programs, but not in production programs. Such a deviatory procedure should be the exception and not the rule.

The FAA views an effective purchasing and receiving inspection system as one that precludes release to production of nonconforming or unsafe articles procured from outside sources. Such a system would ensure that

1) Purchase orders provide specifications or other design data in the detail necessary to ensure procurement of articles or services which meet the requirements of the approved type design [reference chapter 7].

2) All incoming articles conform to approved type design data prior to their acceptance and release to production.

3) Articles which are not designed or manufactured by the production certificate holder are of the same design configuration as specified in the approved type design data.

4) Records are maintained of all inspections and tests performed by or for the holder of a manufacturing approval in controlling the design configuration and conformity of all supplier furnished articles.

5) Inspection/test records are utilized, as appropriate, to document, as evidence of accomplishment, all required inspections, tests, rework, or rejections.[3]

If a manufacturer has met the expectations of the FAA, as just outlined, the conformance to the international quality standards would also be assured. ANSI/ASQC Q9001 and ANSI/ASQC Q9002 both require manufacturers to give consideration to receiving inspection characteristics. "In determining the amount and nature of receiving inspection, consideration shall be given to the amount of control exercised at the subcontractor's (supplier's) premises and the recorded evidence of conformance provided."[4] The major emphasis will be on documentation that provides objective evidence of compliance to the established procedures. This will be the prime characteristic of concern during a conformance audit.

Copies of purchase orders, with their applicable quality clauses applied, must be available to receiving inspection. When the product or service arrives at the manufacturer, the receiving inspection activity shall ensure its conformity to the purchase order requirements, as specified in inspection plans or procedures.

Inspection plans should be created for all products or services that require inspection techniques or methods applied to ensure their conformity. These plans are normally created by an activity within the quality assurance department (hereafter referred to in this chapter as QA). In most larger companies this quality activity is known as quality planning. The plan is initiated after the purchase document has been reviewed by QA and the quality clauses are applied. The same quality activity that creates the inspection plan will also ensure that any special inspection equipment and/or special training that may be needed is identified and that program management is notified. It should be the responsibility of program management to procure any special equipment and to coordinate any special training requirements. This could include the procurement of nondestructive testing (NDT) equipment and the training of personnel, or even the use of simple color coupons to check a product's appearance at receiving. The receiving inspection plans can take various forms and functions. Some companies maintain the receiving inspection plans within a computer database that reduces the amount of paper in the receiving area; others issue hard-copy inspection plans for each scheduled delivery. Each individual manufacturer must find and implement the documented method that works best for its applications. To ensure continued compliance, the receiving activities should be included in an internal audit schedule.

In documenting the receipt of a product or service, a material receipt form (MRF) (Figure 11.1) is typically used. This form is initiated by personnel from the incoming goods (receiving) department and documents the name and address of the supplier; date of receipt; quantities of goods or services; and a detailed description of goods or services, including part number, nomenclature, and, when applicable, serial numbers. The completed form is signed or stamped. This material receipt form shall be assigned a serial number and is maintained as a quality record when complete.

During the initial receipt of the goods or services, the incoming goods (receiving) personnel should inspect the goods or services for any obvious damage and check their identification against the purchase order. If the incoming goods or services are damaged or incorrect goods or services are supplied, the incoming goods (receiving) personnel should notify receiving inspection personnel immediately and the rejected goods or services should be placed in the materials review system. Goods or services that are not obviously damaged and are of correct identification should be forwarded on to receiving inspection for inspection in accordance with applicable plans and procedures. The material receipt form should accompany the goods or services, until the goods or services have been accepted and are in the production system. This material receipt form acts as a cover sheet documenting all of the receiving actions, including creation of rejection documents, receipt of inspection

ACXI Aviation Company X, Inc. Wichita, Kansas				Material Receipt Form			
					Material receipt no: _____		
Date received					Supplier: _____		
Supplier ship. advice no.					_____		
					_____		
ACXI P.O. no.					Supplier code: _____		
Item	Ordered qty.	Rec. qty.	Accepted qty.	Material/part nomenclature	Material/part number	ACXI part number	Serial number
Remarks				Reference documents (C of C, MRB, FAI, EO, etc.)			

Material acceptance				Cost data			
Incoming goods	Quality assurance	Stock room	Customer	Order no.	Dept.	CCN	Initials

ACXI Form 100 (05 Aug. 94)

FIGURE 11.1.   *Sample material receipt form.*

and test reports, receipt of certificates of conformance, and any other data that are applicable to the receipt of those goods or services. This form can be maintained electronically within a computer database or in hard copy. Regardless of what type of document is used, the documented data must be available for review as a quality record (reference chapter 17).

As unfortunate as it may be, some individuals are selling "bogus parts"—products that are either unapproved or used and unserviceable. This includes the resale of parts that already have been disposed as scrap by previous owners. With the opening of global trade opportunities, this undesired condition is expected not only to continue, but to worsen. If during receiving inspection the manufacturer feels that the products it is receiving are unapproved, the FAA should be notified immediately. FAA Form 8120-11 (Figure 11.2) should be initiated by the manufacturer and forwarded to the local FAA MIDO or FSDO, as appropriate. Patience is advised, because the investigation process can be very lengthy.

When source inspection has been carried out on a product, the extent of this inspection should be taken into consideration when determining the requirements for receiving inspection. There is really no reason to perform the inspection process twice. If a product has been accepted by the manufacturer at the supplier's facility, the receiving inspection should consist of an identification and damage check. The exception would be if there were inspection characteristics or test procedures/methods that could not be performed at the supplier's facility and must be performed at the manufacturer's facility to verify conformity.

IN-PROCESS INSPECTION AND TESTING

In-process inspection by quality inspectors is normally performed when a particular characteristic of the product or service will not be verifiable at final inspection. Typical instances that require in-process inspection would be prior to closing an area, prior to application of a surface treatment or covering, prior to machining a raw material (checking material type), prior to bonding processes (checking layup), during torque verifications, or any other instance in which later discovery could have an adverse effect on the quality or safe operation of a product or service. As a rule, in-process inspection by quality inspectors should be performed as infrequently as possible, and only when quality cannot be verified at final inspection. In-process testing shall be performed under the same conditions as in-process inspection.

In-process inspection by the person performing the operation should be an ongoing effort. By delegating noncritical inspection duties

APPENDIX 1.   SUSPECTED UNAPPROVED PARTS NOTIFICATION

OMB Approved: 2120-0052

SUSPECTED UNAPPROVED PARTS NOTIFICATION		
1. Date: November 22, 1991		2. Nomenclature: Support Assembly
3. Part No.: 644179		4. Serial No: 8120
5. Next Assembly Name & No: Housing Assembly, P/N 614113	6. Quantity: 16	7. Make/Model: Boeing 727

8. Part Manufacturer/Distributor:

Name: Amhurst Parts Manufacturers

Street: 795 Richard Road   City: Boston

State/Country: Massachusetts   Zip: 02190

9. Description of Complaint:

During installation of a support assembly P/N 644179 onto the housing assembly
P/N 614113, it was noted that the support assembly looked and weighed different
than usual. An analysis of the parts by Acme Testing Company revealed the
assemblies are dimensionally correct, however, the material used was incorrect.
The material used would crack under prolonged stress and vibration.

The 16 assemblies were purchased from Jones Parts Distributorship, 122 Smith
Road, Boston, MA., 02170 on September 15, 1991. (See attached invoices)

10. Date Suspected Unapproved Part Discovered:
November 1991

11. Location Where Part was Discovered:

Name: Logan Repair Center, Building 101

Street: Logan Airport   City: Boston

State/Country: Massachusetts   Zip: 02190

Check One That Applies:

☐ Manufacturer   ☐ Supplier
☐ Distributor   ☒ Repair Station
☐ Other _____

12. Reporters Name:

Name: Mr. John T. Smith   Telephone No: 617-555-0202

Street: P.O. Box 661   City: Boston

State/Country: Massachusetts   Zip 01921

13. ☐ Check here if you wish your identity to be kept confidential

FAA Form 8120-11 (2-91)

FIGURE 11.2.   *Sample FAA Form 8120-11, Suspected Unapproved*[7]
Parts Notification.

Excerpt from Advisory Circular 21-29A.

to the operator, responsibility for quality is at the source. Through such tools as statistical process control, discrepancies can be detected early in the manufacturing process, thus reducing the risk of later and more expensive rejection. However, delegation of critical inspection points to the operator is strongly discouraged. Such delegation can create unwanted legal liabilities. Inspection delegations can be assigned only after both the operator and the process are qualified and capable. Evidence of this qualification must be available as a quality record.

ANSI/ASQC Q9001 and ANSI/ASQC Q9002 have identical requirements for in-process inspection and testing. "The supplier shall inspect and test the product as required by the quality plan and/or documented procedures; hold product until the required inspection and tests have been completed or necessary reports have been received and verified.[5] The exception would be for product that is released under positive-recall procedures. However, the release of product under positive-recall procedures shall not preclude the requirement for acceptance inspection and/or test. The majority of the in-process inspection requirements are basically restatements within the standard, but with particular emphasis toward in-process inspection.

The FAA requires that all parts and components in process must be inspected and tested for conformity with the type design data at points in production where accurate determinations can be made. For manufacturers who are approved under Production Under Type Certificate Only, this requirement comes from FAR section 21.125 (b)(5). For manufacturers authorized under Production Certificates, the requirement is under FAR section 21.143 (a)(3). PMA manufacturers have the in-process inspection requirement under FAR section 21.303 (h)(5). The designated alteration station will have its requirement under its manufacturing, repair station, or air carrier approval. TSO manufacturers are referred back to the requirements of the Production Certificate for their requirement. Repair stations have their in-process inspection requirements implied within FAR section 145.45. Each of these FAR sections notes this requirement in its own slightly different wording, and some specifically note the requirement for process control while others mention the use of statistical process control as an approved method of control (reference chapter 21). Because all of the FARs require the implementation of in-process inspection, ANSI/ASQC Q9003 is not sufficient to meet the requirements of the FAA.

The method of documenting an in-process inspection is dependent upon the individual manufacturer's internal documentation system and established procedures. In most aviation companies, the inspection is documented on the manufacturing work instructions building the particular product or performing the service. However, there are numerous methods of documenting in-process inspections, including the use of inspection cards and other documents. Whatever method the manufacturer chooses to develop the system, the inspection document must be traceable to the part, and vice versa.

Because the operator or manufacturing person building the part or performing the process is ultimately responsible for his or her own actions, it is primarily that person's responsibility to ensure a quality part or service. Once the operation or process is complete, the stamp or signature of the operator/manufacturing person should be applied to the applicable manufacturing work instructions/inspection record. After the operator/manufacturing person has accepted the in-process steps, a quality inspector will verify compliance to specified requirements. Ideally, once the process has become capable, QA would only audit the process to ensure its continued capability, placing quality inspection in obsolescence. With the increasing implementation of statistical process control, and the delegation of authority and responsibility to the operator for self-inspection, the industry is coming closer to having the QA organization as an auditing agency rather than a policing agency. However, it should not be forgotten that this change in responsibility must be accepted by both industry and federal agencies.

The FAA's interpretation of an effective inspection planning system is one that would provide the means for selecting and controlling procedures governing methods for

a) Selection of appropriate inspection methods and plans for articles to ensure that all characteristics affecting safety will be inspected as required, to ensure conformity to approved design data and to eliminate discrepancies from complete products and spare articles.

b) Ensuring that any defects which might be in a lot accepted under a statistical quality control plan will not result in an unsafe condition in an end product or spare article.

c) The establishing of appropriate inspection stations and the programming of inspections at each stage of production to ensure that parts, assemblies, processes, and assembly operations are inspected, and applicable tests are conducted, in accordance with data, technical materials, and procedures maintained at the station for that particular stage of production.

d) Production planning is commonly achieved through use of fabrication and inspection instructions, shop travelers, checklists, or similar media, which not only provide control over fabrication and assembly operations, but also ensure that necessary inspections and tests will be conducted in the proper sequence, when articles and processes are in an inspectable condition. Such a system would provide for inspection and test appropriate to all phases of the production cycle, from raw materials and related processes and services to the completed product.

e) Production areas would be arranged to provide segregation of manufacturing processes or operations which may adversely affect other operations; for example, separation of precision inspection from each area where grinding, cutting, sanding, or painting operations are performed.[6]

Additionally, manufacturers who produce composite structures will find that there are special FAA requirements for the in-process inspection of their products. Advisory Circular 21-26, Quality Control for the Manufacture of Composite Structures, gives a detailed interpretation of the FAA expectations for a such a quality control system. Some of the test methods that are discussed are audiosonic, radiography, ultrasonic, and mechanical impedance. It is recommended that manufacturers of composite products make themselves familiar with this document.

Once the inspection documents are complete, their disposition must be identified in procedure. All records that show acceptance by the manufacturer for the completion of a process or operation are quality records. These quality records shall be maintained in accordance with internal procedures and the applicable quality standard and FAA manufacturing approval (reference chapter 17).

FINAL INSPECTION AND TESTING

Like in-process inspections and testing, final inspection and testing must be planned and documented, providing detailed instructions of the inspection and test and listing applicable reference documents with their applicable revision status. These inspections and tests are usually, but not necessarily always, more detailed in their undertaking as well as their documentation. The final acceptance of the product should be a joint venture between the manufacturing and quality departments, with both noting acceptance on the applicable inspection record, via stamp or signature.

All three of the international quality standards require final inspection and testing of the product. ANSI/ASQC Q9003 requires that the manufacturer carry out final test and inspection in accordance with the quality plan and/or documented procedures and maintain appropriate records to provide objective evidence of conformance to the specified requirements. This should include the documentation of the actual obtained results from the inspection or test. Additionally, records shall identify the inspection authority responsible for the release of conforming product. This will normally be in the form of the inspector's stamp application. ANSI/ASQC Q9001 and ANSI/ASQC Q9002 have the same requirements, but also include provisions for inspection of purchased items where final inspection is to be performed by the manufacturer at the supplier's facility (source inspection). Additionally, these two international quality standards prohibit the shipment of products until all activities specified in the quality plan and/or documented procedures have been satisfactorily completed and the associated data and documentation are available and authorized.

With particular emphasis on end-item equipment, such as complete aircraft, engines, propeller, and spares certified under a Type Certificate, the FAA has extensive regulation on final inspection and testing of aviation products. Each of the individual manufacturing approvals requires the manufacturer to assure the product is in compliance with the approved type design, and its acceptance is documented. As described in the previous section about in-process inspection, these inspections and test results can be planned and documented on the production planning (manufacturing work instructions). In most cases, end-item products will have a quality acceptance plan and test procedure that must be approved by the FAA. This will normally be a separate inspection/test plan independent of the manufacturing work instructions. It is not uncommon for the customer to request these final inspection/test documents with each delivered product. However, delivery documentation requirements should be addressed in the purchase order, contract, or procurement specification (reference chapter 4). This is normally a characteristic of the contract review process.

SPECIFIC TEST REQUIREMENTS

AIRCRAFT

FAR section 21.127 outlines the specific regulatory test requirements for a complete aircraft. It requires that

> *each person manufacturing aircraft under a Production Under Type Certificate Only, FAR 21 Subpart F, shall establish an approved production flight test procedure and flight check-off form, and in accordance with that form, flight test each aircraft produced. Additionally, each production flight test procedure must include the following:*
>
> > *1) An operational check of the trim, controllability, or other flight characteristics to establish that the production aircraft*

has the same range and degree of control as the prototype aircraft.

2) An operational check of each part or system operated by the crew while in flight to establish that, during flight, instrument readings are within normal range.

3) A determination that all instruments are properly marked, and that all placards and required flight manuals are installed after flight test.

4) A check of the operational characteristics of the aircraft on the ground.

5) A check on any other items peculiar to the aircraft being tested that can best be done during the ground or flight operation of the aircraft.[7]

ENGINES

Like the noted test requirements for an aircraft, both engines and propellers have specific regulated test requirements. FAR section 21.128 requires manufacturers of engines, Produced Under a Type Certificate Only, and excluding rocket engines, to develop procedures and test plans that subject each engine to an acceptable test run that includes the following:

1) Break-in runs that include a determination of fuel and oil consumption and a determination of power characteristics at the rated maximum continuous power or thrust and, if applicable, at rated takeoff power or thrust.

2) At least five hours of operation at rated maximum continuous power or thrust. For engines having a rated takeoff power or thrust higher than rated maximum continuous power or thrust, the five-hour run must include 30 minutes at rated takeoff power or thrust.[8]

Rocket engines also require testing to be performed in accordance with approved statistical techniques and plans.

PROPELLERS

FAR section 21.129 documents the regulatory test requirements for propellers. Each manufacturer of propellers, under a Type Certificate Only, "shall give each variable pitch propeller an acceptable functional test to determine if it operates properly throughout the normal range of operation."[9]

PRODUCTION CERTIFICATE

FAR section 21.143 (a)(3), outlines the requirements for final inspection and testing for manufacturers authorized under a Production Certificate. Each manufacturer must submit for approval data describing the inspection and test procedures necessary to ensure that each article produced conforms to the type design and is in condition for safe operation. This includes a description of the methods used for production inspection of individual parts and complete assemblies, including the identification of any special manufacturing processes involved, the means used to control the processes, the final test procedure for the complete product, and, in the case of aircraft, a copy of the manufacturer's production flight test procedures and checkoff list.[10] When referring to Advisory Circular 21-1B, it is noted that the FAA generally finds acceptable a test procedure that conforms to the identical requirements of the previously noted requirements of products Produced Under Type Certificate Only (FAR 21 Subpart F). So in developing such procedures it may be advisable to structure the test procedures around these requirements, and prior to deviation confer with the applicable FAA offices regarding acceptability.

PARTS MANUFACTURER APPROVAL

FAR section 21.303 (f) outlines the requirements for final testing for products manufactured under the authority of a PMA. PMA manufacturers must make all necessary inspections and tests to determine compliance with the applicable airworthiness requirements; that materials conform to the specifications in the design; that the part conforms to the drawings in the design; and that the fabrication processes, construction, and assembly conform to those specified in the design.

TECHNICAL STANDARD ORDER

FAR section 21.607 outlines the final inspection and test requirements for TSO manufacturers. Each manufacturer of an article for which a TSO authorization has been issued shall manufacture the article in accordance with FAR 21 Subpart O and its applicable TSO, and conduct all required tests and inspections and establish and maintain a quality control system adequate to ensure that the article meets the requirements of FAR 21 Subpart O and its applicable TSO and is in condition for safe operation.[11]

REPAIR STATIONS

Repair stations are required to perform final inspection and testing in accordance with applicable manufacturers' specifications. FAR section 145.45 (f) makes reference to such a requirement.

GENERAL

When a manufacturer is performing any testing of a product, regardless of its stage of completion, procedures should be established that control the conditions of testing. This includes the assurance of the test equipment calibration; the assurance that articles are retested after adjustment or rework has been accomplished after acceptance; and where sampling inspection tests are utilized, other inspections and tests should be implemented as required to assure acceptance of conforming and safe products.

NONDESTRUCTIVE TESTING

Nondestructive testing (NDT) is a special process of verifying a product's conformance, through test, without damaging the product. As design technology advances, so do the methods of substantiating conformance. This means personnel must be continuously trained and equipment must be updated. Within the manufacturer's quality assurance manual, the outline of the NDT control system should be displayed briefly, indicating the core requirements. The specific details of employee certification, use of outside laboratories, calibration control of NDT equipment, and record retention should be documented in an individual procedure. The more involved a company is with the process of NDT, the more the need exists to have stand-alone procedures for each individual type of NDT process.

If NDT is applicable to a company's manufacturing processes, and it will be in most instances, the FAA will require that the procedures documenting the control systems for the individual processes are approved by the FAA prior to implementation. (NDT is a major characteristic of an ACSEP evaluation.) When creating the individual procedures, attention must be given to the acceptance criteria and its assurance that it is realistic and current with present design data. Keeping in line with the guidelines of the American Society for Nondestructive Testing (ASNT) has been the normal rule of acceptance. However, within the concept of the international standards, ISO 9412 provides an international control standard for the process of NDT and can facilitate third-party evaluation and registration of personnel and laboratories.

FORMAL ACCEPTANCE DOCUMENTATION

Formal documentation on a product's final acceptance and its compliance to type design usually takes the form of a certificate. For aircraft that were manufactured under the authority of a Type Certificate Only an aircraft airworthiness certificate, FAA Form 8100-2 (Figure 11.3),

---

UNITED STATES OF AMERICA
DEPARTMENT OF TRANSPORTATION—FEDERAL AVIATION ADMINISTRATION

STANDARD AIRWORTHINESS CERTIFICATE

1. NATIONALITY AND REGISTRATION MARKS	2. MANUFACTURER AND MODEL	3. AIRCRAFT SERIAL NUMBER	4. CATEGORY

5. AUTHORITY AND BASIS FOR ISSUANCE

This airworthiness certificate is issued pursuant to the Federal Aviation Act of 1958 and certifies that, as of the date of issuance, the aircraft to which issued has been inspected and found to conform to the type certificate therefor, to be in condition for safe operation. and has been shown to meet the requirements of the applicable comprehensive and detailed airworthiness code as provided by Annex 8 to the Convention on International Civil Aviation, except as noted herein. Exceptions:

6. TERMS AND CONDITIONS

Unless sooner surrendered, suspended, revoked, or a termination date is otherwise established by the Administrator, this airworthiness certificate is effective as long as the maintenance, preventative maintenance, and alterations are performed in accordance with Parts 21, 43, and 91 of the Federal Aviation Regulations, as appropriate, and the aircraft is registered in the United States.

DATE OF ISSUANCE	FAA REPRESENTATIVE	DESIGNATION NUMBER

Any alteration, reproduction, or misuse of this certificate may be punishable by a fine not exceeding $1,000, or imprisonment not exceeding 3 years, or both. THIS CERTIFICATE MUST BE DISPLAYED IN THE AIRCRAFT IN ACCORDANCE WITH APPLICABLE FEDERAL AVIATION REGULATIONS.

FAA Form 8100-2 (8-82)   GPO 773-933

FIGURE 11.3.   *FAA Form 8100-2, Standard Airworthiness Certificate.*

shall be issued. For engines and propellers manufactured under this same authority, an airworthiness approval tag, FAA Form 8130-3, is issued. Additionally, a statement of conformity is required on FAA Form 8130-9 (Figure 11.4).

> *This statement of conformity must be signed by an authorized person who holds a responsible position in the manufacturing organization, and must include:*
>
> *1) For each product (products other than the complete aircraft, engine or propellers, but certified under the type certificate of one of these items), a statement that the product conforms to its type certificate and is in condition for safe operation.*
>
> *2) For each aircraft, a statement that the aircraft has been flight checked.*
>
> *3) For each aircraft engine or variable pitch propeller, a statement that the engine or propeller has been subjected by the manufacturer to a final operational check.[12]*

For aircraft that were manufactured under the authority of a Production Certificate, FAR 21 Subpart G, the formal final acceptance of

OMB: 2120-0018

STATEMENT OF CONFORMITY

Section I — Aircraft

1. Make	2. Model
3. Serial No.	4. Registration No.

Section II — Engine

1. Make	2. Model
3. Serial No.	

Section III — Propeller

1. Make	2. Hub Model
3. Blade Model	4. Hub Serial No.
5. Blade Serial Nos.	

Section IV — Certification

I hereby certify that:

☐ A. I have complied with Section 21.33(a.)

☐ B. The aircraft described above, produced under type certificate only (FAR 21 Subpart F), conforms to its type certificate, is in a condition for safe operation, and was flight checked on _____
(Date)

☐ C. The engine or propeller described above, presented herewith for type certification, conforms to the type design therefor.

☐ D. The engine or propeller described above produced under type certificate only (FAR 21 Subpart F), conforms to its type certificate and is in a condition for safe operation. The engine or, if applicable, the variable pitch propeller was subjected by the manufacturer to a final operation check on _____
(Date)

Deviations:

Signature of Certifier	Title	
Organization	Date	

FAA Form 8130-9 (11-88) Use Previous Edition

FIGURE 11.4. *FAA Form 8130-9, Statement of Conformity.*

airworthiness is documented with the issuance of an aircraft airworthiness certificate. As referenced in FAR Subpart 21.183 (a), "new aircraft manufactured under a production certificate are entitled to a standard airworthiness certificate without further showing, except that the FAA may inspect the aircraft to determine conformity to the type design and condition for safe flight."[13] This same requirement applies to engines and propellers produced under a Production Certificate. A statement of conformity also is required under the requirements of FAR Section 21.53. Caution must be advised when reviewing FAR section 21.53. It requires an FAA Form 317 to be issued. However, the 317 form was replaced by the 8130-9 over 20 years ago, without a change in regulation. Additionally, FAA Form 8130-9 will be required at first article inspections of a new type-certificated design, including major subassemblies, systems and components, and updates of those inspections after design updates or changes are made.

Some manufacturers may be delegated by the FAA to issue airworthiness certificates themselves, providing they have authorized personnel on staff. However, prior to the issuance of the airworthiness certificate, FAA Form 8130-6, Application for Airworthiness Certificate (Figure 11.5), must be completed. Advisory Circular 21-12A provides detailed instructions on how to complete this form. When the manufacturer has completed the applicable sections of FAA Form 8130-6, it should be submitted, together with any other material that may be required by the regulations for the airworthiness certification being requested, to the appropriate FAA flight standards district office (FSDO), manufacturing inspection district office (MIDO), designated manufacturing inspection representative (DMIR), or designated airworthiness representative (DAR), as appropriate. When the address of the district office that will process the application is not known, it may be obtained from the FAA regional office serving the area wherein the applicant is located. This regional office can normally be found under the Government section of the local telephone book.

Parts or appliances that have been manufactured under a Technical Standard Order (TSO), FAR 21 Subpart O, shall be identified with the applicable TSO number and the manufacturer's identification mark. A certificate of conformance, of the manufacturer's own design, also should accompany the part or appliance. An FAA Form 8130-3, Airworthiness Approval Tag, and its application form, FAA Form 8130-6, also should be issued if the part or appliance is to be exported outside of the United States.

With the creation of the European Community (EC) and the development of the Joint Airworthiness Authority (JAA), Europe has strived for standardization of certification and documentation. The European equivalent to the FAA Form 8130-3 is the JAA Form 1. Shortly after the JAA

FIGURE 11.5. *FAA Form 8130-6, Application for Airworthiness Certificate.*

*U.S.GPO:1989-241-672/90913

VI. PRODUCTION FLIGHT TESTING

A. MANUFACTURER

NAME	ADDRESS

B. PRODUCTION BASIS *(Check applicable item)*

	PRODUCTION CERTIFICATE *(Give production certificate number)*
	TYPE CERTIFICATE ONLY
	APPROVED PRODUCTION INSPECTION SYSTEM

C. GIVE QUANTITY OF CERTIFICATES REQUIRED FOR OPERATING NEEDS ⟶

DATE OF APPLICATION	NAME AND TITLE *(Print or type)*	SIGNATURE

VII. SPECIAL FLIGHT PERMIT PURPOSES OTHER THAN PRODUCTION FLIGHT TEST

A. DESCRIPTION OF AIRCRAFT

REGISTERED OWNER	ADDRESS
BUILDER *(Make)*	MODEL
SERIAL NUMBER	REGISTRATION MARK

B. DESCRIPTION OF FLIGHT — CUSTOMER DEMONSTRATION FLIGHTS ☐ *(Check if applicable)*

FROM	TO	
VIA	DEPARTURE DATE	DURATION

C. CREW REQUIRED TO OPERATE THE AIRCRAFT AND ITS EQUIPMENT.

	PILOT		CO-PILOT		NAVIGATOR		OTHER *(Specify)*

D. THE AIRCRAFT DOES NOT MEET THE APPLICABLE AIRWORTHINESS REQUIREMENTS AS FOLLOWS

E. THE FOLLOWING RESTRICTIONS ARE CONSIDERED NECESSARY FOR SAFE OPERATION *(Use attachment if necessary)*

F. CERTIFICATION — I hereby certify that I am the registered owner (or his agent) of the aircraft described above, that the aircraft is registered with the Federal Aviation Administration in accordance with Section 501 of the Federal Aviation Act of 1958, and applicable Federal Aviation Regulations, and that the aircraft has been inspected and is airworthy for the flight described.

DATE	NAME AND TITLE *(Print or type)*	SIGNATURE

VIII. AIRWORTHINESS DOCUMENTATION (FAA use only)

A. Operating Limitations and Markings in Compliance with FAR 91.31 as Applicable	G. Statement of Conformity, FAA Form 8130-9 *(Attach when required)*
B. Current Operating Limitations Attached	H. Foreign Airworthiness Certification for Import Aircraft *(Attach when required)*
C. Data, Drawings, Photographs, etc. *(Attach when required)*	I. Previous Airworthiness Certificate Issued in Accordance with
D. Current Weight and Balance Information Available in Aircraft	FAR _____ CAR _____ *(Original Attached)*
E. Major Repair and Alteration, FAA Form 337 *(Attach when required)*	J. Current Airworthiness Certificate Issued in Accordance with
F. This Inspection Recorded in Aircraft Records	FAR _____ *(Copy attached)*

FIGURE 11.5. (continued)

Form 1 was released, the FAA released its revised version of the FAA Form 8130-3. This new revised version greatly resembled its European equivalent and had many of the same functions. Unfortunately, this form was not readily accepted by the U.S. aviation industry and was again changed. This was mainly due to the tag's inability to serve as a serviceable tag in maintenance activities. The new form is a mixture of the two previous revisions. Though the new revision is now in issue, many of the previous revision forms are still in the field and will probably be around until the turn of the century, when supply rooms have finally purged products certified on the outdated forms. Until this time, it is important for aviation manufacturers, operators, and service centers to recognize both previous forms, as well as the new, and accept their issuance, when correctly completed. Figure 11.6 exhibits the outdated form, Figure 11.7 exhibits the revised version, and Figure 11.8 exhibits the current issue of FAA Form 8130-3. JAA Form 1 is displayed in Figure 11.9.

Parts, processes, and appliances manufactured under the authority of a Parts Manufacturer Approval (PMA), FAR 21 Subpart K, shall be identified in accordance with the requirements of FAR section 45.15. Each part manufactured under a PMA authorization, in addition to its part number and revision, shall be permanently and legibly marked with the following.

1. The letters *FAA-PMA*.
2. The name, trademark, or symbol of the manufacturer.
3. The name and model designation of each type-certificated product on which the part is eligible for installation.
4. Because of the inspection status requirements, the application of an authorized representative of the manufacturer's inspection department shall also apply his or her acceptance stamp directly to the product.

If the FAA finds that the part is too small or it is otherwise impractical to mark a part with any of the required information, a tag attached to the part or its container must include the required information. If the required marking is so extensive (normally because of numerous installation eligibilities) that to mark on a tag is impractical, the attached tag may refer to a specific readily available manual or catalog for part eligibility information. The other data must be provided on the tag. Additionally, a certificate of conformance, of the manufacturer's own design, should accompany the part or appliance. Like the TSO, PMA products will require an airworthiness approval tag if exported outside of the United States. The issuance of this document is made by either an on-staff DMIR/DAR or through the local MIDO.

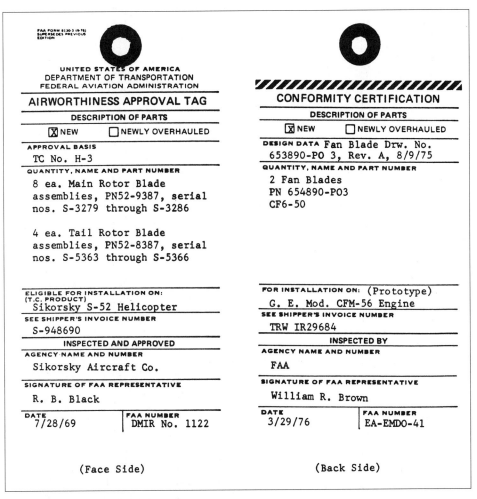

FIGURE 11.6. *FAA Form 8130-3, Airworthiness Approval Tag—Superseded Issue.*

The FAA does provide one interesting exception within the scheme of final inspection and testing. Major assemblies and components, comprising a complete aircraft, manufactured under a Production Certificate may be exported prior to final assembly, inspection, and flight test in accordance with FAR Subpart 21.325 (b) providing (1) the holder of the Production Certificate has established FAA-approved assembly and flight test procedures and (2) the extent of disassembly is the same as an aircraft that has been disassembled for shipment purposes. This exception basically only benefits those manufacturers who manufacture small aircraft and have overseas distributors. The benefit is from not having to

1. Country **UNITED STATES**	2. ☐ Conformity ☐ Airworthiness	**AUTHORIZED RELEASE CERTIFICATE APPROVAL TAG**				3. Certificate Ref No.
4. Organization						5. Work Order/Contract/Invoice
6. Item	7. Description	8. Part No.	9. Eligibility*	10. Qty.	11. Serial/Batch No.	12. Status/Work
13. Remarks						

14. **New Parts:**
Certifies that the part(s) identified above except as otherwise specified in block 13 was (were) manufactured/inspected in accordance with the airworthiness regulations of the stated country and/or in the case of parts to be exported with the approved design data and with the notified special requirements of the importing country.

15. **Used Parts:**
Certifies that the work specified above except as otherwise specified in block 13 was carried out in accordance with the airworthiness regulations of the stated country and the notified special requirements of the importing country and in respect to that work, the part(s) is (are) in condition for safe operation and considered ready for release to service. (over)

16. Signature

17. Name (typed or printed)

18. Date

19. Issued by or on behalf of the Federal Aviation Administration.

FAA Form 8130-3 (9-82)

* Cross-check eligibility for more details with parts catalog

FIGURE 11.7. *FAA Form 8130-3, Authorized Release Certificate Approval Tag—Superseded Issue.*

FAA FORM 8130-3
AIRWORTHINESS APPROVAL TAG
U.S. Department of Transportation
Federal Aviation Administration

1. UNITED STATES	2.	3. System Tracking Ref. No.

4. Organization	5. Work Order, Contract, or Invoice Number:

6. Item	7. Description	8. Part Number	9. Eligibility *	10. Quantity	11. Serial/Batch Number	12. Status/Work

13. Remarks

Limited life parts must be accompanied by maintenance history including total time/total cycles/time since new.

14. New ☐ Newly Overhauled ☐	19. Return to Service in Accordance with FAR 43.9
Certifies that the new or newly overhauled part(s) identified above, except as otherwise specified in block 13 was (were) manufactured in accordance with FAA approved design data and airworthiness.	Certifies that the work specified in block 13 (or attached) above was carried out in accordance with FAA airworthiness regulations and in respect to the work performed the part(s) is (are) approved for return to service.
NOTE: In case of parts to be exported, the special reqirements of the importing country have been met.	

15. Signature	16. FAA Authorization No:	20. Authorized Signature:	21. Certificate Number:

17. Name *(Typed or Printed):*	18. Date:	22. Name *(Typed or Printed)*	23. Date:

FAA Form 8130-3 (11-93)

* (Optional) Installer must cross check eligibility with applicable technical data.

FIGURE 11.8. *FAA Form 8130-3, Airworthiness Approval Tag—Current Issue.*

1. COUNTRY/STAAT F. R. GERMANY	2. LUFTFAHRT-BUNDESAMT AUTHORIZED RELEASE CERTIFICATE - AIRWORTHINESS APPROVAL TAG PRÜFSCHEIN - GERÄTEANHÄNGER	3. CERTIFICATE REF. NO. PRÜFSCHEIN-NR.
4. ORGANIZATION ANERKANNTER BETRIEB		5. WORK ORDER/CONTRACT ARBEITSAUFTRAG/VERTRAG

6. ITEM LFD. NR.	7. DESCRIPTION BESCHREIBUNG	8. PART NO. TEILE-NR.	9. ELIGIBILITY VERWEND-BARKEIT (*)	10. QTY. ANZAHL	11. SERIAL/BATCH NO. WERK/LOS-NR.	12. STATUS/WORK STAND/ARBEITEN

13. REMARKS
BEMERKUNGEN

14. **NEW PARTS:** Certifies that the part(s) identified above except as otherwise specified in block 13 was (were) manufactured/inspected in accordance with the airworthiness regulations of the stated country and/or in the case of parts to be exported with the approved design data and with the notified special requirements of the importing country.

NEUE TEILE: Es wird bescheinigt, daß das/die genannte(n) Teil(e), außer wenn anders in Rubrik 13 festgelegt, in Übereinstimmung mit den geltenden Vorschriften des genannten Staates und/oder bei Ausfuhr von Teilen mit den zugelassenen Musterunterlagen und mit den bekanntgegebenen Sonderforderungen des Einfuhrstaates hergestellt/geprüft wurde(n).

15. **USED PARTS:** Certifies that the work specified above except as otherwise specified in block 13 was carried out in accordance with the airworthiness regulations of the stated country and the notified special requirements of the importing country and in respect to that work the part(s) is (are) in condition for safe operation and considered ready for release to service.

Gebrauchte Teile: Es wird bescheinigt, daß die oben aufgeführten Arbeiten, außer wenn anders in Rubrik 13 angegeben, in Übereinstimmung mit den Vorschriften des genannten Staates und den bekanntgegebenen Sonderforderungen des Einfuhrstaates durchgeführt worden sind und daß das Teil/die Teile sich in einem betriebssicheren Zustand befindet/befinden und für den Betrieb freigegeben ist/sind.

16. SIGNATURE UNTERSCHRIFT		19. ISSUED BY OR ON BEHALF OF THE LUFTFAHRT-BUNDESAMT UNDER AUTHORIZATION REFERENCE. AUSGESTELLT DURCH ODER FÜR DAS LUFTFAHRT-BUNDESAMT IM RAHMEN DER ANERKENNUNG NR.
17. NAME	18. DATE DATUM	

JAA Form One/Hessverlag Braunschweig LBA – Muster Nr. 19

20. (*) Cross-check eligibility for more details with parts catalog – Für nähere Einzelheiten Gegenkontrolle mit Teile-Katalog vornehmen.

FIGURE 11.9. *JAA Form 1, Authorized Release Certificate—Airworthiness Approval Tag.*

perform the final inspection and test process twice, and only once after the aircraft has been assembled at the overseas distributor. However, caution must be used that the overseas operation has authorized personnel to certify the airworthiness of the aircraft.

SHIPMENT OF PRODUCT PRIOR TO DESIGN APPROVAL

The FAA released Advisory Circular 21-32, Control of Parts Shipped Prior to Type Certificate Issuance, to clarify its requirements for shipment of uncertified products. Production approval holders must often ship parts to facilities such as coproducers, subcontractors, repair stations, and commercial air carriers in advance of type certification of a new product, so adequate spares are on hand or are available for incorporation into the product upon Type Certificate (TC) issuance.

Notwithstanding any contractual commitments, production approval holders (manufacturers) located in the United States are responsible for the following.

1. Applicants for type certification of new aircraft engines and propellers are responsible under FAR section 21.53 (a), Statement of Conformity, for submitting to the FAA a statement of conformity to the type design.

2. Applicants for type certification of new aircraft or parts thereof are responsible under FAR section 21.53 (b), Statement of Conformity, for submitting to the FAA a statement of conformity to FAR section 31.33 (a), Inspection and Test, when the aircraft or parts thereof are presented for tests.

Additionally, manufacturers with an approved production inspection system (Production Under Type Certificate Only) are responsible under FAR section 21.130, Statement of Conformity, for submitting to the FAA a statement of conformity which must include the following.

1. For each product, a statement that the product conforms to its type certificate and is in condition for safe operation

2. For each aircraft, a statement that the aircraft has been flight checked

3. For each aircraft engine or variable pitch propeller, a statement that the engine or propeller has been subjected by the TC holder to a final operational check

Production Certificate (PC) holders are responsible for complying with FAR section 21.165 (b) by ensuring that each completed product and part submitted for airworthiness certification conforms to the type design and is in a condition for safe operation.

There must be a documented procedure and/or plan for controlling such parts shipped in advance of a Type Certificate issuance. Production approval holders (approved manufacturers) in the United States who enter into a production program requiring shipment of parts in advance of type certification should present a formal proposal to the FAA detailing how the configuration of those parts will be controlled until the Type Certificate, Approved Production Inspection System, and/or Production Certificate are issued. The proposal (procedure) should be presented to the FAA as soon as practicable to allow review and discussion to determine if the proposal (procedure) will result in a viable program. From a planning standpoint, the production approval holder (approved manufacturer) should give the FAA sufficient lead time to evaluate the proposal as it may be necessary in some instances for the FAA to coordinate with foreign civil air authorities.

The procedure for control of parts shipped prior to Type Certificate issuance should contain the following, at a minimum.

1. The method of tracking part configuration from the time of manufacture through the time of shipment and until the Type Certificate is issued.

2. The method of identifying and segregating parts shipped by the manufacturer and/or its suppliers in such a manner as to preclude their inadvertent installation prior to type design approval.

3. The method of storing parts received by coproducers, subcontractors, repair stations, and commercial air carriers.

4. The method of recall and configuration updating of parts shipped prior to Type Certificate issuance, including parts used during type design testing and customer crew training, that do not meet type design at the time of Type Certificate issuance.

5. The method of notifying facilities to whom parts were shipped prior to Type Certificate issuance concerning the approved or nonapproved status of the parts at the time of the Type Certificate issuance.

6. The proposed use of any designees to conduct conformity inspections on behalf of the FAA as provided in FAR Part 183 (for example, DARs, DERs, and DMIRs). These conformity

inspections would be conducted on each part or lot of parts being shipped in advance of type certification of the product.

Manufacturers in the United States should be prepared to furnish the FAA with any design or quality control data that may be required by foreign civil air authorities to determine conformity to the approved type design of completed products.[14]

The international quality standards have similar, but less exacting, requirements for such uncertified/unqualified products. As noted earlier in this chapter, positive-recall procedures must be developed when required. However, release under positive-recall procedures shall not preclude any necessary inspection and testing activities.

EXPORTING OF PRODUCTS

FAR 21 Subpart L documents the requirements for exporting approved type design products outside of the United States. Additionally, Advisory Circular 21-2F, Export Airworthiness Approval Procedures, lists the various bilateral export agreements with foreign countries, as well as other special requirements. Basically, if an approved product is to be exported outside of the United States, it must be accompanied by an export certificate, unless the foreign civil air authority specifically states that it does not require this document. There are two different types of export certificates; the product's classification will determine which one will be issued.

- A class I product is a complete aircraft, aircraft engine, or propeller, that has been type certificated in accordance with applicable FARs and for which federal aviation specifications or Type Certificate data sheets have been issued; or is identical to a type certificated complete aircraft, aircraft engine, or propeller in all respects except as is otherwise acceptable to the foreign civil air authority of the importing state.

- A class II product is a major component of a class I product (for example, wings, fuselage, empennage assemblies, landing gears, power transmissions, control surfaces, and so on), the failure of which would jeopardize the safety of a class I product; or any part, material, or appliance, approved and manufactured under the Technical Standard Order system in the C series (reference FAR 37).

- A class III product is any part or component that is not a class I or class II product, and includes standard parts (for example, nuts, bolts, rivets of NAS, AN, MS, and MIL specification) as well as some noncritical components (for example, overhead bins, trolleys, and so on). However, certification documents only apply to FAA-approved materials, parts, and processes.

Export airworthiness approvals are issued to exporters or authorized representatives of the exporter of class I and class II products. Class I products will be exported on FAA Form 8130-4 (Figure 11.10) and class II products are exported on FAA Form 8130-3. These certificates must be issued by authorized representatives of the FAA (for example, DARs and DMIRs), and application is made on FAA Form 8130-1 (Figure 11.11).

Export certificates for class III products that are approved under a TC, STC, or TSO are issued on FAA Form 8130-3. Manufacturers who request an export certificate must either have in their employ a designated representative of the FAA who has been authorized to issue that approval (DAR or DMIR), or request FAA support in issuing the certificate. Additionally, the manufacturer must hold for that product being exported a Production Certificate, an approved production inspection system (Production Under a Type Certificate Only), or an FAA-PMA, or TSO authorization. Depending on the requirements of the importing state, distributors of standard hardware may or may not be required to supply an FAA Form 8130-3. This is because the hardware itself is not certified under the regulations of the FAA. However, the FAA is currently working with foreign civil air authorities to develop standardized requirements for standards distributors.

There is one exception to the requirement for certification of exporting product that does not meet type design requirements. If the export airworthiness approval is issued on the basis of a written statement by the importing state as provided in FAR 21.327 (e)(4), the requirements that are not met and the differences in configuration, if any, between the product to be exported and the related type certificated product are to be listed on the export airworthiness approval as exceptions.

SUMMARY

As displayed in this chapter, the inspection and test requirements of ANSI/ASQC Q9003 are not stringent enough to meet the requirements of the FAA. ANSI/ASQC Q9001 and ANSI/ASQC Q9002 complement the FAR requirements well, in that, aside from specific corrective and preventive action requirements, the international quality standards place no additional controls for inspection and testing activities. The inspection and testing requirements of the FARs are the most detailed characteristics of an FAA-approved manufacturer's quality system.

As outlined in this chapter, a manufacturer shall establish quality assurance systems that control the processes of receiving inspection,

The United States of America
Department of Transportation
Federal Aviation Administration
Washington, D.C.

No. _____

Export Certificate of Airworthiness

This certifies *that the product identified below and more particularly described in Specification (s)[1] of the Federal Aviation Administration, Numbered* _____

has been examined and as of the date of this certificate, is considered airworthy in accordance with a comprehensive and detailed airworthiness code of the United States Government, and is in compliance with those special requirements of the importing country filed with the United States Government, except as noted below. This certificate in no way attests to compliance with any agreements or contracts between the vendor and purchaser, nor does it constitute authority to operate an aircraft.

Product:

Manufacturer:

Model:

Serial No.:

New ☐   *Newly Overhauled* ☐

Used Aircraft ☐

Country to which exported:

Exceptions:

_____
Signature of Authorized Representative

_____
Date

_____
District Office or Designee Number

[1] *For complete aircraft, list applicable specification or Type Certificate Data Sheet numbers for the aircraft, engine, and propeller. Applicable specifications or Type Certificate Data Sheet, if not attached to this export certificate, will have been forwarded to the appropriate governmental office of the importing country.*

FAA Form 8130-4 (7-68)   Formerly Form FAA 26

FIGURE 11.10.   *FAA Form 8130-4, Export Certificate of Airworthiness.*

US Department of Transportation Federal Aviation Administration	**APPLICATION FOR EXPORT CERTIFICATE OF AIRWORTHINESS**	FORM APPROVED: O.M.B. No. 2120-0018
		Export Certificate No.

INSTRUCTIONS — This application is to be submitted to an authorized FAA representative (one copy) when the product(s) to be exported is (are) presented for inspection. Use Part I for Class I products and Part II for Class II. For complete aircraft execute items 1 through 11, as applicable. For engines and propellers, omit item 5A. Part III is for FAA use only.

▶ **Part I — APPLICATION FOR EXPORT CERTIFICATE OF AIRWORTHINESS** *(Complete items 1-11)*

1. Application is made for an export certificate of airworthiness to cover the product(s) described below which is (are):

☐ NEW   ☐ USED *(Aircraft)*   ☐ NEWLY OVERHAULED

2. Name and address of exporter	3. Name and address of foreign purchaser	4. Country of destination

5. Description of product(s)

Type (a)	Make and model (b)	Identification No.	Serial Nos (c)	FAA Spec. No. (d)	Operating time (Hours) (e) Since overhaul	Total
A. AIRCRAFT						
B. ENGINES						
C. PROPELLERS						

6. Does the product comply with all applicable Federal Aviation Regulations, Airworthiness Directives, and other FAA requirements?

☐ YES   ☐ NO   *(Explain in "Remarks")*

7. Have applicable special requirements of the importing country been complied with?

☐ YES   ☐ NO   *(Explain in "Remarks")*

8. Date title passed or is expected to pass to foreign purchaser :

9. For overseas shipment, preservation and packaging methods used to protect product(s) against corrosion and damage *(List Spec. No. or Title)*:

Effective duration of above methods:

10. Remarks

11. **EXPORTER'S CERTIFICATION** — The undersigned certifies that the above statements are true and that the product(s) described herein is (are) airworthy and in condition for safe operation except as may be noted under item 10 "Remarks" above.

Signature of applicant or authorized representative	Title	Date

FAA Form 8130-1 (11-88) Supersedes Previous Edition

FIGURE 11.11. *FAA Form 8130-1, Application for Export Certificate of Airworthiness.*

PART II — APPLICATION FOR APPROVAL OF AERONAUTICAL PARTS *(Complete items 12-20)*

12. Name and address of exporter	13. Name and address of foreign purchaser	14. Country of destination

15. Parts are eligible for installation on ⟶	Make and model Class I product	FAA Spec. No.

16. The parts are *(check one)* ⟶   ☐ NEW   ☐ NEWLY OVERHAULED

17. The parts are described *(Check one)*

☐ Below by name, part number, and quantity   ☐ On the attached invoice or packing sheet, by name, part number and quantity ⟶

Invoice/packing sheet No.

Name (a)	Part number (b)	Quantity (c)

18. Have applicable special requirements of the importing country been complied with? ☐ YES   ☐ NO *(Explain in item 10 "Remarks")*

19. Preservation and packaging methods used to protect parts against corrosion and damage *(List Spec. No. or Title)*:

Effective duration of above methods:

20. EXPORTER'S CERTIFICATION—I certify that the foregoing statements are true and that the parts described herein are airworthy, conform to FAA approved design data, and are in condition for safe operation except as may be noted in item 10 "Remarks."

Signature of applicant or authorized representative	Title	Date

Part III — APPROVAL *(FOR FAA USE ONLY)*

21. It is considered that the product(s) described in Part I or Part II is (are) airworthy and conform(s) to pertinent requirements except as noted in item 10. *(Check one)* ⟶ ☐ Part I   ☐ Part II

Signature	Number	Date

(Check one) ⟶ ☐ DMIR   ☐ DAR   ☐ DELEGATION OPTION MFR.   ☐ FAA INSPECTOR

22. Give quantity of approval tags, FAA Form 8130-3, issued for the parts described in Part II. ⟶ Quantity

23. EXPORT FILE SPOT-CHECKED BY:

FAA Supervising Inspector	D.O. No.	Date

★U.S.GPO:1991-0-568-012/40085

FIGURE 11.11.   (continued)

in-process inspection and testing, final inspection and testing, and non-destructive testing. Additionally, manufacturers are required to establish internal procedures for the issuance of formal acceptance documentation, which could include statements of conformity, airworthiness tags, airworthiness certificates, and exporting documents.

When products are to be sent to a customer prior to design or production approval, the FAA has allowed provisions for these activities. However, the manufacturer shall establish internal procedures for such activities, and they shall be approved by the FAA prior to implementation.

As for all of these inspection and test activities, the FAA has special documentation requirements for the indication of acceptance. The manufacturer should be aware of what documentation requirements apply to it. This could be assisted by maintaining a current library of the applicable FARs as well as a complete current set of advisory circulars. Additionally, maintaining a close professional relationship with the local FAA representatives is very important. This could provide an exacting, and the least expensive, source for information.

NOTES

1. DOT/FAA, Federal Aviation Regulation Section 21.143, *Certification Procedures for Products and Parts—Quality Control Data Requirements; Prime Manufacturer* (Washington, D.C.: DOT/FAA, March 1993).

2. ANSI/ASQC Q9001-1994, *Quality Systems—Model for Quality Assurance in Design, Development, Production, Installation, and Servicing* (Milwaukee, Wis.: American Society for Quality Control, 1994), 6, para. 4.10.2.1., Receiving Inspection and Testing.

3. DOT/FAA, Advisory Circular 21-1B, *Production Certificates* (Washington, D.C.: DOT/FAA, 10 May 1976), 7, para. (7)(f), Supplier Control.

4. ANSI/ASQC Q9001-1994, 6, para. 4.10.2.2., Receiving Inspection and Testing.

5. Ibid., para. 4.10.3., In-Process Inspection and Testing.

6. Advisory Circular 21-1B, 9, para. (2), Manufacturing Processes.

7. DOT/FAA, Federal Aviation Regulation Section 21.127, *Certification Procedures for Products and Parts—Tests: Aircraft* (Washington, D.C.: DOT/FAA, March 1993).

8. DOT/FAA, Federal Aviation Regulation Section 21.128, *Certification Procedures for Products and Parts—Tests: Aircraft Engines* (Washington, D.C.: DOT/FAA, March 1993).

9. DOT/FAA, Federal Aviation Regulation Section 21.129, *Certification Procedures for Products and Parts—Tests: Propellers* (Washington, D.C.: DOT/FAA, March 1993).

10. DOT/FAA, Federal Aviation Regulation Section 21.143, *Certification Procedures for Products and Parts—Quality Control Data Requirements: Prime Manufacturer* (Washington, D.C.: DOT/FAA, March 1993).

11. DOT/FAA, Federal Aviation Regulation Section 21.607 (a)(b), *Certification Procedures for Products and Parts—General Rules Governing Holders of TSO Authorizations* (Washington, D.C.: DOT/FAA, March 1993).

12. DOT/FAA, Federal Aviation Regulation Section 21.130 (a), *Certification Procedures for Products and Parts—Statement of Conformity* (Washington, D.C.: DOT/FAA, March 1993).

13. DOT/FAA, Federal Aviation Regulation Section 21.183 (a), *Certification Procedures for Products and Parts—Issue of Standard Airworthiness Certificates for Normal, Utility, Acrobatic, Commuter, and Transport Category Aircraft; Manned Free Balloons; and Special Classes of Aircraft* (Washington, D.C.: DOT/FAA, March 1993).

14. DOT/FAA, Advisory Circular 21-32, *Control of Parts Shipped Prior to Type Certificate Issuance* (Washington, D.C.: DOT/FAA, 14 September 1992).

Chapter 12

CONTROL OF INSPECTION, MEASURING, AND TEST EQUIPMENT

Not unlike most other industries, during the manufacturing and inspection processes of aerospace products, special tools, jigs, equipment, and instruments are used to ensure the correctness of the build and or processes. To ensure the repeatability and accuracy of the special tools, jigs, equipment, and instruments, they must be periodically checked, inspected, adjusted, modified, and repaired. This action is called *calibration*, and includes both metrology and tooling inspection. To simplify reference to these special inspection and manufacturing tools, they will be referred to as *calibrated tooling*.

The three international quality standards all require some level of control over calibrated tooling. The international quality standards state that

> *the supplier shall establish and maintain documented procedures to control, calibrate, and maintain inspection, measuring and test equipment [calibrated tooling], including test software used by the supplier to demonstrate the conformance of product to the specified requirements. Inspection, measuring, and test equipment shall be used in a manner which ensures that the measurement uncertainty is known and is consistent with the required measurement capability.[1]*

This control shall be extended to test software or comparative references such as test hardware that are used as suitable forms of inspection. These shall be checked to prove that they are capable of verifying the acceptability of product, prior to release for use during production, installation, or servicing, and shall be rechecked at prescribed intervals. The extent and frequency of these checks shall be established and records maintained as evidence of control. The international quality standards also require that all calibration and adjustment be performed against certified equipment (also known as standards) having a known valid relationship to nationally recognized standards. Where no such standards exist, the basis used for calibration shall be documented.[2]

ANSI/ASQC Q9001 and ANSI/ASQC Q9002 are identical in their requirements for calibrated tooling. ANSI/ASQC Q9003 is very close to the other two international quality standards in its requirements for calibration, except that the emphasis is only on the control of final inspection, measuring, and test equipment. The international quality standards also have reference to calibrated tooling that is not under the ownership of the manufacturer. If the tooling is rented, on loan, or supplied by the purchaser, it must still meet the calibration requirements. As previously mentioned, reference to tool capability is made. Equipment shall be used in a manner that ensures that measurement uncertainty is known and is consistent with the required measurement capability. This means that if a certain dimension has a tolerance of a noted value, the calibrated tooling (through its own internal tolerances) should not consume so much of the tolerance that the measurement is no longer accurate. Through the requirements of the international quality standards, the calibration system must be controlled by a procedure. This procedure is traditionally a quality assurance procedure, but in consideration of the organization performing as a team, the number of departments involved, and the implementation of the international quality standards, it could be a corporate/company procedure, with only reference made to the control within the quality assurance manual. This would make the procedure interfunctionally effective. There are additional calibration system requirements within the international quality standards, and these will be discussed in developing the system.

The FARs are not as clear as the international quality standards when identifying the requirements for a calibration system. With the exception of FAR Part 145, for repair stations, professional interpretation may be needed. As an example, a manufacturing system under the authority of a Production Certificate, in FAR Subpart 21.143 (a)(3), states that "a description of the methods used for production inspection of individual parts and complete assemblies, including the identification of any special manufacturing processes involved, the means used to control the process, and the final test procedure for the complete product, shall be submitted for approval."[3] In reading these requirements, the need for a calibration system is not entirely clear. In order to obtain the FAA's interpretation of this paragraph, Advisory Circular 21-1B should be reviewed. Among the description of other quality system characteristics, Advisory Circular 21-1B states that "the inclusion of supplementary data [procedures] into the quality manual will be considered helpful in showing acceptable compliance. One of these procedures should include a schedule of inspection and calibration intervals for production jigs and fixtures, precision inspection tools, testing equipment, including gages and recording equipment used in controlling processes."[4] The FAA also has evaluation criteria for the control calibrated tooling within ACSEP.[5]

Advisory circulars are only to be used as reference material, and actual system requirements are to be derived from the individual FARs. But it should never be forgotten that these advisory circulars are the official interpretations of the FAA, and can provide clarification as to what is meant in a particular FAR.

As for the other manufacturing approvals, each has its own reference to calibration, in much the same way the Production Certificate (PC) does. The wording of the individual requirements is much the same as the PC and additional clarification is given in separate advisory circulars. For a manufacturer who produces under a Type Certificate only, the requirement can be found in FAR Subpart 21.125 (a)(4); the requirements for PMA manufacturers are under FAR Subpart 21.303 (h)(4); and those for TSO manufacturers are under FAR Subpart 21.607 (b). Because designated alteration stations (DAS) have the prerequisite of being approved under one of the other manufacturing approvals, the calibration requirements for them are found under the prerequisite approvals.

The quality system requirements for a repair station have a very clear description of the requirements for a calibration system. FAR Subpart 145.47 (b) states that

> the Repair Station shall ensure that all inspection and test equipment is tested at regular intervals to ensure correct calibration to a standard derived from the National Institute of Standards and Technology (NIST) or to a standard provided by the equipment manufacturer. In the case of foreign equipment [aircraft or aircraft components manufactured outside of the United States], the standard of the country of manufacture may be used, if approved by the FAA.[6]

For the repair station, these calibration procedures will normally be a quality assurance procedure. In some cases where the repair station rating is in addition to another manufacturing approval, there will be one repair station manual (RSM) that outlines the core functions of the repair station and references other procedures that are also used under the manufacturing approval. These will provide detailed instructions and requirements, as in the case of the calibration system.

COUPLING THE REQUIREMENTS

In coupling the international quality standards to the individual FAR requirements, it is clear that because the FARs imply written procedures for the control of calibration throughout production and not just at final inspection and test, a conforming quality system will exceed the requirements of ANSI/ASQC Q9003.

When coupling the requirements of ANSI/ASQC Q9001 and ANSI/ASQC Q9002 with those of the various FAA manufacturing approvals, they will be found to be complementary. The FARs state that there will be a system, and the international quality standards provide more details on what that system shall do. Additionally, where the international quality standards require traceability to a national standard of measure, the FARs (through clarification of the advisory circulars) provide direction toward the NIST. In addition, the FARs require that this procedure, in conjunction with the quality assurance manual, be approved by the FAA. The quality system registrar also must approve the manual and associated procedures prior to registration. In addition to the calibration requirements of the international quality standards, ISO 10012-1:1992, *Quality assurance requirements for measuring equipment,* provides international calibration system requirements; however, its use is optional.

DEVELOPING THE SYSTEM

In developing the calibration system, it is recommended to briefly outline it within the quality assurance manual and elaborate within a standalone procedure (corporate/company procedure or quality assurance procedure). This will allow for simplified updating later. Larger companies may find it helpful to separate precision instruments from tooling, because of different departments being responsible for recertification. For example, an inspector's micrometer may be recalled for recalibration by the metrology lab, where fixed tooling will be recertified by the tooling inspection function. However, in smaller companies it is typical for one department to be responsible for all such activities, requiring only one such procedure. In either case, we are going to group all such calibrated tooling into one basket and outline the generic requirements that are applicable to both as referenced in both international quality standards and the FARs.

First, the procedure must be written. For most existing aviation manufacturers, there is probably already one in effect. So in this case, it may need to be revised to incorporate the requirements of the international quality standards. The procedure should outline the responsibilities of each department involved, in such a way that the requirements are easily understandable.

Within the procedure there shall be a description of what equipment is applicable to calibration. This could be a short paragraph stating that "all tooling and equipment that is used for inspection of the product, or may have an adverse effect on the product if not correctly adjusted, shall be subject to recall for calibration and/or inspection." A list also can be part of the procedure, noting the various types of tools that would require calibration. Such tools would include, but by no means be limited to,

Micrometer	Calipers
Gauge blocks	Torque wrenches
Thread gauges	Optical comparators
Thermal couples	Thermometers
Pressure gauges	Transits
Radius gauges	Protractors
Height gauges	Telescoping gauges
Depth gauges	Go–no go gauges
Multimeters	Ohmmeters
Voltmeters	Hertzmeters
Drill templates	Assembly jigs
Holding fixtures	Computer tapes and software
Indicators	Coordinate measuring machines

The control procedure shall include the controls necessary to effectively employ the following characteristics.

- Determination of the necessary measurements and required accuracy
- Selection of appropriate inspection, measuring, and test equipment
- Proper identification of inspection, measuring, and test equipment
- Development of appropriate inspection intervals
- Adjustment and calibration requirements traceable to internationally or nationally recognized standards (FAA requires that the traceability is to nationally recognized standards)
- Definition of proper inspection methods and action to be taken in unsatisfactory conditions
- Indication of calibration status on applicable inspection, measuring, and test equipment
- Quality records retention
- Assessment and documentation of the validity of previous inspection and test results when inspection, measuring, and test equipment is found to be out of calibration

- Assurance of proper environmental conditions
- Requirements to ensure that the handling, preservation, and storage of inspection, measuring, and test equipment is such that the accuracy and fitness for use are maintained
- Safeguarding of facilities to ensure the validity of calibration

RECALL LIST

As previously noted, the list of calibrated tooling is not inclusive of all types of tooling or inspection media that are required to be calibrated, checked, or inspected, but it will provide an idea. But, to ensure that there is no question as to what tooling is to be calibrated and which items do not need it, a master recall list should be created, including the description of the tool/inspection medium, its identification number, the location, and the recertification date. This master recall list should be copied and distributed to all applicable supervisors and centrally posted.

INSPECTION RECORDS

Each tool/inspection medium should have its own inspection record. Ideally, this would be a card-stock form that includes the same data as the master recall list, plus more. This could be a two-part form. The first form would provide the actual inspection requirements, including the method of checking the tool/inspection medium; the acceptance criteria; and what actions to take if the results are unsatisfactory (reference Figure 12.1). If there any special handling instructions or environmental controls necessary, they also should be noted on this form.

The second form (Figure 12.2) should list the actual inspection results. A typical entry would read, "Tool calibrated in accordance with the prescribed requirements, and found OK," or "Inspected tool in accordance with the prescribed requirements, found out of manufacturer's tolerance. Tool adjusted [provide details of adjustment or repair], recalibrated, and returned to service." Additionally, the next calibration date should be listed on the form.

The manufacturer may opt to maintain this data electronically. In this case, the data shall be accessible to all personnel who require data regarding the capabilities and past history of the tool. Such data may be needed when a tool is found out of calibration. This data also should have the capability of being printed out, so it can accompany the tool when it is transferred or sent out for repair/adjustment. With either method, paper or electronic, the records shall be maintained as quality records (reference chapter 17).

Tooling Periodic Inspection Log		
ACXI		Tool S/N: HT0095

Tool ID number	Tool name	
ASHY76885321		Forward spar assembly jig

Tool location	Date initiated	Aircraft model(s)
Bldg. 15, column 7, Mfg.	1 August 1993	ACXI Super Flyer 11A

Periodic inspection process

1. This assembly jig shall be inspected on a 12-month calendar cycle.

2. All inspections shall be in accordance with tool drawing ASHY76885321, latest revision.

3. All out-of-tolerance conditions shall be noted on the appropriate continuation sheet and rectified prior to return to service.

4. When assembly jig is found to be acceptable to the above-noted drawing, place self-adhesive calibration sticker, ACXI Form 113, on the forward-facing structure beam. Ensure that the appropriate calibration due dates are correctly applied.

5. If for any reason this assembly jig is to be placed in storage, remove all outboard-facing details and place in storage box type ACXI 876RS. Wrap all non-painted surfaces in oil paper. Place entire assembly jig in an appropriate size wooden crate. This assembly jig must not be exposed to the outside elements, and shall be stored in warehouse G67.

6. Removal from storage—When removing this assembly jig from storage, carefully remove the contents from applicable storage containers. Inspect all major structures for warpage and corrosion. Inspect all associated details for serviceability. Reassemble jig in accordance with the latest revision of the above-noted drawing. Incorporate any needed changes. Upon acceptance, apply calibration sticker in accordance with the instructions in item 4 of this log.

ACXI Form 115 (05 Aug. 92)

FIGURE 12.1. *Sample tooling periodic inspection log.*

CALIBRATION INDICATORS

After the tool/inspection media has been successfully calibrated, it shall be identified as such. There are two typical methods for such identification—placard entry and sticker application.

Large assembly jigs, holding fixtures, and some drill templates are normally identified with an affixed metal placard. This placard would contain all applicable identification data, and may be accompanied by a calibration status placard, with entries impressed by steel stamps. As the tool is accepted, the inspector applies the next calibration date and the

	Tooling Periodic Inspection Log—Continuation Sheet					
ACXI					Tool SN: HT0095	
Tool ID number ASHY76885321				Tool name Forward spar assembly jig		
Tool location Bldg. 15, column 7, manufacturing				Aircraft model(s) ACXI Super Flyer 11A		
Item	Date	Rev.	Inspection and rework observations		Next due date	Stamp
1.	05 Aug. 93	E	Performed annual inspection in accordance with inspection log planning. Adjusted detail 43 approximately .032 in. inboard. Assy. jig OK for further service.		05 Aug. 93	C1034
2.	03 Aug. 94	F	Incorporated change F. Performed annual inspection in accordance with inspection log planning. No discrepancies noted. Assembly jig OK for further service.		03 Aug. 95	C1034

ACXI Form 116 (05 Aug. 92)

FIGURE 12.2. *Sample tooling periodic inspection log—continuation sheet.*

inspector's stamp. This method should prevent inadvertent loss and damage of the calibration data and provide a visual inspection record.

The most common method of calibration indication is the self-adhesive sticker (reference Figure 12.3). The sticker can be used in almost any type of application. Like the metal placard, the sticker will be identified with the last calibration date, next calibration date, and the inspector's stamp (normally a rubber stamp). The location of the sticker's application should be described in the individual inspection record. This will ensure consistency in the placement and prevent the application of the sticker in an area of the tool that will prevent proper functioning, or that is prone to heavy use and wear. Such stickers are not appropriate for use on tooling whose operation would be prone to damage or loss of the sticker or its data.

INSPECTION INTERVALS

Within the topic of calibration, appropriate intervals of calibration is one of the most disputed subjects. Through the recent decades of aircraft manufacturing, there have been numerous methods developed to determine the appropriate calibration interval for tools. Some have worked and others have failed and caused the production (and scrap) of misman-ufactured parts. The plain fact is that the appropriate interval of calibration for a tool depends on its individual characteristics and environment. To simply say that all tools will be calibrated on an annual basis may not

For installation on larger tools and jigs

For installation on smaller tools
and inspection instruments

FIGURE 12.3.   *Sample calibration indication stickers.*

be good enough. Some tools, because of their high frequency of use, may require more frequent calibration than others. For an example, electrical crimpers that are used daily in a production line environment may need to be checked on a daily basis and calibrated on a monthly schedule. Both the checks and calibrations must be defined and documented.

Tools that are only used a few times a year and are in a stable environment may be placed on a progressive inspection/calibration schedule. One example is a part that is required as a spare and is built on demand. The tool that builds this part is stationary and not affected by any outside influences. Because this tool may be used only once or twice a year, it may be appropriate to perform unit-cycle inspection.

Unit-cycle inspection is an interval method that requires inspection/calibration of a tool after a certain number of units have been produced in it. This is usually a progressive type of interval, starting with the first check after the first production use, or first article inspection. If the tool successfully builds the part, the interval will be lengthened to the next interval length. The more proven the tool becomes, the longer the intervals become. The increments should be determined by a team effort of the tool design, tool inspection, engineering, manufacturing, and quality inspection departments, and should be based on the tool's accuracy and complexity of design.

As each unit cycles through the tool, it is noted on the unit-cycle log (Figure 12.4). As an inspection point in the manufacturing work instructions, "OK to remove from tool," quality inspection approves the removal of the part/assembly from the tool and notes the usage on the form. This form should be installed directly on the tool, when possible, or in the immediate area of the tool. The next calibration/inspection due cycle is noted on the form by leaving the appropriate number of spaces open for usage documentation and placing a bold line and entry noting the inspection requirement when the open spaces are full at the appropriate location on the form.

The international quality standards do not prescribe an interval schedule. Rather, they leave it up to the manufacturer to develop. Keep in mind when establishing intervals that not all tools are the same. Some may require checking and adjustment more often than others. The actual interval shall be based on the individual piece of equipment's ability to maintain its capability and accuracy.

ENVIRONMENTAL CONTROLS

When placing tooling into service, the environments in which it is to function shall be such as to prevent inadvertent adjustments that would invalidate the calibration settings. Characteristics such as temperature,

Unit-Cycle Log			
ACXI Wichita, Kansas			
Tool nomenclature	Tool number		Tool serial number
Last inspection frequency	Present inspection frequency		Tooling insp. log approval (stamp and date)
Load no.	Work order number	Mfg. stamp and date	OK to remove QC stamp and date

ACXI Form 149 (05 Aug. 94)

FIGURE 12.4.   *Sample Unit-Cycle Log.*

humidity, vibration, and concrete thickness may play an important role in keeping the tool in calibration. If there is heavy vehicle traffic in the area, the vibration may throw an assembly jig out of adjustment enough that it can no longer produce a conforming product. The tool design department must consider the environmental characteristics of the area in which the tool is to be used and design the tool to function properly under those conditions. The other option is to change the environmental characteristics of the area, through air-conditioning and heating, or facility improvements (such as thicker concrete or vibration absorbers).

The same is true for smaller precision instruments, such as a torque wrench. If the temperature and humidity vary greatly, the tool may no longer be under controlled conditions, and the required value is no longer accurate. Operators of precision tools must be trained in proper handling techniques and restricted uses during adverse environmental conditions. They must also know what the correct conditions are.

Inspection areas and test facilities also must be protected from the environment. Such areas could include clean rooms, burn chambers, refrigeration chambers, and chemical test laboratories. In some instances, if these delicate areas were allowed to become out of control for any period of time, their capability to continue service may be adversely affected. When applicable, recorders should be applied within these areas to document the continuous acceptable environment. These recorders also must be on a calibration schedule.

HANDLING, PRESERVATION, AND STORAGE

The international quality standards require that the quality system ensures that the handling, preservation, and storage of inspection, measuring, and test equipment is such that the accuracy and fitness for use are maintained. This is mostly directed at tooling and equipment that are susceptible to storage. A section of the tooling procedure can be dedicated to these requirements, or a stand-alone procedure could be created. The size of the company and the number of tools used by the company will mandate the required detail of the procedural instructions. If a company does not depend on much tooling, it is less likely that its employees will need a lot of instruction on how to handle, preserve, and store tooling. However, for larger airframe, engine, and propeller manufacturers, it is quite the opposite. There may be a whole department dedicated to this process.

The procedure should provide instructions for preserving the tooling while it is in storage. This may require the application of a preservative oil, shrink wrapping, or supportive blocking. Additionally, the environment in which the tooling is to be maintained must assure the tool's later usability. These individual steps do not have to be in the procedure—they could be described in the individual inspection record.

When the stored tools are to be returned to service, they must be rechecked for accuracy. This rechecking is actually a recalibration, which shall be noted on the inspection record. This should be the new baseline for the inspection interval.

While tools are in service, handling is very important as well. If a torque wrench is dropped, it must be taken out of service, and the calibration indicator must be voided immediately. The tool must be returned for recalibration and an entry must be made in the inspection record, noting the drop and recalibration actions. The same is true for a large assembly jig. If a fork truck was to accidently bump into the jig, all further processing must stop immediately. The jig must be subjected to rechecking and the incident and corrective measures documented in the individual inspection record.

Personnel who handle these tools must be trained in the proper handling procedures. For example, they must be aware that if the torque wrench drops or the assembly jig is bumped, the tools are subject to recalibration.

SELECTING THE APPROPRIATE TOOL

The international quality standards place emphasis on the correct selection of inspection, measuring, and test equipment. The chosen equipment must be capable of the accuracy and precision necessary. This means that the tool used must be properly matched to the job. The internal tolerance of the tool should not consume the majority of the product's tolerance. For example, if the part has a tolerance of .005, and the tool has a tolerance of .003, in reality, the part is only given a tolerance of .002, because the tool consumes most of it. These examples are basic, but this happens more often than many would think. The industry standard for tool tolerance consumption is 10 percent of the product's tolerance. This will still provide a 90 percent accuracy of part measurement. This would mean that the tool that inspected the part with the .005 tolerance should be capable of maintaining a .0005 internal tolerance.

Ensuring that the operator uses the proper tool can be achieved through numerous means. The most effective method is through training and documentation. Personnel should be trained how to use the tools and should understand how improper use or selection would affect measurement. Additionally, within the inspection planning and manufacturing work instructions, the specific tool required for the job could be noted. The inspector/operator could also note the tool's serial number on the applicable plan, for later traceability. This would prove valuable during system audit.

Who should select the tool? This depends on the type of tool, but this is normally accomplished by the quality engineering department. However, for assembly jigs and fixtures, the tool design department will play a large supportive role.

INITIAL TOOL CERTIFICATION

New tooling and some inspection media must be certified prior to production release. Such equipment would include assembly jigs, holding fixtures, drill templates, computer programs, and special gauges. This is normally accomplished by a combination of inspecting the tooling and inspection media to its appropriate design documents and assuring the product it produced is conforming to its own design documents. As discussed in chapter 5, first article inspections (FAIs) are normally held to verify both product and tooling, as well as design. Off-the-shelf inspection tools do not require FAIs of their own; such an action would be neither cost effective nor logical. However, such off-the-shelf inspection tools, when received, shall be accompanied with the appropriate certifications and be subject to internal calibration requirements.

Like the FAI for the product, the tools and inspection media also should have characteristics plans. Such a plan should document the important dimensional characteristics of the tool/inspection medium, documenting both the required (should be) and actual (is) results. As a final line-item buy off, the inspector should note the FAI serial number of the completed product on the tool's/inspection medium's characteristic plan.

The completed FAI documents for tools and inspection media are to be considered as quality records. Typically, such documents will be maintained in the individual file for the tool or inspection media, in the applicable calibration department (metrology lab or tooling inspection). This would provide a one-stop location for all such calibration documentation. Though the FAA requirement for such document retention is only two years, it is recommended to maintain this data, in its appropriate file, for the life of the tool. This will provide a good life history of the tool/inspection medium.

CUSTOMER ACCESS TO DATA

The international quality standards state that "where the availability of technical data pertaining to the measurement equipment is a specified requirement, data shall be made available, when required by the customer or customer's representative, for verification that the measuring equipment is functionally adequate."[7] This is not really anything new to the aviation industry. However, the right for such audit should be clarified within the contract or purchase order (reference chapter 4, "Contract Review"). Additionally, these customer audits should not be an inconvenience to the manufacturer, providing the inspection records are maintained correctly. This same data also will be required for internal audit surveillance, as well as other second- and third-party evaluations.

SOFTWARE USED FOR INSPECTION

With the advancement of technology, computers have become a necessary part of the aviation industry. As a result, the FAA has released an advisory circular (AC 21-36) titled *Quality Assurance Controls for Product Acceptance Software.* The international quality standards also provide requirements for software control when used for inspection purposes. In actuality, the international quality standards make no difference between inspection software and any other type of inspection media. All of the requirements noted earlier in this chapter also apply to inspection software. Examples of this type of software include numerical control programs, automated test stand software, coordinate measuring machine programs, automated process control software, and automated manufacturing cell controllers. The content of this section does not cover flight software.

As noted time and again, advisory circulars are not regulations, but they are the official FAA interpretation of the FARs. Advisory Circular 21-36 provides a good outline of what characteristics should be incorporated into an inspection software control system. It covers release methods, documentation, software configuration management, identification, change control process, media distribution/retrieval system, and applications. It is recommended that all aerospace manufacturers make themselves familiar with this document, because it is only a matter of time until the content of this advisory circular finds itself in a FAR.

Though the international quality standards do not differentiate between inspection software and hardware, it is recommended that the quality system has different procedures for the control of both. This is primarily because each has its own special characteristics as do the means and possibly the personnel responsible for control.

The procedure shall define the criteria for acceptance of the software. This is normally accomplished through inspection of the product produced by it. If the product is acceptable, then, normally, so is the software. The procedure may also allow for emergency nonroutine use of nonreleased software in the acceptance process. This will be required often when used in a development or prototype product program. However, there must be a means of locating and recalling the product that was manufactured, inspected, or tested by the nonreleased software, when necessary. If unreleased software is used for product acceptance, the product involved must be identified as nonconforming until such time as the exact same version of the software used is released. Each product affected should be identified by serial number to ensure recall if necessary. The product should not be shipped, unless an FAA-approved alternate means of product acceptance is used, until all product acceptance software has been released. The recall system shall not be considered an acceptable alternative means of product acceptance for shipment of products.[8]

The procedure also should include the method to identify what documentation should be available with the software. The documentation may be in electronic or hard copy format and should detail the requirements satisfied by the software. If electronic documentation is used, the FAA reserves the right for audit. The FAA representative must be allowed to review the documentation upon request. Additionally, the documentation must also meet the requirements of the international quality standards, with regard to document control (reference chapter 6).

The procedure should cover the management of the software configuration. The configuration management may be administered by the production approval holder (PC, PMA, TSO), the supplier (software supplier or hardware supplier), or a third party, such as the original development activity. However, the responsibility remains with the production approval holder to ensure that all subject software is properly configured. The configuration management shall include instructions for the identification of the software and documentation (chapter 6). The procedure should also define how software programs, which are not functionally interchangeable, are distinguished from each other. "Only identical copies of master programs are to be considered functionally interchangeable."[9]

The change control process also must be described within the procedure. The objective of the change control is to ensure that all changes have been approved, tested, and correctly implemented, and that only the proper version of the program and its documentation are available for use. The change control procedures should provide explicit instructions regarding how and by whom the software and documentation may be changed. This may require support from multiple departments. The instructions should ensure that procedures exist to verify that all approved changes are properly incorporated. Quick-fix changes may be allowed, but the procedures should identify the method to be used to report those changes back to the change control authority and ensure that the changes are properly documented and incorporated.

The media distribution and retrieval methods should ensure that all software can be recovered or restored in case of a disaster. This disaster preparation may be accomplished by duplicating master copies and ensuring that the master copies and duplicates are stored separately. Methods should be developed to ensure that master copies, archive duplicates, and user copies of the controlled software remain current and accurate. Additionally, the procedure should describe the method to ensure that archive media and operational copies maintain the integrity of the stored data over time. Floppy disks and tape back-ups will eventually lose their data and should be replaced every couple of years. Presently, there are a number of innovative methods (for example, chip writing) available that will store data much longer without derogation. As noted earlier, the control system should ensure that only controlled software is delivered to the users and can be recalled when needed.

As for hardware, the procedure controlling software shall provide guidelines for the selection of software and its applications. Software is susceptible to consumption of tolerance (primarily because of hardware mismatch) and in some cases may not be appropriate for the application.

Attention to training also should be given within the control procedure. The operator should be given the responsibility for verifying that the software is being used correctly. Auditing personnel must be trained in order to effectively audit the process. Additionally, personnel must be trained in the proper methods of handling and storage of the software media to preclude damage to the program.

Specific software programs may interfere with and be dependent upon operating system software. In addition, specific software programs may interfere with and be dependent upon other interrelated software programs. The procedure should include the methods that ensure that the functionality and accuracy of the specified inspection software program is maintained when revisions and/or updates occur to interrelated inspection or operating system software.

The procedure, as well as the quality assurance manual requiring the procedure's use, shall be submitted to the FAA for approval prior to implementation. Many larger companies will have an independent software quality department. If this is not the case, the FAA requires that the organization responsible for software quality assurance shall have functional independence sufficient to allow objective evaluations to be made.

The organization responsible for software quality assurance should have adequate authority, responsibility and freedom to identify and evaluate problems to ensure corrective action is completed on deficiencies discovered and shall:

1) Ensure all software tasks are clearly and adequately described in documented procedures/plans.

2) Verify that suppliers who use controlled software and related digital input/output data for product acceptance implement appropriate controls.

3) Have final authority for formal release of software and related digital input/output data used for product acceptance.

4) Ensure corrective action has been taken on any deficiencies previously discovered.[10]

QUALITY ASSURANCE AUDITING ACTIONS

Quality assurance (QA), within its auditing function, must ensure that the procedures are created that will ensure the effective implementation of a calibration system. Calibration in itself will be a large part of the internal audit scheme. Calibration is also one of the most common areas that will be found discrepant in a second- or third-party quality system evaluation. Because of this, QA should also ensure that the established training is effective and that the appropriate personnel are aware of the proper handling, storage, use, and selection methods of inspection, measuring, and test equipment.

SUMMARY

The controls exerted by a manufacturer to maintain the accuracy of inspection, measuring, and test equipment could be termed the manufacturer's calibration efforts. Calibration is a clear requirement of all three of the international quality standards, and is implied throughout the FARs. In order for a manufacturer to obtain a clear interpretation of the FAA's requirements, it is necessary to review the associated advisory circulars. Within the ACSEP evaluation criteria, the FAA evaluates a manufacturer's ability to control calibrated tooling.

Procedures shall be created that will control the calibration system, and are to be approved by the FAA as part of the overall quality system approval process. The quality system registrar will require the same. Though ISO 10012 provides a metrological confirmation system, its use is not mandatory.

The calibration system shall ensure that all tools, instruments, and equipment used to inspect, test, or verify a product or process, or whose out-of-tolerance condition would adversely affect the quality or safe operation of the product, be routinely subjected to inspection and/or test to verify its continued accuracy. This shall be accomplished in intervals that have been determined based on the individual tool's complexity, use, and ability. Records of all such actions shall be maintained as quality records.

All calibration activities shall be traceable to the national standards. In the United States this national standard is governed by the NIST.

In order to ensure that calibrated tools are returned for calibration activities, a recall list should be created. A controlled recall list will provide the organization a single source document that identifies the status of all calibrated tooling in the organization. In addition to the recall list, a method of recall notification shall be established that will ensure positive recall of calibrated tooling when due.

Within the control procedure, the manufacturer shall also establish a method to visually identify a tool's calibration status. This is usually accomplished through the implementation of calibration placards or self-adhesive stickers that contain the appropriate data. Unit-cycle inspection cards are another method used, though primarily on larger assembly jigs.

Personnel must be trained in the correct usage of such calibrated tools. This would include correct use in adverse environmental conditions; proper handling, preservation, and storage methods; and the correct selection of tools. This training shall be documented and maintained as quality records.

New products and tools shall undergo a certification process. The process is much like that of a new product; however, it will vary depending upon the tool type, complexity, accuracy, and usage. Software used as an inspection medium also shall be certified prior to implementation. The FAA has established some guidelines for the control and certification of such software. These guidelines are outlined in Advisory Circular 21-36.

As for all of the elements of the quality system, the FAA and the quality system registrar shall be allowed access to the manufacturer's facility and records to verify conformity. With regard to calibration, this will include the design data needed to develop the control measures.

NOTES

1. ANSI/ASQC Q9001-1994, *Quality Systems—Model for Quality Assurance in Design, Development, Production, Installation, and Servicing* (Milwaukee, Wis.: American Society for Quality Control, 1994), 6, para. 4.11.1., General.

2. Ibid., 6–7, para. 4.11. Control of Inspection, Measuring, and Test Equipment.

3. DOT/FAA, Federal Aviation Regulation Section 21.143 (a)(3), *Certification Procedures for Products and Parts—Quality Control Data Requirements: Prime Manufacturer* (Washington, D.C.: DOT/FAA, March 1993).

4. DOT/FAA, Advisory Circular 21-1B, *Production Certificates* (Washington, D.C.: DOT/FAA, 10 May 1976), 3, para. (5)(c), Quality Control Data Requirements.

5. DOT/FAA, Federal Aviation Order 8100.7, *Aircraft Certification Systems Evaluation Program* (Washington D.C., DOT/FAA, 30 March 1994), Appendix 6, Section 7.

6. DOT/FAA, Federal Aviation Regulation Section 145.47 (b), *Repair Stations—Equipment and Materials: Ratings Other Than Limited Ratings* (Washington, D.C.: DOT/FAA, August 1993).

7. ANSI/ASQC Q9001-1994, 7, para. 4.11.1., General.

8. DOT/FAA, Advisory Circular 21-32, *Control of Parts Shipped Prior to Type Certificate Issuance* (Washington, D.C.: DOT/FAA, 14 September 1992).

9. DOT/FAA, Advisory Circular 21-36, *Quality Assurance Controls for Product Acceptance Software* (Washington, D.C.: DOT/FAA, 11 August 1993), 4, para. (4)(b)(3)(i), Identification.

10. Ibid., para. (4)(c), Quality Control Systems.

Chapter 13

INSPECTION AND TEST STATUS

In order for a product's acceptance status to be known, it must be in some way identified. There are various means of identification, most of which have been discussed in previous chapters. This chapter will discuss the special requirements for inspection and test status identification and provide a model for stamp control.

IDENTIFICATION OF INSPECTION AND TEST STATUS

The FAA considers any evidence of inspection approval (for example, inspector's stamp) placed on inspection records, test reports, or physical articles as documentation that the article, process, or manufacturing operation has been accepted by the holder of the manufacturing approval. This brings up another area that requires documented control—the use and control of manufacturing and inspection stamps. All three of the international quality standards, under the element of inspection and test status, require that "the inspection and test status of product shall be identified by suitable means, which indicate the conformance or non-conformance of product with regard to inspection and tests performed."[1] ANSI/ASQC Q9001 and ANSI/ASQC Q9002 both require that "the identification of inspection and test status shall be maintained, as defined in the quality plan and/or documented procedures throughout production, installation, and servicing of the product to ensure that only product that has passed the required inspections and tests (or released under an authorized concession) is dispatched, used, or installed."[2] ANSI/ASQC Q9003 has the same identification and documentation requirements, but they are only applied to final inspection and testing.

As outlined in chapter 11, TSO and PMA products have specific identification requirements for the finished products. TSO products shall be identified with their TSO number and the manufacturer's mark. PMA products shall be identified with the letters *FAA-PMA;* the manufacturer's name, trademark, or symbol; and the installation eligibility data. FAR Part 45 outlines the requirements for end-item identification and is discussed in more detail in chapter 9, "Product Identification and Traceability." The requirement to indicate inspection status is not as boldly pronounced as other requirements. But it is a requirement of each of the individual FAA manufacturing approvals, and the description for its control must be outlined in a procedure. Advisory Circular 21-1B interprets the various manufacturing approval requirements and provides the clearest view of what is required. It states that "identifying articles or controlling documentation with appropriate stamps or marks traceable to the individual inspector, is a means of ensuring that only those articles and processes which have been accepted and found to conform to FAA-approved design data are used in the product."[3]

If an article has passed through a point officially designated for inspection (for example, receiving, manufacturing inspection point, final test), the omission of any required stamps or signatures that were designated to be applied at that point to the physical articles, inspection records, or test reports, may be considered as noncompliance with approved quality control data and procedures. If discovered by the FAA (such as during an ACSEP evaluation), the manufacturer's approval may be jeopardized. If found during an internal audit, a corrective action investigation report should be initiated immediately, and the subject product must be segregated and held in bond until its conformity is substantiated. The corrective action investigation report shall investigate the nonconformance and achieve corrective action that will prevent the nonconformance from recurring.

Whatever method the manufacturer develops to identify the product, it must be outlined within a procedure. This procedure may be either a quality assurance procedure or a company procedure/policy. Often the procedures for inspection and test status identification will be rolled into other identification procedures, such as those discussed in chapter 11. It is up to the manufacturer to decide, but it must also be addressed in the quality assurance manual. When the procedures are complete they shall be submitted to the FAA, along with the rest of the quality system procedures, for review and approval. The FAA does have the right to require any changes it feels are necessary to ensure the control of the system.

IDENTIFICATION OF REJECTED PRODUCTS

Identification methods for products that fail inspection and test shall be developed. These instructions are normally contained within the procedures for control of nonconforming materials (as will be discussed in chapter 14). FAR section 21.125 (a)(9) requires that "those materials and parts that are determined by the Material Review Board to be serviceable must be properly identified and reinspected if rework or repair is necessary. Materials and parts rejected by the Material Review Board must be marked and disposed of to ensure that they are not incorporated in the final product."[4] The scrapping process must be stringently controlled to ensure that these rejected parts do not later become "bogus parts."

In encompassing the above requirements, the procedures for the control of identification of inspection status shall have provisions for identifying accepted products, parts that are rejected, parts that have been rejected but later found acceptable, and for identifying parts that are to be scrapped.

STAMP CONTROL

The various FARs place emphasis on personnel being trained and authorized for the functions they perform. The FARs also require the application of inspection status to the physical articles, inspection records, or test reports. The most common method for accomplishing this is through the use of controlled stamps. By identifying articles or controlled documentation with appropriate stamps traceable to the individual mechanic, technician, or inspector, an acceptable means has been created that ensures that only those articles and processes that have been accepted and found to conform to FAA-approved data are used in the product.

Though signatures are also acceptable as a means of acceptance, they are not recommended unless applied to certificates or other formal documents. Signatures applied to manufacturing documents can become messy and illegible, particularly when individuals use their artistic license. Additionally, signatures cannot be easily applied to a product, as required in many instances. However, when signatures are used as an indication of acceptance, a controlled master list, indicating acceptance authorizations and specimens of the signatures shall be maintained by the manufacturer and distributed where required. This would normally be a responsibility of one of the quality activities.

Though not a requirement, the issuance of stamps is by far the preferred method of acceptance indication. The issuance of stamps should not be limited to quality personnel. Any departmental activity that requires acceptance actions should have its own, self-distinguishing stamp design. Manufacturing planners should have their own stamp design that indicates approval of planning and its changes. The same can apply to engineering, procurement, administration, and, of course, quality personnel. Each individual stamp shall be controlled by some method, normally a number that identifies the individual using it. A controlled document that identifies the stamp to its holder, documents the authorization of the holder, and includes any special remarks, shall be maintained by the manufacturer. This is most commonly a quality assurance activity, and in many larger companies the information is in an electronic database. Regardless of how the data are stored, the information must be readily accessible to those who require it. Figure 13.1 displays a sample stamp issuance form.

As for all of the other characteristics of a quality system, procedures must be created that will describe the control the manufacturer will exercise over the use and issuance of acceptance stamps. Normally, the quality assurance manual will outline the requirements and refer to individual procedures that provide more in-depth details of the control system. Whether the manufacturer decides to implement the use of stamps throughout the company or just for inspection purposes will determine whether the procedure should be a quality assurance procedure or a company procedure/policy. In either event, the procedure should provide controls for the issuance of the stamps, use of the stamps, inventory control of the stamps (normally a company-wide inventory every six to 12 months), and instructions about what to do in the event that stamps are lost. Figure 13.2 displays a sample stamp inventory control form.

Misuse of stamps is a critical offense, particularly within the aviation industry. If it has been discovered or suspected that an individual is misusing his or her stamp, an investigation must be initiated immediately. The individual must be removed from any acceptance process that may have adverse effects on the quality of the product or its safe operation. A corrective action investigation report form may be used to investigate the suspected offense. If the individual is found guilty, the company must decide on appropriate corrective action; however, whatever action is taken must be documented. The action may include termination of employment and sometimes even legal actions, depending on severity and intent.

It does not matter how cautious people are, they lose things; and controlled stamps are not immune to this unfortunate fact of life. The manufacturer must create instructions within the control procedure that describe the process of notifying those who need to know that the stamp has been lost. Figure 13.3 displays a sample notification memo. Once a stamp has been lost, the controlled number should not be used for a long enough period that any documents that may have been accepted by the individual stamp number are no longer in the system. This will prevent the potential for fraud if the stamp is later found. If a stamp is found later and turned in to the appropriate departmental agency, the duration for bonding that stamp may be shorter. Additionally, when employees terminate their employment with the company, their stamps must also be turned in and remain in bond for the specified period of

Inspector/Stamp Registration

ACXI
Wichita, Kansas

Name: _____

Job description: _____

_____

Inspection authority: _____

_____

Validation period: From: _____   To: _____

Limitations: _____

_____

Remarks: _____

_____

Requires eyeglasses   ☐ Yes   ☐ No

FAA ratings
(Check applicable)   ☐ Airframe   ☐ Powerplant   ☐ Inspection
                                                              authorization

Other: _____

Stamp					
Date issued					
Date returned					

Inspector signature   Supervisor signature   QA head signature

ACXI Form 107 (05 Aug. 94)

FIGURE 13.1.   *Sample stamp registration form.*

Stamp Inventory

ACXI
Wichita, Kansas

Stamp type: _____

Serial numbers: _____

_____

_____

Inventory month/year: _____

Stamp impressions (Place in numerical order)

Inventory completed by: Reviewed by:

_____   _____
Signature   Signature

ACXI Form 108 (05 Aug. 94)

FIGURE 13.2. *Sample stamp inventory form.*

Aviation Company X, Inc._____ **ACXI**
1234 W. Main Street
Wichita, Kansas 67213
316-729-7948

Internal Memo

To: All ACXI employees
From: J. P. Flyer, Director, Quality Assurance
Subject: Notification of lost and returned stamps
Date: 5 August 1994
Memo reference: M94-119
Copies: Posted at info boards, inspection stations, file

Reference quality assurance procedure (QAP) 118, revision C, this memorandum announces the change of status of acceptance stamps.

The following stamps have been returned to stamp control.

Manufacturing: 018, 026, and 039
Quality control: 004 and 009

The following stamps have been declared lost. If found, they are to be immediately returned to stamp control.

Manufacturing: 057 and 098
Quality control: 019

Reference paragraph 5.3 of QAP 118, revision C, the acceptance of documents with stamp impressions of acceptance stamps that have been declared lost shall be rejected. All documents in use with noted stamp impressions shall be reaccepted by the original accepting individual or supervisor thereof, prior to document closure.

Signed,

J. P. Flyer
Director, Quality Assurance

FIGURE 13.3.   *Sample lost/returned stamp notification memorandum.*

time. It is purely at the discretion of the manufacturer to establish appropriate time spans. However, during both the FAA and registrar audits, these criteria will be examined for effectiveness.

SUMMARY

Both the international quality standards and the FARs require the identification of a product's inspection and test status. The method developed to identify products is up to the manufacturer; however, the identification must be traceable to the inspector who accepted the product. It is common in the aviation industry to use stamps as a method of identification. This identification process must be controlled by a procedure and is often incorporated into the core identification control procedure.

If stamps are used, they must be controlled. This control will include issuance forms and periodic inventories. The correct usage and control of the stamp system must be controlled by a procedure and is subject to approval by the FAA.

The main concern behind the requirement for inspection and test status identification is the prevention of unauthorized parts (bogus parts) being included in the product. In the aviation industry this could be a lethal discrepancy.

NOTES

1. ANSI/ASQC Q9001-1994, *Quality Systems—Model for Quality Assurance in Design, Development, Production, Installation, and Servicing* (Milwaukee, Wis.: American Society for Quality Control, 1994), 7, para. 4.12., Inspection and Test Status.

2. Ibid.

3. DOT/FAA, Advisory Circular 21-1B, *Production Certificates* (Washington, D.C.: DOT/FAA, 10 May 1976), 5, para. (9)(d)(4), Inspection/Identification.

4. DOT/FAA, Federal Aviation Regulation Section 21.125 (a)(9), *Certification Procedures for Products and Parts—Production Inspection System: Materials Review Board* (Washington, D.C.: DOT/FAA, March 1993).

Chapter 14

CONTROL OF NONCONFORMING PRODUCT

"Get it right the first time" and "zero defects" are nice thoughts, but in real life mistakes happen, for whatever reason. In aviation, if left undetected (and they rarely are), even the smallest of mistakes can cost lives. In the topic of nonconforming material, the requirements of the international quality standards and those of the FARs have a lot of similarity. Those who are familiar with the requirements of MIL-Q-9858A will see some similarities to it in the international quality system requirements.

The international quality standards state that "the supplier shall establish and maintain documented procedures to ensure that product that does not conform to specified requirements is prevented from unintended use or installation. This control shall provide for identification, documentation, evaluation, segregation (when practical), disposition of nonconforming product, and for notification of functions concerned."[1] For established aircraft manufacturers this does not sound like anything new, but few would have a formal notification system to inform all functions concerned.

Various sections of FAR Part 21 discuss the processing of nonconforming materials. However, in Part 21.125, Production Inspection System: Materials Review Board, the handling of nonconforming material is best described in detail. In comparison to the international quality standards, the only noticeable difference between the two is that the FAR does specifically identify and require a material review board (MRB) for the disposition of nonconforming materials, while the international quality standards require notification. Additionally, the FARs have special reporting requirements for certain failures and suspected unapproved parts (reference chapter 11).

The following are considered nonconforming materials.

- A part that does not conform to engineering specifications, for *any* reason other than a superseded design
- A part that has been damaged

The following is not a nonconforming condition (often a heated topic between engineering and quality personnel).

- A part that has been superseded by a new design

This condition should be handled solely by engineering on engineering documents. This condition falls under the requirements of design control. If a part is to become obsolete because of an engineering change, who is best qualified to determine any further use for that part? Engineering. Typically on a design change, statements like "use existing materials until stock is exhausted," "scrap previous revision," or "rework previous revision in accordance with modification instructions," will be on the new revised drawings. Asking a quality inspector to create a rejection document for a superseded part is only massaging a weak design change system.

MATERIAL REVIEW BOARD

According to FAR section 21.125, the material review board shall include representatives from the inspection and engineering departments. It does not specify who will chair the board; but in most companies, depending on the company's size, either the head of quality control or the head of engineering will be the chair. Typically, in smaller companies quality will have the chair position and in larger companies engineering will. The FAR does not prohibit representatives from other disciplines being members of the board. Actually, it is preferable to round out the material review board with representatives from the departments that have an active role in the production, planning, and design of the product. However, the members of the board shall be qualified to submit their input. The qualification criteria for members should be addressed within the appropriate control procedure. The following is a representation of how a typical material review board may look.

Chair: Head of quality or engineering
Secretary: Assistant to chair (nonvoting)
Member: Quality inspection
Member: Quality assurance (quality engineering)
Member: Design engineering
Member: Liaison engineering
Member: Program management
Member: Manufacturing planning
Member: Manufacturing

Member: Scheduling

Member: Procurement

Member: Any other specialist that can provide constructive input

The actual structure for the individual organization should be customized to fit its activities. The simpler the structure, the better. However, the structure must be documented and the authority and responsibilities of the individuals must be defined.

DISPOSITIONS

When a nonconformance is presented to the material review board, a documented disposition of the product may be

- Rework to meet specified requirements
- Accept as is without repair by concession
- Accept with repair by concession
- Regrade for alternative applications
- Return to vendor
- Scrap

Does every discrepancy have to go before a formal board hearing? Absolutely not. As long as a system is in place that routes the nonconforming part from quality to engineering and back to quality with a documented disposition, the intent is met. However, those quality and engineering representatives must be authorized in writing as MRB representatives. Additionally, quality inspection personnel can perform initial screening operations by performing preliminary review. This is an action that many companies use to separate those discrepancies that can be returned to drawing specification through minor rework. Anything other than rework must go through the material review system.

Rework is any process performed on a nonconformance that will return the product to the approved design specification requirements without any deviation. That means a repair is anything other than rework. So if a nonconformance is cleared through corrective actions and the product is serviceable but not 100 percent to drawing specifications it is repaired.

Accepted as is is another disposition that is commonly used. This disposition can only be given when the acceptance of the condition will have no adverse effect on fit, form, function, safety, or, in aesthetic applications, appearance.

Regraded for alternative applications is a disposition that is not normally used in aircraft applications, other than regrading to surplus for resale. Once a material or product has been determined unfit for use for its intended design, it is very unlikely that it could be found airworthy for other applications. Parts that have a tooling or shop aid value must be identified as tooling in such a manner as to prevent any use as a production article. Some investment can be regained by selling the materials via a scrap dealer. As an example, some major airframe manufacturers have public sales facilities and organizations that have as their sole responsibility the resale of surplus materials. Extreme caution and control must be exercised to prevent these regraded and scrapped parts from becoming bogus parts. Such parts must be physically rendered unusable.

Scrap dispositions are just that—scrap. This disposition is given to nonconforming materials that cannot be accepted as is, reworked, or repaired. The scrap process itself requires careful monitoring to preclude inadvertent return to the production activity. These materials must remain segregated until final disposition can be carried out. In an effort to limit the number of instructions required in procedures, it is recommended that the engineering disposition on the nonconforming control document (rejection tag) describe the method of scrapping.

After all nonconformances have been either reworked or repaired, the condition must be reinspected for acceptability.

All nonconformances must be documented, regardless of severity. Rejection documents are usually of a company's own design; however, some smaller companies may use preprinted over-the-counter standard forms. Recommended are two different types of rejection forms: one for the documentation for the material review process for other than rework items, and the other for preliminary review rework items. Preliminary review (PR) is both a process and an authority. The process is a determination of severity relating to the discrepancy. The authority is a delegation to an individual to perform the process. In many organizations trained quality inspectors are delegated this authority. Such delegation must be documented.

The document for preliminary review items is usually a document that can accommodate many items and is often used as a listing of the inspection results. This type of document has been called a "squawk sheet" or a "discrepancy list" (Figure 14.1). As the inspection is performed, the nonconformances are noted. By applying the inspector's stamp after each write-up, the mechanic and others will know whom to consult for additional information regarding the entry. Prior to any rework activities, the discrepancies are given a preliminary review to ensure that they are indeed rework items. After reworking the discrepancy, the mechanic applies his or her stamp in the space provided and submits the form to inspection for review. After the discrepancy has been resolved by rework and the inspector has found the condition acceptable to applicable specifications or disposition, the discrepancy is accepted by the application of the inspector's stamp. For discrepancies that are determined to be other than rework, the entry shall be transferred to a formal MRB rejection document.

The formal MRB rejection document (Figure 14.2) documents the other-than-rework discrepancy and provides an engineering disposition, an inspection buy off, and, ideally, a closed-loop corrective action section. The company procedure should provide requirements for the completeness of the document prior to closeout. Initially this document is created by an inspector and submitted to a quality inspection individual with preliminary review authority. The document is reviewed for completeness and correctness, then forwarded to engineering. An authorized engineer dispositions the nonconformance and returns the document to an authorized quality inspection MRB member. The document is reviewed for any special quality concerns and corrective action activity is initiated. The MRB document is then provided to manufacturing for work. If required, in-process inspections are performed as scheduled and documented on this record. After the condition has been repaired, the nonconformance is reinspected for acceptability.

CORRECTIVE ACTION

If corrective action is part of the manufacturer's MRB document, as recommended, the MRB document should not be closed out until corrective action is achieved. The corrective action statement shall address the root cause and the actions taken to prevent recurrence. If additional time is required to perform a corrective action investigation, the nonconformance can be transferred to a stand-alone corrective action document and assigned a case number. This will allow the control number for the corrective action investigation to be entered onto the rejection document, so it can be closed out. Meanwhile, the corrective action investigation continues and a closed-loop system is created. However, for manufacturers that are operating under FAR Part 21, Subpart K, Parts Manufacturing Approval (PMA), the requirement for corrective action does not come from the FAR, but from the international quality standards. Corrective action is discussed in greater detail in chapter 15.

NOTIFICATION

If the nonconformance is very complex and requires additional research for the disposition, it may go before a formal board. As outlined earlier,

Aviation Company X, Inc.
Wichita, Kansas

Discrepancy List

DL SN: D-000029

Part no.	Part name	Work order no.	Aircraft model	Customer	
Item nos.	Detailed description of discrepancy	Noncomformance code	Validating inspection stamp	Production acceptance stamp	QC acceptance stamp

ACXI Form 104 (05 Aug. 94)

FIGURE 14.1. *Sample discrepancy list.*

Aviation Company X, Inc.
Wichita, Kansas

Failure and Rejection Report

Report serial no: W-000249

Page 1 of ____

Type or print using ballpoint pen only. Do not write.
Destruction, unauthorized change or unauthorized removal of this FRR is cause for dismissal.

1. Reference (other FRR or cont. sheet)	2. Date			3.	4. Appearance affected	5. Part no./Assembly no.	Chg/rev.	5a. Model or std. item	6. Airline
	Mo.	Day	Year	☐ MRB action ☐ Prelim. review	☐ Yes ☐ No				

7. Supplier (GFAE/BFE/BDE/CFE/ACXI)	Code (on PO)	8. Work order number	9. Part serial no.	10. Qty. in lot	11. Qty. reject	12. Part/assembly name

13. Purchase order no.	14. Dept rejected in Loc/Code	Dept.	15. Nonconformance code	16. Responsible agency Loc/Code	Dept.	17. Responsible Change Loc/Code	Dept.	18. Responsible Change approval	19. Aircraft no.	20. Customer

Reason for rejection

Disposition instructions

Corrective action

21. Detailed description of discrepancy

25. Specific intructions

29. ☐ Local action   ☐ Corrective action investigation   ☐ Statistical analysis

30. Corrective action statement

31. Cause code

32. CA effectivity

33. CA signature — Date

34. CA approval — Date

21a. Drawing and revision

22. Reported by (stamp)

23. Approved by

Rejection clearance

35. Rework/repair acceptance and/or rejection clearance

	Production	Quality inspection	Customer	36. OK to file

Progressive rework inspection

24.	Manufacturing stamp/date	Inspection stamp/date
Progressive inspection and authorized inspection stamp		

26. Disposition authority	Quality inspection		Engineering		Customer	
	Accept	Rework	Repair	Scrap	ROK	RTV

27. Disposition quantity breakdown	Rework	Repair	Scrap labor	Scrap material

28. Cost data

ACXI Form 153 (05 Aug. 94)   Distribution: White–QA; Green–QA Records (interim); Blue–Engineering; Card–Production

FIGURE 14.2.   Sample failure and rejection report.

ACXI

Failure and Rejection Report Continuation Sheet

Report
serial no: _____

Type or print using ballpoint pen only. Do not write.
Destruction, unauthorized change or unauthorized removal of this FRR is cause for dismissal.

Page _____ of _____

ACXI Form 153 (05 Aug. 94)   Distribution: White–QA; Green–QA Records (interim); Blue–Engineering; Card–Production

FIGURE 14.2. (continued)

this board can address questions about material availability, schedules, human resources, and regulatory requirements. However, the material review board must have a means of notification for such proceedings. Typically, a manufacturer will hold weekly material review board meetings on a routine basis. However the system is established, it must be documented. Additionally, those departmental activities that require knowledge of nonconforming materials shall also be notified. Such notification must be developed to accommodate the individual organization and demographics. Typically, either a centrally located board, holding all rejection documents, or a computer print out will meet this requirement. For dispositions such as use as is, scrap, and regrade as surplus, the manufacturing departments may have little or no action, other than being aware that the documentation and conditions exist.

BUYER-FURNISHED MATERIALS

The international quality standards require that additional consideration shall be given to nonconformances on customer-supplied product, also called *buyer-furnished* materials. The quality assurance manual must provide instructions on how nonconformances are to be handled on such materials. Additionally, any special actions should be clarified within the contract review process. In some instances a customer will provide the manufacturer with written authorization to perform MRB actions on its property. If so, the nonconformances shall be treated in the same fashion as other internal MRB actions. The exception should be for scrap and use-as-is dispositions. The customer should always be informed that some of its material is about to be scrapped before it is done. Informing the customer could prevent later confrontations.

If MRB authority has not been delegated from the customer to the manufacturer, the customer shall be notified of the nonconformance, in accordance with the customer-approved internal procedures. It is then the customer's responsibility to provide an MRB disposition. All dispositions, whether from the customer or the manufacturer, shall be documented. In this case a copy of the customer's disposition or rejection document should be attached to the manufacturer's rejection document. Eventually these will become part of the quality records.

REPORTABLE NONCONFORMANCE

For nonconformances that affect aircraft or products in service, the regional department of the Federal Aviation Administration shall be notified within 24 hours of determination of a failure, malfunction, or defect.[2] This action should be described briefly within the contents of the quality assurance manual and expanded in detail with quality assurance procedures. All reportable failures and defects shall be documented on FAA Form 8010-4, Malfunction or Defect Report (Figure 14.3). The FAA has allowed provisions for nonconformances that have been identified on weekends and holidays. If a report is due on a Saturday or Sunday, it may be delivered on the following Monday. If a report is due on a holiday, it may be delivered on the first following workday. The FAA recognizes only U.S. federal holidays. Telephone numbers and names and titles of FAA contacts should be available within the quality control department, in the form of memorandums. Additionally, the responsibility and authority of personnel for notification should be described.

As referenced in FAR Part 21.3, the following occurrences must be reported.

1. Fires caused by a system or equipment failure, malfunction, or defect

2. An engine exhaust system failure, malfunction, or defect that causes damage to the engine, adjacent aircraft structure, equipment, or components

3. The accumulation or circulation of toxic or noxious gases in the crew compartment or passenger cabin

4. A malfunction, failure, or defect of a propeller control system

5. A propeller or rotorcraft hub or blade structural failure

6. Flammable fluid leakage in areas where an ignition source normally exists

7. A brake system failure caused by structural or material failure during operation

8. A significant aircraft primary structural defect or failure caused by any autogenous condition (fatigue, understrength, corrosion, and so on)

9. Any abnormal vibration or buffeting caused by a structural or system malfunction, defect, or failure

10. An engine failure

11. Any structural or flight control system malfunction, defect, or failure that causes an interference with normal control of the aircraft or that derogates the flying qualities

12. A complete loss of more than one electrical power generating system or hydraulic power system during a given operation of the aircraft

OMB No. 2120-0003

DEPARTMENT OF TRANSPORTATION FEDERAL AVIATION ADMINISTRATION	OPER. Control No.		8. Comments *(Describe the malfunction or defect and the circumstances under which it occurred. State probable cause and recommendations to prevent recurrence.)*		DISTRICT OFFICE	
MALFUNCTION OR DEFECT REPORT	ATA Code				OTHER	
	1. A/C Reg. No. N-				COMMUTER	
Enter pertinent data	MANUFACTURER	MODEL/SERIES	SERIAL NUMBER		FAA	
AIRCRAFT 2.					MFG	
POWERPLANT 3.					AIR TAXI	
PROPELLER 4.					MECH	
5. SPECIFIC PART *(of component)* CAUSING TROUBLE					OPER	
Part Name	MFG. Model or Part No.	Serial No.	Part. Defect Location		REP STA	
6. APPLIANCE COMPONENT *(Assembly that includes part)*					SUBMITTED BY	
Comp/ Appl Name	Manufacturer	Model or Part No.	Serial Number		OPERATOR DESIGNATOR	
					TELEPHONE NUMBER ( ) —	
Part TT	Part TSO	Part Condition	7. Date Sub.			

Optional Information:

Check a box below, if this report is related to an aircraft

☐ Accident; Date _____   ☐ Incident; Date _____

FAA Form 8010-4 (10-92)   SUPERSEDES PREVIOUS EDITIONS

FIGURE 14.3.   *FAA Form 8010-4, Malfunction or Defect Report.*

13. A failure or malfunction of more than one attitude, airspeed, or altitude instrument during a given operation of the aircraft

However, the noted conditions are not required to be reported if

1. It is determined that the condition was caused by improper maintenance or improper usage;
2. It is known that the condition has already been reported to the FAA by another person or organization; or
3. It has been reported under the accident reporting provisions of Part 430 of the regulations of the National Transportation Safety Board.

Information that shall be included in such reports is

1. Aircraft serial number
2. The serial number and model numbers, to include applicable part numbers, of any components that have failed, malfunctioned, or have defects
3. Description of the nature of the failure, malfunction, or defect
4. Time, date, and location of failure, malfunction, or defect[3]

If the product does not interface with a completed aircraft or functional system, the FAA still requires that a reporting system be in place. For such manufacturers—with no physical interfacing of operating systems, engines, propellers or rotors, or complete aircraft—a short paragraph within the quality assurance manual stating that a reporting process will be implemented when warranted is normally sufficient. However, if the organization does interact with reportable products, a stand-alone quality assurance procedure would be more appropriate. This will cut down on the weight of the quality assurance manual and allow space for a detailed description of responsibilities, authority, and conditions. This quality assurance procedure should be especially clear and simple to ensure that the reporting is carried out correctly, in what would more than likely be a hectic time after such a failure. The use of flowcharts would increase the clarity of the requirements.

The international quality standards have additional coordination requirements.

> *Where required by the contract, the proposed use of product which does not conform to specified requirements shall be reported for concession to the customer or customer's representative. The de-*

scription of the nonconformity that has been accepted, and of repairs, shall be recorded to denote the actual condition.[4]

This can be achieved by transmitting the previously discussed failure and rejection report (Figure 14.2) to the customer and recording the customer's acknowledgment/acceptance directly on the form.

SUMMARY

The control of nonconforming materials is a requirement of all the international quality standards as well as the applicable FARs. In actuality, the international quality standards and the FARs have many similarities. These similarities are even more evident when the ACSEP evaluation criteria are reviewed. All nonconforming material must be identified, documented, evaluated, segregated, and dispositioned, and all concerned departmental activities must be notified.

The applicable FARs require the establishment of a material review board. The function of this board is to develop appropriate dispositions for nonconforming conditions. Additionally, this board should review the cause of such discrepancies, in a production sense, to determine preventive measures. As will be discussed in the next chapter, corrective action may be achieved on the rejection document; however, it may be referred to the corrective action board. Members of each of these boards shall be qualified based on education and/or experience. The qualifications criteria should be documented within a procedure.

Materials belonging to the customer may require special disposition actions. These special actions should be clarified within the contract review phase and documented in quality plans.

The FAA has established special reporting requirements for certain products. As outlined in this chapter, the manufacturer shall establish procedures that will control the reporting process. Where required by individual contract, this reporting process may also require customer acceptance of a concession.

NOTES

1. ANSI/ASQC Q9001-1994, *Quality Systems—Model for Quality Assurance in Design, Development, Production, Installation, and Servicing* (Milwaukee, Wis.: American Society for Quality Control, 1994), 6, para. 4.13.1., General.

2. DOT/FAA, Advisory Circular 21-9A, *Manufacturers Reporting Failures, Malfunctions, or Defects* (Washington, D.C.: DOT/FAA, 26 May 1982); and DOT/FAA, Federal Aviation Regulation Section 21.3 (e)(1), *Certification Procedures for Products and Parts—Reporting Failures, Malfunctions, and Defects* (Washington, D.C.: DOT/FAA, March 1993).

3. DOT/FAA, Federal Aviation Regulation Section 21.143, *Certification Procedures for Products and Parts—Quality Control Data Requirements: Prime Manufacturer* (Washington, D.C.: DOT/FAA, March 1993).

4. ANSI/ASQC Q9001-1994, 7–8, para. 4.13.2., Review and Disposition of Nonconforming Product.

Chapter 15

CORRECTIVE AND PREVENTIVE ACTION

The process of identifying a discrepancy, investigating its root cause, incorporating measures to correct the condition, and establishing methods to prevent recurrence is corrective action. The process itself requires training and discipline. If it is allowed to go by the wayside just a few times, then the integrity of the process is questionable. Without an effective corrective action system, the manufacturer will realize the same discrepancies time and time again. Management must support this process without compromise. Without the needed management support, the corrective action system will have no chance for success.

Though corrective action is not a requirement of the FARs, it is referenced in various advisory circulars, including the ACSEP evaluation criteria.[1] It is also a major element of the international quality standards. ANSI/ASQC Q9001 and ANSI/ASQC Q9002 state that "the supplier shall establish and maintain documented procedures for implementing corrective and preventive action."[2] They additionally require that "any corrective or preventive action taken to eliminate the causes of actual or potential nonconformances shall be to a degree appropriate to the magnitude of problems and commensurate with the risk encountered" (ANSI/ASQC Q9001, 8, para. 4.14.1., General). This means that when corrective or preventive action is undertaken, it will be taken against the root cause of the nonconformance. Going after a symptom will not fix the disease. Additionally, by the requirement of preventive action, the manufacturer's management is required to take a proactive role in preventing the occurrences of nonconformances. If the manufacturer is pursuing ANSI/ASQC Q9003 conformance, corrective action is a requirement to be applied to final inspection and test discrepancies as well as customer complaints, and documented control procedures are not required.

CREATING THE PROCEDURES

When creating the procedures, corrective and preventive action should be mentioned in the quality assurance manual, where reference is made to individual quality assurance procedures that discuss the appropriate actions in detail. In this case, two procedures should be created for the control of the corrective action process—one for internal corrective action and another for supplier corrective action. Within these procedures, instructions shall be established that include

> *(a) The effective handling of customer complaints and reports of product nonconformities;*
>
> *(b) Investigation of the cause of nonconformities relating to product, process and quality system, and recording the results of the investigation;*
>
> *(c) Determination of the corrective action needed to eliminate the cause of nonconformities; and*
>
> *(d) Application of controls to ensure that corrective action is taken and that it is effective (ANSI/ASQC Q9001, 8, para. 4.14.2., Corrective Action).*

By creating two different procedures, these requirements can be approached in two different directions. Both should be simple and easy to maintain. Keep in mind though, if the system design is too complex it will be bound for breakdowns and failure.

What nonconformances require corrective action? All of them. The only question is to what degree. Some discrepancies are clear, and their cause and action can be addressed in the corrective action section of the rejection tag. The minimum requirements that should justify a formal corrective action investigation should include one or more of the following:

- High cost
- Repetitive occurrences
- Written request from management
- Nonconformance on supplier parts or processes
- Nonconformance to customer-furnished material

Most other conditions could be handled directly on the rejection document.

The procedures for preventive action can be documented in much the same manner as those for corrective action. They can be outlined within the quality assurance manual and controlled by a quality assurance procedure. The procedure for preventive action shall include

> *(a) The use of appropriate sources of information such as processes and work operations which affect product quality, concessions, audit results, quality records, service reports, and customer*

complaints to detect, analyze, and eliminate potential causes of nonconformities;

(b) Determination of the steps needed to deal with any problems requiring preventive action;

(c) Initiation of preventive action and application of controls to ensure that it is effective; and

(d) Confirmation that relevant information on actions taken is submitted for management review (ANSI/ASQC Q9001, 8, para. 4.14.3., Preventive Action).

Whereas the corrective action process is a reactive activity, the preventive action process is proactive. The nonconformance does not actually exist; only the potential for it does. By giving consideration to the characteristics just noted and becoming involved in the quality process, management has the opportunity to support continuous improvement.

THE CORRECTIVE ACTION BOARD

The procedures for corrective action should identify an organization (usually quality assurance, or QA) that is responsible for orchestrating the process. In some larger companies corrective action departments are created. It is also recommended that medium and large sized companies create a corrective action board (CAB) to conduct a roundtable of critical nonconformances. This will allow for team interaction and representation from various departments and backgrounds. Normally, the head of quality assurance, or his or her designee, will chair the board. Typically the CAB will be structured as shown here.

Chair: Head of quality assurance

Secretary: As designated by chair (nonvoting)

Member: Manufacturing

Member: Engineering

Member: Procurement

Member: Planning

Member: Scheduling

Member: Facilities

Member: Any other department or individual that can provide constructive input

These departmental representatives can be at any level within their departmental organization as long as they are delegated the organizational freedom and authority to perform as active members. Decisions must be made, and changes committed to, without having to solicit prior departmental approval.

CAB meetings should be held as required, and the frequency will depend on the size of the company. Holding them too often can cause redundancy, while meetings too far apart are not effective. Normally, the chair will call for a board meeting when deemed necessary. Like the material review board, the corrective action board does not have to hear every nonconformance problem. Only those conditions that are complex in nature or require interdepartmental support should go before the board.

Some of the responsibilities that a corrective action board should have are

- Ensuring timely and effective correction throughout the company
- Directing allocation of personnel and resources for multiprogram corrective action activities
- Addressing production problems/issues that cannot be resolved locally
- Identifying a corrective action investigator
- Supplying corrective action to customers
- Communicating results to affected personnel

If a corrective action board is not established, the administrative responsibility should be delegated to the quality assurance department. Its staff shall be delegated the organizational freedom and empowered to pursue and obtain effective corrective action. However, the quality assurance department should only have to orchestrate and monitor the process. The departmental management in which the discrepancy occurred should be ultimately responsible for investigating cause and establishing effective corrective action.

The results of the corrective action board can be useful in the development and assessment of preventive actions. Whereas the corrective action process has its own board, the preventive action process can be integrated into all other processes. By analyzing discrepancies and asking if such a condition could occur in another process or project, a simple preventive action process is established. The second question should be, How do we prevent something like this from occurring on this process or project. An example would be a part that is experiencing corrosion in the field. It has been determined that the raw material is at fault. The question must be asked if this same material was used in other projects. If so, an investigation must be undertaken to determine effectivity of the discrepancy. Once the discrepancy is resolved, we must develop a means to prevent this discrepancy from happening again. One such action might be tighter receiving inspection on the raw material or supplier corrective action.

Preventive action should be part of every process, not just those that are producing product. Preventive action reviews can be included in

- Purchase order/contract reviews
- Design reviews
- Nonconformance reviews
- Tool design reviews
- Management reviews
- Any other activity that performs a process

INTERNAL CORRECTIVE ACTION INVESTIGATIONS

For internal corrective actions, QA should initiate the appropriate corrective action form and forward it to the departmental head who is ultimately responsible for the nonconformance. The responsibility for determining the root cause and establishing an effective corrective action should be given to the individual who is responsible for the process. After the root cause is determined and corrective action is obtained, QA shall audit for compliance. The audit shall be performed prior to further processing and again at a later time as a follow-up audit. The follow-up audit should be scheduled at the time of the first compliance audit, but can be dependent upon fluctuating production schedules. This audit shall ensure that the measures taken are effective in preventing nonconformance recurrence.

The investigation should be controlled by a serialized cover sheet (Figure 15.1). Typically these cover sheets are called *corrective action investigation reports* (CAIRs) and should include the following:

To be completed by the initiator
- Control number
- Date the form was initiated
- Name, title, and department of the requester
- Part number or process and nomenclature of the discrepancy
- Customer information, when applicable
- Thorough description of the nonconformance, to include times and location
- Requester's signature

Corrective Action Investigation Report (CAIR)			
Aviation Company X, Inc.	Control number		Date
Requester's name	Title		Department
Part no./Process type/Audit type		Part nomenclature/Process name/ Audit standard	
Model/Product/Department	Customer (N/A for system audits)		Project
Description of nonconformance and suspected cause	Additional sheets attached? ☐ Yes ☐ No		
Requester's signature		Reviewer's signature	
Determined root cause	Additional sheets attached? ☐ Yes ☐ No		
Corrective action and effectivity	Additional sheets attached? ☐ Yes ☐ No		
Follow-up and closeout results	Additional sheets attached? ☐ Yes ☐ No		
CAB Remarks	Signed when complete and closed		
	CAB signature and title		Date

FIGURE 15.1. *Sample corrective action investigation report.*

To be completed by the responsible department
- Name, title, and department of responsible individual
- Root-cause response
- Corrective action measures to prevent recurrence

- Effectivity of corrective action (when the corrective action measures become effective)
- Signature of responsible individual

To be completed by an authorized corrective action investigator after the corrective action has been verified and accepted
- Acknowledgment of acceptance by signature and title
- Date of acceptance
- Date of follow-up audit

To be completed by the follow-up auditor after verification of compliance
- Indication of corrective action acceptance status (if not, enter new CAIR number)
- Signature, title, and date of auditor

Other applicable corrective action investigation documents should be attached to the cover sheet, creating a file. When additional sheets are attached, their quantity should be noted on the cover sheet. Controlling the issuance of the CAIRs, a log sheet could be used, as displayed in Figure 15.2. This log sheet can provide a quick reference of the CAIRs' status.

SUPPLIER CORRECTIVE ACTION

Supplier corrective action activities have many of the same characteristics that an internal corrective action investigation has. The procedure shall describe how a supplier is to be notified, and who is responsible for doing so. Again, QA should take a leading role in orchestrating the process. However, program management also should be responsible for supporting the process efforts. Both purchasing and quality assurance should ensure that the manufacturer has a contractual right to require corrective action when needed. This can be accomplished by ensuring the application of a quality clause to the applicable contract or purchasing documents that define this requirement (reference chapter 7).

For most supplier fault discrepancies, investigations should be initiated. Typically the form that is used as a cover sheet is called a *supplier corrective action notice* (SCAN) (Figure 15.3). These SCANs have many of the same characteristics that a CAIR does. However, SCANs should also include a suspense date for supplier reply. Many companies will allow their suppliers two different suspense dates, depending on their geographical locations. However, with most companies operating daily with fax machines, the rationale of slow overseas mail is no longer valid.

Corrective Action Investigation Report (CAIR) Status Log

ACXI
Wichita, Kansas

CAIR serial no.	CAIR issued to	Discrepancy	Issue date	Name of auditor	Response due date	Response received date	Proposed follow-up date	Date CAIR closed

ACXI Form 154 (05 Aug. 94)

FIGURE 15.2. *Sample corrective action investigation report status log.*

Recommended is one suspense period of not more than 10 working days to provide a response of corrective action. If a supplier is unable to provide immediate corrective action, it should request an extension. If extensions are granted, they should be based on valid reasons. Though there may be exceptions, extension intervals of not more than five days at a time should be used. These extensions should be noted on the SCAN, with the new due date. Like the CAIR, the SCAN should be controlled by a log sheet, as displayed in Figure 15.4.

Additionally, when dealing with foreign suppliers, local holidays and company-wide vacation shutdowns should be considered when calculating the response due date. As the fourth of July is celebrated in the United States as Independence Day, in Germany the third of October is celebrated as tag der Deutsche einheit, Fete Nationale is celebrated on 14 July in France, and in Canada, on the first of July, Canada Day is observed as a national holiday.

If a supplier's corrective action statement is not acceptable, the SCAN should be rejected. In this case, a new corrective action should be requested on a new SCAN with reference to the prior.

To perform a follow-up audit of the supplier, at its facility, is often not economical. In this case the follow-up audit should be performed at receiving inspection. The applicable receiving inspection plan should note when and how an audit is to be performed. Recurring discrepancies will require new investigations and the issuance of new SCANs.

NOTICE OF REJECTION

Sometimes rejections on supplier services and products are not severe enough to launch a formal corrective action investigation. However, the supplier must still be formally informed of the nonconforming condition. In such cases a notice of rejection (NOR) can be used. NORs are controlled documents issued by the manufacturer, documenting the nonconforming condition. Sometimes NORs may provide a suggested corrective action. However, they do not request a corrective action response.

NORs are useful in documenting a condition that may not be considered significant yet, but has the potential to become so later. They are also useful in documenting conditions for statistical analysis of conditions. They should not be used in cases where a SCAN should be initiated, as previously described. Persons who have the responsibility to pursue corrective action must be trained in the appropriate issuance of such a document. Exclusive use of NORs will not ensure that discrepant conditions are resolved. If a couple of NORs have been issued for the same problem or to the same supplier, a SCAN may be the more appropriate vehicle.

Supplier Corrective Action Notice

SN:

Aviation Company X, Inc.
1234 W. Main St.
Wichita, Kansas 67213
Phone 316-729-7948
Fax 316-729-9949

SCAN
ACXI FORM 114
(05 AUG 94)

1. Supplier _____
   Address _____
   _____
   _____

Supplier code:

2. Part number	3. Nomenclature	4. PO no.	5. Date recd.

6. ACXI QA rep. name	7. ACXI QA rep.title	8. Date issued	9. Qty. recd.	10. Qty. rej.

11. Description of discrepancy:

11a. Corrective action required no later than:

Supplier response   Additonal sheets attached ☐

12. Root cause:

13. Corrective action:

14. Effectivity:

15. Name	Title	Signature	Date
Telephone		Fax	

ACXI Form 114 (05 Aug. 94)

FIGURE 15.3. *Sample supplier corrective action notice.*

Supplier Corrective Action Notice (SCAN) Status Log

ACXI
Wichita, Kansas

SCAN serial no.	Supplier's name	Rejection tag no.	Issue date	Name of issuer	Response due date	Response received date	Proposed follow-up date	Date SCAN closed

ACXI Form 155 (05 Aug. 94)

FIGURE 15.4. *Sample supplier corrective action notice status log.*

The use and retention of NORs must be controlled in a control procedure and can be folded into the same procedure that controls the issuance of the SCAN. The basic design of the NOR is normally simple, but it must be serial number–controlled to ensure traceability.

SUMMARY

Effective corrective action will reduce or, ideally, prevent recurrence of a nonconformance. The establishment of preventive action activities will prevent similar nonconformances from occurring in similar and unrelated processes and projects. The requirements for corrective and preventive action are derived primarily from the international quality standards. The individual FARs make no reference to this activity; however, the various ACs (including the ACSEP evaluation criteria) do.

In most companies, a corrective action board will be established, with the head of quality assurance as the chair. This board should only review those corrective action cases that are complex, high cost, repetitive, or recurring on customer-furnished product, or when requested by management. Otherwise, corrective action can be achieved by the corrective action system in the material review process. The responsibility for investigating the root cause and obtaining corrective action is that of the individual responsible for the process. Quality assurance should only perform an orchestrating role within the process. Preventive action review will normally be integrated into other meetings and reviews.

The process of corrective and preventive action shall be documented. However, ANSI/ASQC Q9003 does not require preventive action and documented procedures are not required for corrective action activities. The establishment of documented procedures is primarily accomplished by a brief overview of the requirements in the quality assurance manual, with details in the quality assurance procedures. The individual results of the corrective action process may be documented on a corrective action investigation report, which serves as a cover sheet for the investigation file. For supplier corrective action activities, a supplier corrective action notice can be used in the same way as a CAIR. When complete, these corrective action records shall be considered as quality records. Notice of rejection documents also can be issued to suppliers for minor conditions of discrepancy but the use of such documents must be closely monitored to prevent overuse. Preventive action reviews can be documented by inclusion in the applicable minutes of meeting or review.

Though there may be some up-front costs associated with the corrective action process, the costs of not implementing an effective system are far greater. If not implemented, the manufacturer will most definitely realize repetitive discrepancies and throw good money after bad. However, the key is management support. Without such support, the system is bound for compromises and credibility will be lost. With the support of management, the organization can, as a team, combat the problems at hand and prevent them from recurring.

NOTES

1. Federal Aviation Order 8100.7, *Aircraft Certification Systems Evaluation Program* (Washington D.C.: DOT/FAA, 30 March 1994), Appendix 6, Section 11.

2. ANSI/ASQC Q9001-1994, *Quality Systems—Model for Quality Assurance in Design, Development, Production, Installation, and Servicing* (Milwaukee, Wis.: American Society for Quality Control, 1994), 8, para. 4.14.1., General.

Chapter 16

HANDLING, STORAGE, PACKAGING, PRESERVATION, AND DELIVERY

One of the largest consumers of a company's profits is damage of materials and product during fabrication, processing, assembly, storage, and delivery. This often occurs because of management's lack of adequate planning and control. However, some companies have gone to great lengths to combat this problem, and have even created departments whose sole responsibility is to develop new methods and techniques to protect the product.

All three of the international quality standards address the requirements for handling, storage, packaging, preservation, and delivery. However, ANSI/ASQC Q9003 only requires the manufacturer to establish and maintain documented procedures for completed product after final inspection and test. It also requires the protection of these products during delivery, provided the requirement is stipulated within the individual contract.[1]

ANSI/ASQC Q9001 and ANSI/ASQC Q9002 are more encompassing in their requirements, and are identical in their requirements for the control of these processes. They are both broken down into six subsections.

- General
- Handling
- Storage
- Packaging
- Preservation
- Delivery

Within General, the requirements for establishing procedures for the individual subsection are stipulated.

The FAA also has requirements for storage and protection. Manufacturers who are authorized under FAR 21 Subpart F, Production Under Type Certificate Only, will find the requirement under FAR section 21.125 (b)(3). PMA manufacturers have their requirement under FAR section 21.303 (h)(3). Designated alteration stations will have their requirement stated either within their repair station or air carrier certification requirements, whichever is applicable. Repair stations have their requirement for storage and protection of product stated within FAR section 145.45 (c). The requirements for the TSO manufacturer are traced back to the requirements of the Production Certificate. The Production Certificate does not have this requirement stated explicitly. Within certain paragraphs of FAR 21 Subpart G, the requirement for the protection and proper storage of materials and products is implied, but not specifically stated. The other manufacturing approval regulations are mostly identical in their wording for the requirement. They state that "materials subject to damage and deterioration must be suitably stored and adequately protected."[2] Only after Advisory Circular 21-1B is reviewed is the FAA's interpretation for the Production Certificate clearly found.

The FAA feels that an effective storage and issuance system would ensure

1) That only those articles which are identified as having passed company inspection are received into stores.

2) Identification, segregation, and protection of articles in storage.

3) Periodic reinspection and disposition of materials subject to deterioration from prolonged storage.

4) Protection from damage of articles being delivered to fabrication or shipping areas or while stored in these areas prior to use.

5) Incorporation of applicable design changes prior to release of stored articles for installation in the product.[3]

Though advisory circulars are not firm regulatory requirements, as stated earlier, they are the official interpretation of the FAA with regard to the individual FARs. There is always opportunity for discussion with regard to interpretation; however, experience has found that developing a system within the parameters of the applicable FARs and using the advisory circulars as models will normally result in success.

In the following comparisons of the international quality standards, it will be found that they are complementary to the FAA manufacturing approval requirements.

HANDLING

Under the Handling subsection of the international quality standards, "the supplier shall provide methods of handling product that prevent damage or deterioration."[4] Such methods could include additional instructions within manufacturing work instructions, training of personnel in the importance of proper handling of materials and product, the implementation of special protection devices and barriers, and the modification of tooling and equipment.

How methods are developed to prevent damage and deterioration during handling processes is very much dependent on the type of product. What may be sufficient for one manufacturer may not be for another. The best method for determining what would be most effective is to create internal work groups. These work groups should consist of members from each department affected and have representation from both the general workforce and management. Decisions that are made at these team meetings must be implementable, so management representatives must have the authority to make changes. Additionally, responsibility and authority should be given to every person in the workforce to fix or identify problems as they are found.

The generic requirements for proper handling of materials and product should be addressed in the quality assurance manual. If the manufacturer has special requirements for handling, these can be addressed in either individual work instructions or stand-alone procedures.

STORAGE

ANSI/ASQC Q9001 and ANSI/ASQC Q9002 both state that "the supplier shall use designated storage areas or stockrooms to prevent damage or deterioration of product, pending use or delivery." They also require that effective control over the receipt and dispatch to and from such areas is maintained. The International Standards continue, "in order to detect deterioration, the condition of product in stock shall be assessed at appropriate intervals."[5] ANSI/ASQC Q9003 has these same requirements, only applied to product pending delivery. In comparing the requirements of ANSI/ASQC Q9001 and ANSI/ASQC Q9002 to the interpretation of the FARs, as noted in Advisory Circular 21-1B, as well as a review of the ACSEP evaluation criteria,[6] the requirements are almost identical.

The manufacturer should address the requirements for storage of materials and products within the quality assurance manual. However, depending on the size of the manufacturer, these requirements may be described in greater detail in a stand-alone procedure. Many companies may desire to make this a quality assurance procedure, as they traditionally are; however, because it affects more than just quality assurance, it would be more appropriate as a company procedure/policy. However, the decision remains the manufacturer's as to what type of procedure this should be. One way or another, some reference must be made in the QAM.

The procedure should be inclusive of all the actions of the stockroom and storage areas, and include responsibilities and authorities of individual departments. It may also address the use of special control plans when required by contract. It must address the authorized access of personnel into these controlled areas. Though not specifically stipulated within the FARs, a controlled access list must be maintained. This list shall document who is authorized to enter the controlled stock areas and must be signed by a responsible person within the manufacturer's management. As the list is updated, revisions must be distributed to those within the organization who require a copy. Normally, the FAA will not require a copy. However, if a manufacturer has been assigned an on-site FAA representative, he or she may require copies of all changes to controlled documents.

In addition, the procedure shall provide requirements for the verification of materials and parts prior to release from the stockroom/storage area. This includes the verification of shelf life status, inspection for damage or deterioration, and ensuring that the material or product has not been superseded by revision. The revision verification is not required within the storage section of the international quality standard, but is required by various subparts within FAR Part 21. The inspection and testing sections of the international quality standards have similar requirements regarding revision status.

If material or product is found discrepant, it must be processed in accordance with the established procedures for material review (see chapter 14). This, too, should be addressed within the control procedure, referencing the applicable material review procedure.

PACKAGING AND PRESERVATION

Packaging and preservation are two separate elements of the 1994 revision of the international quality standards. However, because these two processes are so interrelated, we will discuss them together within this section.

The requirements for packaging and preservation are not for any one specific stage of production. They are general requirements, affecting materials and parts in the stockroom and assembly and fabrication areas, and for finished products that are to be shipped. The international quality standards state "the supplier shall control packing, packaging, and marking processes (including materials used), to the extent necessary to ensure conformance to specified requirements." These procedures shall also control the "appropriate methods for preservation and segregation of product when the product is under the supplier's control."[7] The extent of the manufacturer's control should be defined and documented within the contract review process.

The quality assurance manual should address these requirements, and may refer to a stand-alone procedure to outline the requirements in greater detail. This could normally be accomplished within the procedure developed to control the storage requirements. The procedure should address the methods the manufacturer implements in packaging materials and products, to include the preservation of such. The simplest method for controlling packaging and preservation requirements is through the use of individual plans. These plans can be either stand-alone or integrated into the manufacturing work instructions. This will allow for the development of packaging and preservation instructions for the characteristics of each individual product. The completion of packaging and preservation processes should require inspection verification and documentation of that verification. This verification document could be a final acceptance on a work order and will become a part of the quality records.

Additionally, it must be made perfectly clear within the contract review process if there are to be any special packaging and preservation requirements. If so, it should be the responsibility of program management to procure what is needed and coordinate any special training. Where the exchange of responsibility occurs during shipping should be specified within the individual contract. There is not a specified or typical point of responsibility exchange; it depends on demographics and type of product. Wherever the exchange is made, it should be clearly defined within the contract, and the appropriate personnel should be informed.

If the manufacturer is responsible for the product during shipping, the method of shipping and the route must be considered when designing packaging and preservation requirements. For example, if a product was manufactured in Miami and shipped by truck to Los Angeles, it would have an extensive journey before it. The product could be taken on various routes to reach its destination: the humid southern route, the bumpy central route, or the mountainous northern route. Environmental conditions, as well as the potential for shock damage, should be considered. This may require the use of moisture adsorbents and shock absorbers to protect the product. The same applies to products that are shipped overseas. If sent via ship, the packaging must protect the product from the highly corrosive conditions of sea air and spray. It is easy for a manufacturer to think that it is the shipping company's responsibility if the product is damaged. This is not always true. If the product is damaged because of neglect in packaging, then it is the manufacturer's responsibility. However, it really does not matter whose responsibility it is; if the customer receives damaged goods, it will probably not be very happy, especially when its own schedules may be affected.

After the product has been packaged, the packaging should be labeled with the contents. This will preclude having to tear the packaging apart to see what is inside. The identification should include part number, nomenclature, and, when applicable, serial number, lot/batch data, and purchase order/contract number. When the product has been assigned to a specific aircraft, the aircraft's identification number should be included. The application of an inspection stamp also should be applied, to provide evidence of final acceptance. However, this also can be accomplished by indication on the attached label or tag (reference chapter 13).

DELIVERY

As noted earlier, the product shall be protected after final inspection and test, and this may include during delivery. The specific details for delivery should be explicitly outlined within the contract. This will prevent later dispute of the requirements. The manufacturer should address the generic requirements for the control of delivery of the product within the quality assurance manual. Like the other requirements of this chapter, delivery requirements can be included in the same procedure as storage and packaging. However, the manufacturer will most likely find that the requirements for delivery will have to be addressed in individual plans or work instructions. This is because various customers have different requirements, and normally no two are the same.

The requirement for the issuance of certificates should also be addressed within the procedure. Such certificates could include airworthiness approval tag, aircraft airworthiness certificate, statement of conformity, inspection and test reports, or any other document that may be required by the FAA or desired by the customer.

QUALITY ASSURANCE ACTIONS

In addition to the normal activities of inspection and issuance of certifying documents, the quality assurance function should perform audit surveillance of the systems outlined in this chapter. The primary responsibility for ensuring that the requirements of handling, storage, packaging, and delivery are fulfilled is that of those who perform the individual operations and their managers. But quality assurance must also ensure that the internal procedures conform to the applicable quality standards and FARs. If quality assurance discovers nonconformance during any of these audits, the discrepancies should be noted on a corrective action investigation report and the cause investigated. It is very important, if the control system is to be successful, that shortcuts are not taken that may cause the materials and products to be susceptible to damage or deterioration. This one area of control, if properly implemented and monitored, can save a company money, materials, labor hours, and, in some cases, a schedule and reputation.

SUMMARY

Process control procedures are required to document the requirements and controlling actions of handling, storage, packaging, preservation, and delivery of the product. This requirement comes from both the international quality standards and the applicable FAR sections. ANSI/ASQC Q9003 requires such controls only for product after final inspection and test, whereas ANSI/ASQC Q9001 and ANSI/ASQC Q9002 both require controls throughout the entire production process. The applicable FARs require that the manufacturer ensures that materials subject to damage and deterioration are suitably and adequately protected. Advisory Circular 21-1B and the ACSEP evaluation criteria provide additional insight as to the FAA's desired control over this process.

All five of these processes should be considered at the beginning of a program and should be part of the contract review process. If there are special requirements, these should be identified and plans should be created accordingly. Program management should be responsible for ensuring that needed materials are provided and personnel are appropriately trained. This should include all activities from receiving to shipping to transport.

The responsibility for protecting the product does not always stop at the shipping dock. Delivery routes also should be considered when developing the packaging requirements. Such proactive analysis could prevent unwanted damage of the materials en route to the customer. Regardless of fault, if the customer receives damaged goods, that customer will not be happy. If customer appreciation is an element of concern of the manufacturer, then appropriate measures should be taken to prevent mishaps. Though not every accident can be prevented, with planning and implementation of necessary protection materials, and a lot of common sense, the majority can be.

A few dollars invested today in protecting what has already been produced will save many dollars tomorrow in having to produce a replacement or repair the damage.

NOTES

1. ANSI/ASQC Q9001-1994, *Quality Systems—Model for Quality Assurance in Design, Development, Production, Installation, and Servicing* (Milwaukee, Wis.: American Society for Quality Control, 1994), 5, para. 4.15.1., General.

2. DOT/FAA, Federal Aviation Regulation Section 21.303 (h)(3), *Certification Procedures for Products and Parts—Replacement and Modification Parts* (Washington, D.C.: DOT/FAA, March 1993).

3. DOT/FAA, Advisory Circular 21-1B, *Production Certificates* (Washington, D.C.: DOT/FAA, 10 May 1976), 10, para. (10), Storage and Issuance.

4. ANSI/ASQC Q9001-1994, *Quality Systems—Model for Quality Assurance in Design, Development, Production, Installation, and Servicing* (Milwaukee, Wis.: American Society for Quality Control, 1994), 8, para. 4.15.2., Handling.

5. Ibid., para. 4.15.3., Storage.

6. DOT/FAA, Federal Aviation Order 8100.7, *Aircraft Certification Systems Evaluation Program* (Washington D.C.: DOT/FAA, 30 March 1994), Appendix 6, Section 12.

7. ANSI/ASQC Q9001-1994, 8, para. 4.15.4., Packaging, para. 4.15.5., Preservation.

Chapter 17

CONTROL OF QUALITY RECORDS

Quality records serve as the primary objective evidence of a quality system, and are typically the one element of the quality system the auditor seeks most. Quality records can be either documentation of system processes or product operations and conformance acceptance. Typically, such records are manufacturing planning with inspection buy offs, test reports, material review documents, receiving inspection plans, internal audit results, external audit results, and calibration documents. Other functional documents, such as purchase orders and engineering drawings, should be treated as quality records. The control of quality records is a requirement of both the international quality standards and the various FAR sections that control aviation manufacturers.

RECORD RETENTION

Quality records are any documents that record data that demonstrate achievement of the required quality process. These documents can be of the traditional paper system or the ever-advancing paperless systems of computer technology. However, in either case the data must be maintained and protected.

Because a purchase order documents the terms and conditions of a procurement action, it conveys a design requirement that can be audited against. Engineering drawings, with their noted revision level, document a condition of build. In conjunction with the manufacturing planning, the drawing is part of the inspection record. This does not mean that a copy of the drawing has to be filed with each inspection record, but drawings do have to be retrievable to the revision of the documented build. Some sort of drawing archive system must exist, but not necessarily with the rest of the quality records. The same is true for purchase orders. The procurement department may decide to maintain these documents either close at hand or at an off-site location. However, the requirement remains the same—all quality records shall be protected from deterioration and be retrievable.

The international quality standards do not mandate specific time spans for retention, but they do require that the retention times and the method of retention are defined within a procedure. Additionally, document identification, collection, indexing, access, filing, storage, maintenance, and final disposition actions must be controlled within a procedure. The various sections of FAR Part 21 require that inspection records be retained by the manufacturer for at least two years.[1] However, for product liability reasons, many manufacturers have opted to maintain their records for greater lengths. It is not uncommon for an aircraft manufacturer to keep the quality records for as long as two years after the aircraft has been retired from service. In any event, the manufacturer must identify, within the contents of the quality assurance manual, the time span for maintaining such documents.

SPECIAL LIABILITY

For manufacturers of aircraft and components, it would be recommended to maintain quality records to the extent of federal liability laws. Fortunately for much of the American aviation industry, there has been a recent change in aviation liability legislation. The new law limits an aircraft manufacturer's liability for its products to 18 years. This represents the closing of the open-end liability and may eventually have a positive effect on the insurance premiums of manufacturers. Prior to this change a manufacturer's liability increased over the years with each additional unit it manufactured. A manufacturer can be held liable for such elements as

- Negligence in fabrication and workmanship
- Defects in quality control
- Inadequate testing
- Use of materials of inadequate quality
- Failure to exercise reasonable care in the design of the product[2]

ARCHIVE

The method of retention and the archive location are usually dependent upon the facility environment, size of company, and commodity being produced. If the manufacturer is small, with limited staff support, and manufacturing noncritical products, the documents will probably be maintained in a fireproof filing cabinet on-site. On the other end of the scale, if the manufacturer is large, accumulating almost the products' weight in quality records, and producing a long-life, complex product such as an engine or aircraft, the on-site retention may be limited to 12 months of activity, with the older documents going to an off-site location for archiving.

The international quality system requirement for storage of quality records is for the records to be stored in "a suitable environment to prevent damage or deterioration and prevent loss."[3] In order to comply with the minimum requirements of international quality standards, the quality records should be maintained in a locked fireproof cabinet, with controlled access. However, because of the pure volume of documents, many manufacturers may opt for off-site storage. Salt mines are typical candidates for archives because of their dryness and normally secured access. There are also some companies that are purely in the business of document archival. They can provide a full-service operation, including pickup, indexing, storage, and retrieval that can include transfer to electronic media. However, for the long run, an internal cost analysis should be performed to determine what is right for the individual organization.

READILY RETRIEVABLE RECORDS

The international quality standards require quality records to be readily retrievable. The definition of *readily retrievable* is one that is often debated. It is highly recommended that this term is clearly defined within the individual quality assurance manual or quality assurance procedures. For one person a couple of hours is readily retrievable, and for another a few days is appropriate. However, in a quality audit, if the definition is not provided the auditors may develop their own. In any event, this period of time should remain reasonable. If the inability to readily retrieve a document has an adverse effect on a process, such as having to stop operations because a document is not yet available, then it is too long. Defining the term with respect to various applications will allow additional flexibility.

Creating individual definitions for *readily retrievable* and placing the definitions within the individual control procedures will allow the organization the flexibility of having different departments responsible for maintaining their own records. For example, the procurement department may be able to archive up to two years of records on-site, while the engineering department only has the capacity of maintaining drawings of present revision levels. The procurement department may have a recall time of minutes, where the engineering department will require hours or days. Creating internal standards and documenting what is acceptable within a procedure may prevent future internal and extrinsic conflict.

Normally, records that have been closed out within the past 12 months should be retrievable within a couple of hours. Records that have been closed in excess of one year, and have a lesser likelihood of being needed as often as newer records, could be maintained at a remote location with recall times of days. In no case should it take longer than one week to retrieve any record, regardless of location.

DOCUMENT IDENTIFICATION

Document identification should be kept as simple as possible, to avoid confusion that can result from an overelaborate system. As described in chapter 6, document numbers should have some relation to their function. With regard to a rejection document, the form number could be the same number as the individual control procedure number that covers it. Additionally, use of serial numbers on the forms will provide individual traceability. The documentation of this serial number will provide control for the indexing process. For example, if quality assurance procedure 123 pertains to failure and rejection reporting, the failure and rejection report could be labeled form number 123.

For records that document a specific inspection activity, such as a completed manufacturing plan with quality buy offs, material review documents, and test reports, additional identification is required. This identification shall provide individual records with a traceable trail to the product or process they represent. There are many variations of this traceability. Some can be linked to a master charge account that is further linked downstream to an individual product. Other documents are identified with an aircraft fuselage number or component serial number. In the case of processing, a lot/batch number is utilized.

DOCUMENT DISTRIBUTION

Per the international quality standards, the document distribution system shall be documented, including the responsibility for records collection. After the documents are closed out, a closed-loop method for collecting the documents must be established. Within this process, steps must be taken to prevent inadvertent loss or damage. The indexing or inventory control of the documents will provide a record of their status and location. It is recommended that the procedure identify a department or function that is responsible for all activities of quality records retention. In most larger aviation companies this is the sole function of the quality records department.

ELECTRONIC MEDIA

As mentioned earlier, the method of storage can vary greatly depending on the individual organization and complexity of the commodity. Storage of paper documents is rather straightforward; however, the storage of electronic media can be more complex. Storing records on computer disks, tapes, and chips can free up numerous shelves and enhance recall time. When networked, the documents can be retrieved at a moment's notice from any computer terminal connected to the system, enhancing the flow of information. However, while both software and hardware are becoming ever more reliable for the storage of data files, for various reasons they are still susceptible to data loss. This means that if records are to be stored via electronic media, backup systems are mandatory. This can be achieved by maintaining backup copies of the information in electronic file. It is highly recommended that these backup disks be maintained at an off-site location (different than the primary locations). Many smaller companies that maintain such documents utilize safety deposit boxes at their banking facilities.

Maintenance of these backup copies is also essential to ensure reliability. Data can be lost through an electrical storm, static electricity discharge, or fluke. By replacing the backup files periodically, the organization's success of maintaining electronic media data will be enhanced.

FINAL DISPOSITION

After the documents have reached their maturity of retention, the method of disposal must be defined within the procedures. Whether the documents are simply thrown in a wastebasket or shredded and burned, the specific method shall be specified. The author has found that prior to disposal of the records, the customer usually prefers the option of assuming custody. This option should be outlined within a control procedure describing the steps of such a transaction, to include the method of notification and document shipping. Whatever method is appropriate, a final disposition log should be maintained documenting the final action.

SUMMARY

Quality records are just as important as the product itself. Without objective evidence that the required actions were performed as prescribed, the product cannot be accepted, nor can the quality system be found complying. The international quality standards, and the applicable FARs require manufacturers to establish and maintain documented controls (procedures) for the identification, collection, indexing, access, filing, storage, maintenance, and disposition of quality records. These quality records will be identified with traceability to the product they represent.

When these records are complete in their place of origin, the manufacturer shall have established control procedures for their collection and indexing. The better the indexing system, the more proficient the retrievability process. Because various departments have different records requirements, it may be advantageous to define the retrievability requirements for each department differently. This can be accomplished in individual departmental procedures; however, it needs to be governed by the quality assurance manual.

The international quality standards require that these quality records be maintained as specified by the applicable contract. However, the FAA requires that these quality records be maintained for a minimum of two years. Because of legal product liabilities, the manufacturer may desire a longer retention. For most major component and airframe manufacturers this is normally for two years after the retirement of the product. Retention times should be developed by each organization to meet its own unique needs as well as those of its customer. The location for such storage activities and the required facilities also shall be considered. Both of these characteristics will affect the protection and the retrievability of the records. Electronic media will require special precautions, including backup storage.

Once the retention time of the records has expired, the manufacturer shall dispose of the documents as specified in internal procedures. This could include destroying the documents, transferring them to electronic media for long-term storage, or sending the records to the customer. These final actions also shall be controlled by a procedure and/or individual plans.

In addition to maintaining these quality records, the international quality standards require that the records be maintained in a suitable environment in such a manner as to preclude deterioration, damage, or loss. And, as contractually agreed upon, access shall be made available to the customer. Such access shall always be made available to the FAA and the quality system registrar.

NOTES

1. DOT/FAA, Federal Aviation Regulation Section 21.125 (a)(2), *Certification Procedures for Products and Parts—Production Inspection System: Materials Review Board* (Washington, D.C.: DOT/FAA, March 1993); Federal Aviation Regulation Section 21.303 (h)(9), *Certification Procedures for Products and Parts—Replacement and Modification Parts* (Washington, D.C.: DOT/FAA, March 1993); and Federal Aviation Regulation Section 145.61, *Repair Stations—Performance Records and Reports* (Washington, D.C.: DOT/FAA, August 1993).

2. V. Foster Rollo, *Aviation Law: An Introduction* (Lanham, Md.: Maryland Historical Press, 1985).

3. ANSI/ASQC Q9001-1994, *Quality Systems—Model for Quality Assurance in Design, Development, Production, Installation, and Servicing* (Milwaukee, Wis.: American Society for Quality Control, 1994), 9, para. 4.16., Control of Quality Records.

Chapter 18

INTERNAL QUALITY AUDITS

There are basically three types of audits: internal, external, and extrinsic. External audits are audits performed outside the company on a supplier. Extrinsic audits are audits that are performed by third-party organizations such as registrar and regulatory agencies (FAA). However, this chapter is concerned with the internal audit process. The internal audit is an audit performed by the organization itself to evaluate its own performance and adherence to standards and requirements.

An effective internal auditing system is probably the most valuable tool a company can develop. If properly implemented, internal audits can discover waste, material and labor misuse, and noncompliance to procedure. All of these are consumers of a company's profit margin. Once identified, the condition is documented and an investigation is conducted. The investigation also should be documented each step of the way. The goal is to find the root cause of the discrepant condition and to establish effective corrective action that will prevent recurrence of the condition.

Because the FAA concerns itself primarily with a quality control system, and not a quality assurance system, it places the majority of its emphasis on inspections. Though some may argue that internal audits are implied for the control of processes that affect quality or safe operation, the requirement for internal auditing does not come from the FAA. At the writing of this book, there is no firm statement within the FARs. However, there is a requirement for internal auditing in the ACSEP evaluation criteria,[1] and it is one of the system elements that can warrant the extension of FAA compliance audits. Many aviation manufacturers will already have internal auditing systems established, primarily because of compliance with other quality standards, such as military standards. In most cases, those internal auditing systems will require little or no modification to meet the requirements of the international quality standards. However, the emphasis is on documentation.

All three of the international quality standards require the establishment of an internal auditing system and are identical in their requirements. (Prior to the 1994 revision, ANSI/ASQC Q9003 did not require internal auditing activities.) They state that "the supplier shall establish and maintain documented procedures for planning and implementing internal quality audits to verify whether quality activities and related results comply with planned arrangements and to determine the effectiveness of the quality system."[2]

The audits and follow-up actions shall be carried out in accordance with documented procedures. Most appropriately, this would be a quality assurance procedure. The quality assurance organization (QA) also should have the responsibility for the management of the system. However, this does not mean that only quality personnel are to perform internal audits. Internal audits should be performed by those members of the manufacturer's organization that are qualified to perform audits. The only conditions, according to ANSI/ASQC Q9001, are that the audits "shall be carried out by personnel independent of those having direct responsibility for the activity being audited" (9, para. 4.17., Internal Quality Audits). These personnel should be familiar in the area under audit and be trained in auditing methods. They should also have the authority and access needed to perform the audit and document the results.

INTERNAL AUDITORS

Presently, the Registrar Accreditation Board (RAB), does not have provisions for the certification of internal auditors. This may change in the foreseeable future. The Institute for Quality Assurance—International Register of Certificated Auditors (IQA-IRCA), in the United Kingdom, already has a scheme for the certification of internal auditors. However, the use of only certified internal auditors is not yet a requirement for organizations registered under one of the international quality standards. That, too, may change in the foreseeable future.

Training is very important for potential internal auditors. Presently, there are numerous third-party companies providing such training. However, caution is advised when selecting an outside training agency. There are numerous suppliers of training who have become overnight ISO experts, as well as overnight trainers. When selecting a training supplier, always check the supplier's background. As when approving a processor for a special process, ensure that the supplier is qualified to perform the training process. This can be accomplished by asking the professionals in the field, or in some cases, such as for lead auditor training courses, asking for the supplier's registration credentials. Both the RAB and IQA-IRCA register training organizations and require them to meet a stringent training plan when presenting the courses. The IQA-IRCA also registers training companies for internal auditing courses. Additionally, by attending only registered training courses, the attendees receive official documentation noting their attendance and, when successful, the passing of tests that are required for RAB/IQA-IRCA certification of the personnel.

It is not necessary to send every employee to outside training—only those who are responsible for performing audits. The manufacturer should establish a primary team of auditors, with representation from quality, manufacturing, engineering, procurement, administration, product support, and any other department that may be required to ensure the compliance of special processing, internal procedures, and external requirements. This primary team also can perform as trainers and instruct others in the methods of internal auditing. However, in order to obtain certification from the IQA-IRCA (and possibly later from the RAB), the internal auditors must have attended a certified training course. When the manufacturer selects the auditing team, consideration should be given to the traits of an effective auditor. An auditor must be technically competent, unbiased, observant, a listener, impartial, inquisitive, tenacious, patient, analytical, confidential, and diplomatic. If the internal auditors possess these traits, then the process of auditing becomes more qualified.

SCHEDULING THE INTERNAL AUDIT

The international quality standards state that the "internal audits shall be scheduled on the basis of the status and importance of the activity to be audited" (ANSI/ASQC Q9001-1994, para. 4.17., Internal Quality Audits). This means that some areas of activity may be audited more than others, and some less than others. If a process or activity has a higher likelihood of adversely affecting quality or safe operation of the product, then the controls for that process will be more stringent than for a process that has a lesser impact. As noted earlier, the quality assurance department should be responsible for the management of internal audits, and this includes their scheduling.

The simplest method of scheduling internal audits is by creating an annual audit schedule (Figure 18.1). This annual audit schedule will map out the internal auditing activities for the entire year, with the exception of some special audits. Individual areas of concentration can be selected and scheduled, and, as stated earlier, more critical areas will be scheduled more frequently. For most areas, it is sufficient to audit once or twice a year. The scheduling of the audit can be represented by a diagonal mark in the applicable month and category blocks on the annual audit schedule. Additionally, the results of the audit can be indicated on the annual audit schedule. Conformance can be indicated by entering two more lines in the applicable block. Indications of nonconformances will be discussed later in this chapter. As in the performance of audits on suppliers (reference chapter 7), discrepancies should be identified

Internal Audit Schedule—1995

ACXI
Wichita, Kansas

Survey	Jan.	Feb.	Mar.	Apr.	May	Jun.	Jul.	Aug.	Sept.	Oct.	Nov.	Dec.
Planning control												
Process control												
Calibration												
Material review												
Tool inspection												
Receiving inspection												
NDT												
Stamp control												
Stockroom control												
Assembly methods												
Electrical assy. and bonding												
Functional testing												
Painting and decoration												
Identification												
Sealing												
Housekeeping												
Packaging and shipping												
Reading logs												
Training												

Legend:
- Audit scheduled
- Audit acceptable
- Category I discrepancy
- Category II discrepancy

ACXI Form 147 (05 Aug. 94)

FIGURE 18.1. Sample internal audit schedule.

within their appropriate categories. This will be discussed shortly; however, first the audit must be scheduled.

After the annual audit schedule is created, it should be used to create visibility within the organization. Though internal audits may be performed unannounced, this is not a good practice. Auditing personnel are put into a bad light when they surprise a department by an unannounced audit, particularly when the department is under the gun to finish a project. Unannounced audits should only be carried out when conditions warrant them, such as in cases of repetitive noncompliance or during some follow-up audits.

Prior to any internal audits that require more than one auditor, the leader of the auditing team should be selected and given all administrative responsibilities for the performance of the audit. This includes selection of auditors, preparation of the itinerary, submission of the final audit report, and ensuring that follow-up activities are performed.

Two weeks prior to the internal audit, the audit team leader should notify the function being audited of the scheduled audit. Normally, this is accomplished via memorandum (Figure 18.2), and because of the posted annual audit schedule, it should not be a surprise. This notification should include time and date of the audit, audit scope and objectives, name(s) of the auditor(s), and a request to the audit target to advise the auditor if the time is not convenient. This allows both parties to properly prepare for the audit and to clear their schedules for the event. Sometimes it is necessary to reschedule audits; this should not pose a problem. However, rescheduling should not become a chronic condition.

The scope of the audit relates to the amount of the quality system or process that should be reviewed to assure that the activities are in compliance with the applicable requirements. For an aviation manufacturer this can be compliance to a quality standard (international quality standards), FARs, and/or customer requirements. In the case of an internal audit, management, together with QA, should determine which quality system elements, procedures, and work instructions are to be audited at the particular scheduled audits.

When establishing the objectives of the audit, the depth of the audit should also be considered. Shallow or superficial audits are brief, top-layer evaluations of a system. Superficial audits will not confirm whether or not procedures or operations are in compliance with specified requirements. The auditor must go deeper into the nuts and bolts of the process to ensure compliance. This is called a *deep audit*, also known as an *adherence audit* or *compliance audit*. It is up to management and QA to determine when and where the superficial or deep audits are to be performed. However, the exclusive implementation of superficial audits

Aviation Company X, Inc._____ **ACXI**
1234 W. Main Street
Wichita, Kansas 67213
316-729-7948

Internal Memo

To: John Smith, Engineering Manager
From: J. P. Flyer, Director, Quality Assurance
Subject: Notification of internal audit
Date: 5 August 1994
Memo reference: M94-109
Copies: B. Allen, file

Dear Mr. Smith:

This is to confirm the scheduling of the upcoming audit of your department's quality system.

Date of audit: 12 September 1994
Time of audit: Beginning at 0745

The audit scope and objectives are to verify the compliance to the following procedural documents:

   —Engineering Procedure 315, Revision D, Drawing Change Control
   —Engineering Procedure 316, Revision F, Drawing Identification

The audit team will consist of B. Allen (team leader), and S. Frye.

Please contact the undersigned if the scheduled audit date and time are agreeable to you.

       Regards,

       J. P. Flyer
       Director, Quality Assurance

FIGURE 18.2. *Sample internal audit notification memorandum.*

will not ensure that the systems are in control. The rule of thumb is to start out at a superficial level and then go a little deeper. If all is well, and the auditor feels comfortable with the results, then the audit should be concluded. However, if minor discrepancies are found, then the auditor should go deeper, until a level of confidence is achieved or all of the possible discrepancies are found.

INTERNAL AUDIT PLANS

The internal audit plans, often referred to as checklists, should be developed in much the same way as plans for supplier audits (as was shown in Figure 7.3). This audit plan should guide the auditing team through the audit process. The applicable quality standards and internal procedures should be used to structure the audit plan characteristics. The individual control procedures should also be evaluated during the internal audit. Though the control procedures should have been checked for compliance to quality standards and company policy *prior to* release, ensuring this compliance would additionally assure the procedure release system and ensure the updating process. When developing the audit plan, caution must be exercised not to include items that would not produce objective evidence. This would bound that particular element to failure.

The audit plans should also document the type of objective evidence presented to demonstrate conformance. Additionally, when nonconformances are discovered, the applicable corrective action investigation report serial number should be noted within the remarks section of the audit plan.

Once completed, these audit plans and associated documents should be treated as quality records and be maintained appropriately (reference chapter 17).

PERFORMING THE INTERNAL AUDIT

As for any audit, the internal audit should be broken down into four sections. The first section would be the entry meeting. For smaller companies such a formality, or protocol, may seem redundant, but this entry meeting sets the scene for the audit and ensures that everyone has the same mission. The entry meeting should introduce the audit team and audit target, clarify the scope and purpose of the audit, explain how the audit is to be carried out, define the reporting structure, and describe the purpose and structure of the final meeting and final report.

The next section is the actual performance of the audit. This is accomplished by following the audit plan and collecting evidence. Interviewing, examination of documents, and observation of activities are methods of collecting evidence. During the audit, it is recommended that when objective evidence is obtained, whether to confirm conformance or discrepancy, the audit target should sign the evidence or report, verifying the authenticity of the evidence.

The evaluation of the results should be the next section of the audit. This is normally accomplished without the presence of the audited function, but with the entire auditing team. At this point, the team should decide on the severity of discrepancies and determine further actions. As noted earlier, it is important that one team member performs as the audit team leader and has the authority to accept or reject the findings. Within this evaluation section of the audit process, reports, including corrective action investigation reports, are created. The final report is not usually created until after the entire audit process is complete, including the exit meeting.

The final section of the audit process is the exit meeting. Again the auditing team is introduced to the audited group. An overview of the audit results are presented. The audited group should be informed of when the final audit report will be issued. This should be accomplished within five working days for internal audits, and 10 working days for external (supplier) audits. Finally, the response dates for corrective actions to documented discrepancies should be agreed upon, and the potential time frames for follow-up audits should be discussed and established.

NONCONFORMANCES AND FOLLOW-UP AUDITS

As in the performance of supplier audits, internal audit discrepancies should be categorized into severity of nonconformance.

Category 1 nonconformances are major or unacceptable discrepancies and alone are cause to reject the internal audit. These nonconformances should be documented on a corrective action investigation report. Such nonconformances would include the procedure or department not addressing an element of the applicable international quality standard or FAR requirements, a departmental activity that is in direct contravention of the applicable international quality or FAA requirement, or a departmental activity that is in direct contravention of a procedure and that will have consequential effect on the quality or safe operation of the product or the service.

Category 2 nonconformances are also called *minor* or *conditional discrepancies.* Category 2 nonconformances should also be documented on corrective action investigation reports, but do not necessarily warrant the red flag of rejection. As for suppliers, as long as there are not more than three incidents of the same discrepancy type encountered in the audit, the department or process should be conditionally approved, providing the discrepancy does not adversely affect quality or safe operation of the product or present an unsafe condition (such a case would upgrade the discrepancy to a category 1). However, if more than three of the same discrepancies exist of the same type, they should be upgraded to a major (category 1) nonconformance. Category 2 nonconformances are isolated incidents of nonconformance with a system or procedural requirement that has no direct consequential effect on the quality of the product or service.

Category 3 findings are observations or comments of the departmental operation. These are not nonconformances; these are only observations. The comments and observations are not requirements for change, but should provide a view to improvement, and can include measures for cost reduction.

Category 1 nonconformances can be indicated on the annual audit schedule by completely filling in the box. Category 2 nonconformances can be indicated by shading in the lower corner of the box. Category 3 conditions should not be shown on the annual audit schedule. Additionally, after an area under audit has been found nonconforming, a follow-up audit should be scheduled. The difference between a category 1 and category 2 follow-up audit is usually its depth. In a category 2, a superficial follow-up audit and verification of corrective action implementation may be sufficient. Category 1 nonconformances are more prone to deep audits for verification of corrective action implementation.

As stated earlier, when the nonconformances are discovered during internal audit, they shall be documented. This documentation would be most appropriate on a corrective action investigation report. The actions for the corrective action investigation for internal audit discrepancies are the same as for any other corrective action investigation. The international quality standards do require that the results of the audits shall be documented and brought to the attention of the personnel having responsibility in the area audited. They also require that management personnel responsible for the area take timely corrective action on the deficiencies found by the audit. The term *timely corrective action* should be defined within the auditing control procedure. Five working days is normally sufficient. Because the international quality standards place the responsibility for establishing corrective action on the shoulders of those responsible for the discrepancy, the importance of management's role in quality becomes ever more clear.

Based on the results of the corrective action investigation, a follow-up audit shall be scheduled to ensure effectiveness of corrective action measures and conformity of the specific area. Either a complete audit or just a partial audit, checking the previously discrepant area, can be performed. This should be based on a case-by-case analysis of the discrepancy and the decision of the auditor. Additionally, when these follow-up audits are scheduled, they should be indicated on the annual audit schedule. This is normally accomplished by entering another diagonal line in the appropriate, later date, box.

THE FINAL AUDIT REPORT

The audit team leader should be responsible for the issuance, completeness, and accuracy of the final audit report (Figure 18.3). As for many of the other controlled forms displayed in this book, the final

Internal Audit Report			
ACXI Wichita, Kansas			Page 1 of
Department audited	Type of audit	Audit criteria	Audit report serial no.
Date of audit	Audited dept. representative	Title	Telephone no.
Audit team leader	Telephone no.	Previous audit date	Previous audit reference
Persons contacted in audited department		Other audit team members	
Summary of audit			
Signature of audit team leader and date		Signature of head of QA and date	

ACXI Form 165 (05 Aug. 94)

FIGURE 18.3.   *Sample internal audit report.*

ACXI Wichita, Kansas	Internal Quality System Audit Report Status Log						
Audit report serial no.	Department audited	Type of audit	Audit date	Audit team leader	Procedures/criteria audited	Date audit report issued	CAIRs issued

ACXI Form 157 (05 Aug. 94)

FIGURE 18.4.   *Sample internal quality system audit report status log.*

audit report should be controlled by a log sheet. Figure 18.4 displays such a log sheet.

The final audit report should contain the following information, as applicable.

- Name and/or number of organization/department audited
- Scope and objectives of the audit
- Details of the audit itinerary or timetable
- Name and title of audit team members and audited department's representatives
- Identification of the audit criteria (for example, quality system standard, quality manual requirement, procedure requirement, work instructions, contract, FARs, or other regulatory agency)
- Record of the nonconformances and applicable corrective action investigation request serial numbers
- Results or summary of the audit
- Audit distribution list

The final audit report should also perform as a cover sheet for the entire audit package and be inclusive of all associated documents. When completed, the final audit report and its associated documentation should be considered as a quality record and be stored accordingly (reference chapter 17).

SUMMARY

By identifying nonconformances within the internal systems of an organization, investigating the root cause, and establishing effective corrective action, internal audits can be one of the organization's most powerful tools. Though this activity is not an FAA requirement, it is viewed favorably by FAA auditors and is an element of the ACSEP evaluation criteria. The international quality standards require that manufacturers establish and maintain documented procedures for planning and documenting internal quality audits to verify whether quality activities or related activities comply with planned arrangements and to determine the effectiveness of the quality system.

The careful selection of personnel for auditing activities is very important. Contrary to many beliefs, auditors do not have to be members of the quality organization. They can come from any department, as long as they have the necessary training in auditing activities, experience in the discipline under audit, and the organizational freedom and access to perform the audit without any outside interference. The international quality standards require that internal auditors be independent of those having direct responsibility for the activity under audit.

Scheduling of the internal audit should be performed on an annual interval, with a posted annual audit schedule. This annual audit schedule can perform as both a schedule and a status log. Notification of the internal audit should be accomplished using much the same methodology as supplier audits. An internal memorandum should be sent to the prospective audit target at least two weeks prior to the scheduled audit. The actual scheduling of the internal audit shall be on the basis of the status and importance of the activity to be audited.

The performance of the internal audit should be preceded by an entry meeting. As for any other type of audit, the entry meeting will set the scene for the audit process. When performing the internal audit, an audit plan should be used, guiding the process through the verification steps. This audit plan will be similar to the one utilized for the supplier audits and should be developed to accommodate the process characteristics of each individual department.

If nonconformances are discovered during the internal audit process, they shall be documented. A corrective action investigation report should be utilized to document the entire investigation and corrective action process. As for any corrective action activity, the effective implementation of the corrective action measures shall be verified through follow-up audit.

As the performance of the internal audit is concluded, an exit meeting should be performed to address the results. After the exit meeting, the audit team leader is responsible for issuing a final audit report. This report should serve as the cover sheet for the entire audit process and be maintained as a quality record when complete. The implementation of a status log would assist in the control of the final audit reports.

NOTES

1. DOT/FAA, Federal Aviation Order 8100.7, *Aircraft Certification Systems Evaluation Program* (Washington D.C.: DOT/FAA, 30 March 1994), Appendix 6, Section 15.

2. ANSI/ASQC Q9001-1994, *Quality Systems—Model for Quality Assurance in Design, Development, Production, Installation, and Servicing* (Milwaukee, Wis.: American Society for Quality Control, 1994), 9, para. 4.17., Internal Quality Audits.

Chapter 19

TRAINING

To different degrees within the organization, training is a requirement in all three international quality system standards. ANSI/ASQC Q9001 and ANSI/ASQC Q9002 are identical in requirement.

> *The supplier shall establish and maintain procedures for identifying the training needs and provide for the training of all personnel performing activities affecting quality. Personnel performing specific assigned tasks shall be qualified on the basis of appropriate education, training, and/or experience, as required. Appropriate records of training shall be maintained.[1] [reference chapter 17]*

ANSI/ASQC Q9003 has the same requirements as the other two international quality standards, with the exception of applicability to only final inspection and test activities.

With relation to the individual FAA manufacturing approvals, there is little or no reference to training in the various parts of the FARs. However, in the regulations of the designated alteration station and the repair station, the requirements for training and experience of personnel affecting quality are very exacting, and could compare to the training requirements of ANSI/ASQC Q9003. However, for an organization to meet the requirements of ANSI/ASQC Q9001 and ANSI/ASQC Q9002 the training must be expanded to all personnel who directly affect quality during production and installation. This includes the person who builds the product, the person who cleans the product, and the person who packages the product. Anyone who comes in contact with the product, either physically or through the system (for example, quality auditors, manufacturing planners, engineers, and contract personnel) must be trained and qualified for their specific assigned tasks. This training must be documented and maintained as quality records. The ACSEP evaluation criteria also require the control for training but are not as encompassing as the international quality standards.[2]

The control procedure itself does not have to be a quality procedure, nor should the quality assurance department have the responsibility to manage the training activities. However, training procedures must be addressed in the quality assurance manual. Training should be a company-wide effort and be outlined in a corporate document, as either a procedure or policy. The procedure/policy should be a stand-alone document and include all requirements and responsibilities relating to training. Identification for the need of training, method for accomplishment of training, and documentation of training, are some areas that should be covered in this procedure/policy.

Primarily, the role QA shall perform in training is in verifying that the procedure/policy has been established and monitoring the actions for compliance. This monitoring is accomplished through internal audits. As discussed in chapter 18, "Internal Quality Audits," these audits are to be performed by trained, qualified personnel. These personnel do not have to be full-time QA personnel. But, when they are performing the auditing functions, they shall be trained, be unbiased, and report to QA.

IDENTIFYING TRAINING NEEDS

The need for training within the organization can range from being obvious to hidden. Some of the obvious indicators for the need of training are the introduction of new equipment and machinery, advancing technologies, job changes within the company, and new employee hiring.

However, in some cases neither the employee or the supervisor may realize that there is a need for training. These scenarios are usually detected as product rejections, and are often noticed too late. The customer may already be in possession of the product and discover the discrepancy. Not all discrepancies are caused by the lack of training, but many are. For example, the customer complains about an installation corroding prematurely. It is later discovered that the corrosion prevention process was not correctly complied with. In this case it could result in both a training problem and a possible work instructions problem.

When personnel have documented experience in the specific tasks, training may become redundant. In these cases, there would be no reason to provide the training unless the process has changed or there is a performance problem. However, this experience must be documented in the employee's records.

TRAINING DOCUMENTATION

Like the requirements for personnel information on the material review board and in demonstration of competency levels of the design control process, the training documentation of an employee profile must also be created and maintained. Again, to simplify the process, it is recommended that the organization use one form for all three requirements—

MRB, design competency, and training. This one form can have even more expanded uses when the organization decides to pursue individual FAA authorizations. All of the data necessary to be provided to the FAA can be extracted from this one source. In addition, an attachment can be created that documents both training and activity on specific projects. To limit the number of paper documents an organization has to file, these records can be maintained in a computer database. As discussed in chapter 17, this electronic filing must have fail-safe characteristics to prevent loss of the data. This is usually accomplished with the creation of backup disks.

Experience and competency can most easily be demonstrated by certificates and licenses issued to employees from certifying agencies. To make employees' training and personnel records inclusive, copies of certificates and licenses should be in the record file. If an electronic file is maintained, either a paper file should also be maintained for retention of the certificate or license, or an electronic scanning method should be used to save the document electronically.

In the case of the aviation industry, the majority of the recognized certifications are issued by the FAA. However, there are other important certifications and licensing performed by other organizations and agencies, including the Department of Labor, American Society for Quality Control, the Society of Manufacturing Engineers, American Society for Nondestructive Testing, foreign governmental agencies, and numerous others. The following is a summary of typical certifications realized within the aviation industry and their qualifying characteristics.

Airframe and powerplant mechanic (A & P) license is a rating issued by the FAA under the provisions of FAR 65 Subpart D. The license can be for an airframe rating, for a powerplant rating, or for both. The holder of such a license must remain current within the spectrum of FAR 65.83.

Journeyman mechanic is a certificate issued to aviation mechanics who have successfully completed an apprenticeship program governed by the Department of Labor.

Inspection authorization (IA) license is a rating issued by the FAA under the provisions of FAR 65.91. This rating can be applied for after the applicant has held an A & P license for a minimum of two years. Like the requirements for an A & P, both a written and an oral exam must be successfully completed before a license can be issued. Every IA must have access to an IA library. This library, usually on microfiche, contains Type Certificates and airworthiness directives for every type of aircraft type certificated by the FAA. IAs must renew annually under the guidelines of FAR 65.93.

Certified mechanical inspector (CMI) is a certification issued to inspectors who have passed a written test and with documented related work experience. This certificate is issued by the American Society for Quality Control and is not directed toward aviation.

Designated airworthiness representative (DAR) is an authorization given to individuals and/or organizations that the local FAA office has acknowledged as its quality field representatives. There are no examinations required for this authorization; however, the applicant must meet the requirements of FAR 183.33. Advisory Circular 183-33A provides detailed guidelines for application, responsibilities, and durations. DARs must renew their certification annually. There are DARs for both manufacturing fields and maintenance applications, each requiring their own certification. Application for a DAR rating is made on FAA Form 8110-14 (Figure 19.1).

Designated engineering representative (DER) is much like the DAR, in that authorization comes from the local FAA office, no examination is required, and authorization is based on the education and experience of an individual. However, DERs are authorized to perform engineering activities within the parameters of their specific specialties (electrical, structural, engines, propellers, and acoustical). The authority of the DER is outlined in FAR 183.29, and application is made on FAA Form 8110-14.

Designated manufacturing inspection representative (DMIR) is an authorized quality field representative of the FAA; that is, like the DAR and DER, the DMIR is authorized by the local FAA office. DMIRs are certified on the basis of their experience, and perform under the guidelines of FAR 183.31. Application is made on FAA Form 8110-14.

Certified quality technician (CQT) is a certification issued by the American Society for Quality Control to applicants who have passed a written examination and can demonstrate experience. The CQT is a paraprofessional who supports quality engineers in quality technology. CQTs, under supervision, create inspection plans, select sampling plans, prepare procedures, train inspectors, perform audits, and analyze and troubleshoot quality problems.

Certified quality engineer (CQE) is a certification issued by the American Society for Quality Control to applicants who have passed a written examination and can demonstrate related experience. The CQE should have the abilities to develop and operate quality control systems, apply and analyze testing and inspection procedures, use metrology and statistical methods to diagnose and correct improper quality control practices, understand human factors and motivation, understand facility quality cost concepts and techniques, develop and administer management information systems, and audit quality systems for compliance. CQEs must remain current by participating in approved continuing education.

Certified internal quality auditor is a certification issued by the Institute of Quality Assurance—International Register of Certificated Auditors (IQA-IRCA) in the United Kingdom. It is issued to individuals who

Organizations complete only the applicable blocks and attach separate resumes with the names, signatures, titles and qualifications of those persons who would actually perform the authorized functions.

STATEMENT OF QUALIFICATIONS (DAR—DMIR—DER—DPRE—DME)	Form Approved OMB-2120-0035

US Department of Transportation
Federal Aviation Administration

3. U.S. CITIZEN ☐ Yes ☐ No

INSTRUCTIONS: Print or type all entries except signatures.

1. NAME (Last, first, middle) **OR ORGANIZATION** — PHONE NUMBER — **4. SOCIAL SECURITY NO.**

2. ADDRESS (Number, street, city, state, and ZIP code) — **5. DATE OF BIRTH**

6. DESIGNATION SOUGHT

☐ Designated Manufacturing Inspection Representative (DMIR)
☐ Designated Mechanic Examiner (DME)   ☐ Airframe Rating   ☐ Powerplant Rating
☐ Designated Parachute Rigger Examiner (DPRE)   ☐ Seat   ☐ Back   ☐ Chest   ☐ Other
☐ Designated Engineering Representative (DER)
  ☐ Structural Engineering   ☐ Engine Engineering
  ☐ Powerplant Engineering   ☐ Propeller Engineering
  ☐ Systems and Equipment Engineering   ☐ Flight Analyst
  ☐ Acoustical Engineering   ☐ Flight Test Pilot
☐ Designated Airworthiness Representative (DAR)
  ☐ Manufacturing Function(s)
  ☐ Engineering Function(s)
  ☐ Maintenance Function(s)

NOTE: A separate application must be submitted for each discipline, i.e. manufacturing, engineering, maintenance.

DAR applicants shall identify specific function(s), currently authorized in AC 183-33, for which appointment is sought:

7. EXPERIENCE RESUME FOR NUMBER OF YEARS, AS APPROPRIATE, PERTINENT TO DESIGNATION SOUGHT. (Use additional sheets if necessary)

Dates From	To	Employer's Name	Position Title and Duties

8. EDUCATION AND TRAINING HIGH SCHOOL LEVEL AND ABOVE PERTINENT TO DESIGNATION SOUGHT

Dates From	To	Name of School	Curriculum or Study Program	Degrees Received

9. FAA CERTIFICATES NOW HELD PERTINENT TO DESIGNATION SOUGHT

Type	Certificate No.	Rating	Date Each Rating Issued

10. EMPLOYER'S RECOMMENDATION (To be completed for DER and DMIR only)

I recommend the person identified above be appointed as: ☐ Designated Engineering Representative ☐ Designated Manufacturing Inspection Representative

Date	Primary Business	Signature

11. LOCATION WHERE DESIGNEE FUNCTIONS WILL BE PERFORMED (To be completed for DAR, DME and DPRE only)

Address	Telephone No.

12. CERTIFICATION: I certify that the above statements are true to the best of my knowledge and that I am familiar with the Federal Aviation Regulations pertinent to the designation sought.

Date	Signature

FAA Form 8110-14 (3-83) SUPERSEDES PREVIOUS EDITION

FIGURE 19.1.   *FAA Form 8110-14, Statement of Qualifications.*

13. ACTION RECORD *(For FAA Use Only)*		
Designee's Name/Organization Name		**Designation Number**
Date Applicant Interviewed		**Date Certificate of Authority Expires**
Date References Verified		
Date Applicant Notified ☐ Accepted ☐ Denied		**Signature of Approving Authority**

14. RECORD OF APPROVAL

☐ Designated Manufacturing Inspection Representative (DMIR)

☐ Designated Mechanic Examiner (DME)   ☐ Airframe Rating   ☐ Powerplant Rating

☐ Designated Parachute Rigger Examiner (DPRE)   ☐ Seat   ☐ Back   ☐ Chest   ☐ Other

☐ Designated Engineering Representative (DER)
   ☐ Structural Engineering   ☐ Engine Engineering
   ☐ Powerplant Engineering   ☐ Propeller Engineering
   ☐ Systems and Equipment Engineering   ☐ Flight Analyst
   ☐ Acoustical Engineering   ☐ Flight Test Pilot

☐ Designated Airworthiness Representative (DAR)
   ☐ Manufacturing Function(s)
   ☐ Engineering Function(s)
   ☐ Maintenance Function(s)

NOTE:
A separate approval is required for each discipline

Function(s) Authorized *(Identify specific functions authorized including any limitations)*

15. RECORD OF SUBSEQUENT ACTIONS

Type			New Address and Telephone No *(If changed)*	Date Status of Designee Amended	FAA Official
Annual Renewal	Change of Address	Cancellation			

FIGURE 19.1. (continued)

meet the specific experience and training requirements outlined by the IQA-IRCA to qualify them as internal auditors, and have successfully passed a written examination.

Certified quality auditor (CQA) is a certification issued by the American Society for Quality Control to applicants who successfully pass a written examination and can demonstrate related experience. The requirements to become a CQA are very similar to those of the CQE. The CQA should have the understanding of standards and principles of auditing and auditing techniques of examining, questioning, evaluating, and reporting to determine a quality system's adequacy and deficiencies. The CQA must remain current, like the CQE, through attendance and participation in approved continuing education.

Quality systems lead auditor (QS-LA) is a certification that is issued from an accredited body. In the United States, the accrediting body is the Registrar Accreditation Board (RAB); in the United Kingdom it is the IQA-IRCA. Lead auditors must meet a number of stringent requirements that include experience documentation, attendance in training, and successfully passing a written examination. Lead auditors must have the ability to supervise quality auditors within a team at second- and third-party locations, thoroughly understand the standards (ISO) and principles of auditing, interface with upper-level company executives, and document audit results as required by the standards. QS-LAs must renew their certifications annually based on work activities.

Certified nondestructive test (NDT) *inspector* is a certification that is issued by the American Society for Nondestructive Testing to individuals who have met the specified training and experience requirements and have demonstrated their ability in test. There are three varying levels of this certification. Once recognized in the United States, ISO 9412 could promote certification credentials of these individuals, in much the same fashion as quality system auditors.

FAR TRAINING REQUIREMENTS

Though the various chapters of the FARs place emphasis on authorized personnel and facilities, only the requirements for the repair station, designated alteration station, and, to a lesser degree, Type Certificate explicitly state a requirement for training or experience.

TYPE CERTIFICATE

Under the requirements of a Type Certificate, FAR 21.37 states that flight test pilots working for a Type Certificate holder shall hold an appropriate pilot certificate to make test flights. There are no other references to personnel qualifications or training.

DESIGNATED ALTERATION STATION

With regard to training and experience, to be eligible for a designated alteration station authorization, FAR 21.439 (a) requires that the organization must

> —*Have adequate facilities and personnel, in the United States, appropriate to the products that it may operate or maintain under its certificate; and*
>
> —*Employ, or have available, a staff of engineering, flight test, and inspection personnel that can determine compliance with the applicable airworthiness requirements of FAR 21 Subpart M, Designated Alteration Station.[3]*

In addition, a DAS must also have at least one member of the staff that meets *all* of the following qualification requirements.

> —*A thorough working knowledge of the applicable requirements of FAR 21 Subpart M, Designated Alteration Station;*
>
> —*A position, on the DAS staff, with the authority to establish alteration programs that ensure that altered products meet the applicable DAS requirements;*
>
> —*At least one year of satisfactory experience in direct contact with the FAA while processing engineering work for type certification or alteration projects;*
>
> —*At least eight years of aeronautical engineering experience; and*
>
> —*The general technical knowledge and experience necessary to determine that altered products, of the types for which a DAS authorization is requested, are in condition for safe operation.[4]*

The majority of these requirements are necessary because a DAS will be required to have its own DER on staff.

REPAIR STATION

Under the personnel requirements of the repair station, FAR 145.39 is precise in the requirements for repair, supervisory, and inspection personnel. The FAR requires a repair station to "provide adequate personnel who can perform, supervise, and inspect the work for which the repair station is to be rated."[5] Not every mechanic requires a certification or a license, but uncertified mechanics shall have demonstrated their abilities on the basis of practical tests or employment records. It is not mandatory, but by exclusively employing licensed mechanics (reference

FAR 65 Subpart D) as supervisors, the organization can eliminate the need to certify repairmen (FAR 65, Subpart E).

The FAR requires that the repair station have enough supervisors for all phases of its activities. The FAR does not provide any distribution ratios, other than for supervision of apprentices and students. Unless the apprentices and students are integrated into groups of experienced workers, there should be at least one supervisor per 10 apprentices and students. For the work groups, the number of supervisors must be sufficient to produce airworthy work. Though the supervisors must have direct control over their working groups, they do not necessarily need to be at management levels. Qualified mechanics with the appropriate authority will meet the requirement.

Each person who is in charge of maintenance operations of the repair station (supervisors) shall be appropriately certificated as a mechanic or repairman under FAR 65. In addition, the supervisors shall have had at least 18 months of practical experience in the procedures, practices, inspection methods, materials, tools, machine tools, and equipment generally used in the work for which the station is rated. (Experience as an apprentice or student does not count in computing the 18 months of experience.)

For repair stations that have an airframe rating, at least one supervisor shall have the experience in the methods and procedures prescribed by the FAA for returning an aircraft to service after 100-hour, annual, and progressive inspections. An FAA-authorized inspector will meet these requirements.

Each limited repair station shall have employees with detailed knowledge of the particular maintenance function or technique for which the station is rated. This can be demonstrated by certificates of completion/attendance of a factory school, or by employment records that indicate long experience with the product or technique involved. This normally applies to commodities such as radios, instruments, propellers, rotor blades, and other complex components.

SUMMARY

Training must be an essential part of every organization's quality system. Though the major FAA production approval requirements do not make mention of the need, the requirements for the DAS and the repair station do. Training is also addressed in the ACSEP evaluation criteria. The three international quality standards all require documented training for personnel who affect quality.

ANSI/ASQC Q9001 and ANSI/ASQC Q9002 both require that the manufacturer establish and maintain procedures for identifying the training needs and provide for the training of all personnel performing activities affecting quality. Such training should not be limited to the production and quality organizations, but rather should apply to the entire organization. Additionally, the international quality standards require that personnel be assigned to tasks based on the appropriate education, training, and/or experience requirements of the individual task.

To provide objective evidence of conformance, the manufacturer must establish and maintain records of all such training activities. This should include maintaining records of employee experience. All such records must be maintained as quality records.

NOTES

1. ANSI/ASQC Q9001-1994, *Quality Systems—Model for Quality Assurance in Design, Development, Production, Installation, and Servicing* (Milwaukee, Wis.: American Society for Quality Control, 1994), 9, para. 4.18., Training.

2. DOT/FAA, Federal Aviation Order 8100.7, *Aircraft Certification Systems Evaluation Program* (Washington D.C.: DOT/FAA, 30 March 1994), Appendix 6, Section 1.

3. DOT/FAA, Federal Aviation Regulation Section 21.439 (a), *Certification Procedures for Products and Parts—Eligibility* (Washington, D.C.: DOT/FAA, March 1993).

4. Ibid.

5. DOT/FAA, Federal Aviation Regulation Section 145.39 (a), *Repair Station—Personnel Requirements* (Washington, D.C.: DOT/FAA, August 1993).

Chapter 20

SERVICING

When products leave the manufacturer, they will sometimes require servicing. This servicing can be a result of warrantee claims, design improvement, design error, normal scheduled maintenance, or repair activities. In the aviation industry, this servicing activity is often referred to as *product support*.

ANSI/ASQC Q9003 makes no requirement for the servicing of products. ANSI/ASQC Q9001 and ANSI/ASQC Q9002 both state that "where servicing is a specified requirement, the supplier shall establish and maintain documented procedures for performing, verifying, and reporting that the service meets the specified requirements."[1] For ANSI/ASQC Q9002 this is a new element of the 1994 revision. However, within the aviation industry the serving of FAA-approved products is highly regulated. As such, the requirements of the individual FARs are in excess of the international quality standards and take precedence.

Servicing can also be one of the most complex processes of the organizational system. There are basically four approved methods for the manufacturer to service product after delivery. Original equipment manufacturers (OEM) may perform some servicing activities on their own produced products in accordance with the requirements of FAR Part 43. Two other methods are found under FAR Part 145 and are the manufacturer's maintenance facility (MMF) and the domestic repair station. The final method is through field approvals using the services of a DER and a DAR.

ORIGINAL EQUIPMENT MANUFACTURERS

FAR Part 43 provides the core requirements for all maintenance, preventive maintenance, rebuilding, and alteration of any aircraft having a U.S. airworthiness certificate; foreign-registered civil aircraft used in common carriage of mail under the provisions of FAR Parts 121, 127, or 135; and airframe, aircraft engines, propellers, appliances, and component parts of such aircraft. It does not apply to experimental aircraft. Within FAR Part 43 there are various exceptions and provisions. For the purpose of this chapter only the requirements of the manufacturer and repair station will be displayed.

FAR Section 43.3 (i) states that a manufacturer may

> *(1) Rebuild or alter any aircraft, aircraft engine, propeller, or appliance manufactured by [it] under a type or production certificate;*
>
> *(2) Rebuild or alter any appliance or part of aircraft, aircraft engines, propellers, or appliances manufactured by [it] under a Technical Standard Order Authorization, an FAA—Parts Manufacturer Approval, or Product or Process Specification issued by the [FAA]; and*
>
> *(3) Perform any inspection required by Part 91 or Part 125 of [the FARs] on aircraft it manufactures, while currently operating under a production certificate or under a currently approved production inspection system for such aircraft.[2]*

These requirements are rather straightforward, but it must be stressed that these provisions only apply to manufacturers. Organizations that perform as suppliers and do not produce the product under their own FAA production approval or type design approval are not manufacturers, but rather suppliers. For suppliers, such servicing activities under FAR Part 43 would have to be performed under the supervision and authority of the FAA production approval holder.

Additionally, all design data must be FAA approved. This mostly applies to rebuilding and alteration activities and can be achieved by various methods. One method is by having an FAA-authorized DER, on staff or under contract for the required application, who has the authority to approve alterations. A manufacturer could also directly solicit the support of the FAA engineering function for such an approval. These types of approvals are called *field approvals* and are normally only for one unit, though they can have higher effectivities. For standard alterations that affect a number of units, a Supplemental Type Certificate (STC) is usually applied for (see chapter 5, "Design Control").

The concept of rebuilding also should be defined. Rebuilding is not repairing. FAR Section 43.2 (b) states that

> *no person [manufacturer] may describe in any required maintenance entry or form an aircraft, airframe, aircraft engine, propeller, appliance, or component part as being rebuilt unless it has been disassembled, cleaned, inspected, repaired as necessary, reassembled, and tested to the same tolerances and limits as a new item, using either new parts or used parts that either conform to*

new part tolerances and limits or to approved oversized or under-sized dimensions.³

This means that the rebuilt product must be as good as new and capable of being classified as reworked (reference chapter 14).

There are documentation requirements for each of these activities. Rebuilding and inspection activities shall be documented in the appropriate equipment record. These are commonly referred to as logbooks. FAR Part 43 provides exacting requirements for each type of entry, including inspection statements. Major alterations must be documented on FAA Form 337. This form will be discussed later in this chapter, but for this application it should be completed by a supervisory person within the quality inspection department.

Under the authority of FAR Part 43 manufacturers are not authorized to perform maintenance or repairs on products that have been delivered and are in service.

MANUFACTURER'S MAINTENANCE FACILITY

If a manufacturer is to perform maintenance or preventive maintenance on products it produced, it may opt to pursue certification under FAR Part 145 Subpart D as a manufacturer's maintenance facility (MMF).

The holder of a certificate issued under [FAR Part 145 Subpart D] may maintain and approve for return to service any article for which it is rated, and perform preventive maintenance on that article, if certificated mechanics or repairmen are employed directly in charge of the maintenance and preventive maintenance.⁴

This certification does not authorize repair activities.

In order for a manufacturer to obtain an MMF rating, it must first formally apply. This is normally accomplished in letter form to the FAA manufacturing inspection district office (MIDO) responsible for the applicable manufacturing facility. Most manufacturers will have an FAA primary inspector (PI) assigned to them, and these actions should be coordinated through this FAA representative. Additionally, accompanying the application for approval, revisions to the quality assurance manual addressing these activities, as well as any new or revised procedures controlling the operations of the manufacturer's maintenance facility, should be supplied.

In most cases, manufacturers will briefly describe the functions and responsibilities of the manufacturer's maintenance facility in the quality assurance manual, and create new stand-alone procedures to fully describe the operations and control of processes. In larger companies, it is often the case that the manufacturer creates a new department to control all servicing and warranty work and titles this department Product Support. The procedures that control the processes of the manufacturer's maintenance facility could be placed under this department's jurisdiction, or they could be developed as company procedures/policies. Smaller companies may wish to create these procedures as quality assurance procedures. It really depends on the structure of the organization and the desires of management.

Once the MIDO has received the request, it is its option to perform an audit. As for any audit, the MIDO representatives will evaluate the manufacturer's procedures and abilities to conform to both the internal procedures and FAR requirements. Once a manufacturer has been approved, it may apply these actions at any location or facility, providing the certification does not note limitations.

There are additional performance requirements for these maintenance activities. With the exceptions of maintenance performed for an air carrier or commercial operator, under the continuous airworthiness requirements of FAR Parts 121 and 127, and for airplanes under the inspection program requirements of FAR Part 125, all maintenance and preventive maintenance operations shall be performed in accordance with the applicable sections of FAR Part 43.

DOMESTIC REPAIR STATIONS

Some manufacturers will find it more advantageous to apply for a repair station rating under FAR Part 145 Subpart B. Whereas a manufacturer's maintenance facility may only perform maintenance and preventive maintenance on products of its own production, repair stations may perform these activities, as well as alterations, repairs, and certain inspections, regardless of production origin. Application for a domestic repair station rating is made to the flight standards district office (FSDO) having jurisdiction over the repair station.

The domestic repair station will be required to have an inspection system that meets both the generic and special requirements of FAR Part 145. These special requirements include personnel qualification, special housing, and facility requirements. As noted in document control, repair stations also have special requirements when advertising. Basically any document or advertising tool, including letterhead, that implies that the facility is an FAA-approved repair station shall also have the repair station's approval number noted. The repair station certificate must also be displayed at a place in the repair station that is normally accessible to the public and is not obscured.

A certified Domestic Repair Station may:

> *(1) Maintain or alter any airframe, powerplant, propeller, instrument, radio, or accessory, or part thereof, for which it is rated;*
>
> *(2) Approve for return to service any article for which it is rated after it has been maintained or altered; in the case of a station with an airframe rating, perform 100 hour, annual, or progressive inspections, and return aircraft to service; and*
>
> *(3) Maintain or alter any article for which it is rated at a place other than the repair station, if—*
>
> > *(a) the function would be performed in the same manner as when performed at the repair station and in accordance with FAR Section 145.57 to 145.61 [performance requirements];*
> >
> > *(b) all necessary personnel, equipment, material, and technical data is available at the place where the work is done; and*
> >
> > *(c) the inspection procedures manual of the [repair] station sets forth approved procedures governing work to be performed at a place other than the repair station.[5]*

However, as for all such activities, the work must be performed in accordance with FAA-approved data. For such repairs it is common to pursue a field approval through an FAA-authorized DER.

As for the manufacturer's maintenance facility, the repair station shall perform maintenance, preventive maintenance, alterations, or inspections in accordance with the standards of FAR Part 43. Activity performed on air carrier or commercially operated aircraft shall be in accordance with FAR Part 121 or FAR Part 127 and comply with the requirements of FAR Part 121 (except 121.363, 121.369, 121.373, and 121.379) or Subpart I of Part 127 (except 127.131, 127.134, 127.136, and 127.140), as applicable. These individual sections of FAR 121 and FAR 127 provide additional performance requirements. In addition, these repair stations shall perform that work in accordance with the applicable air carrier's or commercial operator's manual.

When a repair station performs a major repair or alteration on a type design article (for example, airframe, powerplant, propeller, or appliance), it shall be documented on FAA Form 337 (Figure 20.1). This form shall be completed by only authorized members of the repair station's staff, such as the qualified inspector. The qualified inspector must be a person employed by the repair station who has shown by experience as a journey worker that he or she understands the inspection methods, techniques, and equipment used in determining the airworthiness of

			Form Approved
			OMB No. 2120-0020

US Department of Transportation **Federal Aviation Administration**	**MAJOR REPAIR AND ALTERATION** (Airframe, Powerplant, Propeller, or Appliance)	**For FAA Use Only** Office Identification

INSTRUCTIONS: Print or type all entries. See FAR 43.9, FAR 43 Appendix B, and AC 43.9-1 (or subsequent revision thereof) for instructions and disposition of this form. This report is required by law (49 U.S.C. 1421). Failure to report can result in a civil penalty not to exceed $1,000 for each such violation (Section 901 Federal Aviation Act of 1958).

1. Aircraft

Make	Model
Serial No.	Nationality and Registration Mark

2. Owner

Name (As shown on registration certificate)	Address (As shown on registration certificate)

3. For FAA Use Only

4. Unit Identification   **5. Type**

Unit	Make	Model	Serial No.	Repair	Alteration
AIRFRAME	~~~~~~~~~~~~~ (As described in Item 1 above) ~~~~~~~~~~~~~				
POWERPLANT					
PROPELLER					
APPLIANCE	Type				
	Manufacturer				

6. Conformity Statement

A. Agency's Name and Address	B. Kind of Agency	C. Certificate No.
	U.S. Certificated Mechanic	
	Foreign Certificated Mechanic	
	Certificated Repair Station	
	Manufacturer	

D. I certify that the repair and/or alteration made to the unit(s) identified in item 4 above and described on the reverse or attachments hereto have been made in accordance with the requirements of Part 43 of the U.S. Federal Aviation Regulations and that the information furnished herein is true and correct to the best of my knowledge.

Date	Signature of Authorized Individual

7. Approval for Return To Service

Pursuant to the authority given persons specified below, the unit identified in item 4 was inspected in the manner prescribed by the Administrator of the Federal Aviation Administration and is ☐ APPROVED ☐ REJECTED

BY	FAA Flt. Standards Inspector	Manufacturer	Inspection Authorization	Other (Specify)
	FAA Designee	Repair Station	Person Approved by Transport Canada Airworthiness Group	
Date of Approval or Rejection	Certificate or Designation No.	Signature of Authorized Individual		

FAA Form 337 (12-88)

FIGURE 20.1.   *FAA Form 337, Major Repair and Alteration.*

the article concerned. Qualified inspectors must also be proficient in using various types of mechanical and usual inspection aids appropriate for the article being inspected. Preferably, such personnel, especially the chief inspector, are certified under FAR Part 65 as authorized inspectors

(IAs). This certification demonstrates the individual's experience to meet the requirements of the repair station. At a minimum, qualified inspectors must be licensed as mechanics or repairmen, under FAR Part 65. Advisory Circular 65-24 provides general information regarding the certification of a repairman. Authorized persons must also complete the necessary documentation for the return-to-service activities. With the 1994 revision of FAA Form 8130-3 (see Figure 11.8), return to service can be documented on an official form. FAA Order 8130.21, Revision 1/3/94, provides instructions for this form's use.

There are also personnel requirements on the manufacturing side of the operations. Anyone directly in charge of maintenance functions of a repair station must also be certificated as a mechanic or repairman, under the requirements of FAR Part 65. They must also have 18 months of practical experience in the procedures, practices, inspection methods, materials, tools, machine tools, and equipment generally used in the work for which the station is rated. Experience as an apprentice or student mechanic does not count toward the 18 months of experience. Additionally, at least one person in charge of maintenance functions for a station with an airframe rating must have had experience in the methods and procedures prescribed by the FAA for returning aircraft to service after 100-hour, annual, and progressive inspections. An IA meets these requirements.[6]

FAR Part 145 also requires each limited repair station to have employees with detailed knowledge of the particular maintenance function or technique for which the station is rated. The experience shall be based on attendance at a factory school or long experience with the product or technique involved.[7] Evidence of this training and experience shall be maintained as quality records.

As previously mentioned, repair stations have additional housing and facility requirements. The majority of the requirements are based on good business practices, such as providing a controlled environment and adequate lighting. However, depending on the individual rating there are special requirements. These special requirements relate mostly to the required tooling or facilities for a special process, such as ventilation systems for fabric work and painting. In some cases, the minimum size of the facility is also regulated. The repair station with an airframe rating must provide suitable permanent housing for at least one of the heaviest aircraft within the height class it is rated. If location of the station is such that climatic conditions allow work to be done outside, permanent work docks, of appropriate design, may be used.[8]

The same applies to component repair stations. Such repair stations shall provide suitable "facilities for properly protecting parts and assemblies during disassembly, cleaning, inspection, repair, alteration, and assembly; so that work being done is protected from weather elements, dust, and heat; workers are protected so that the work will not be impaired by their physical efficiency; and maintenance operations have efficient and proper facilities."[9] The actual requirements for housing and facilities are rather extensive and should be reviewed for individual applicability.

When a repair station is approved, it will be authorized to perform only the activities for those ratings it possesses. There are six basic ratings: airframe, powerplant, propeller, radio, instrument, and accessory. Each of these main ratings is broken down into smaller, more specific ratings. For example, radio ratings have three subratings: communication equipment, navigational equipment, and radar equipment. Each of these ratings must be applied for separately. Prior to the acceptance of any service work, the manufacturer should ensure that the approved ratings the repair station holds are appropriate for the intended service. This would normally be accomplished during the contract review phase.

FOREIGN REPAIR STATIONS

FAR Part 145 Subpart C has provisions for the certification of repair stations located outside of the United States. Application for such a rating is made to FAA through the international field office (IFO) having jurisdiction over the foreign repair station.

> *A repair station certificate with appropriate rating may be issued for a foreign repair station if the FAA determines that it will be necessary for maintaining or altering United States registered aircraft and aircraft engines, propellers, appliances, and component parts thereof for use on United States registered aircraft.*[10]

Foreign repair stations are required to meet the same requirements as domestic repair stations, except for those of personnel requirements. FAR Section 145.75 provides additional personnel requirements for foreign repair stations.

The personnel requirements are not based on certifications or licenses, but rather on the ability to prove competency. This demonstration is at the discretion of the FAA and can include oral and/or practical tests. No person may be responsible for supervision or final inspection of work on an aircraft of United States registry at a foreign repair station unless he or she can read, write, and understand English.

The documentation requirements for a foreign repair station are the same as for a domestic repair station. However, the IFO having jurisdiction over the foreign repair station may require special reporting procedures at its discretion.

REPORTS OF DEFECTS OR UNAIRWORTHY CONDITIONS

As discussed in chapter 14, "Control of Nonconforming Product," the FAA must be notified of any serious defects or recurring unairworthy conditions in FAA-approved product. The requirements for both the domestic repair station and foreign repair station are the same.

Within 72 hours after any serious defect is discovered it must be reported to the FAA. Such reporting is normally documented on FAA Form 8010-4, Malfunction or Defect Report (shown in Figure 14.3), and made to the FAA office having jurisdiction over the repair station. However, actual reporting can take any form the FAA requires. Using alternative methods of reporting is common when a defect or malfunction is discovered that could result in an imminent hazard to flight.[11] OEMs and MMFs will report such defects and malfunctions under the reporting procedures discussed in chapter 14 and required by FAR Part 21.3.

SUMMARY

Unlike many other industries, parts and products cannot simply be returned to the aviation manufacturer for servicing, rework, repair, or alteration. The manufacturer must hold the appropriate approvals and ratings from the FAA. This is one of those cases where the requirements of the FARs take precedence over the international quality standards. The FARs have exacting requirements for this element of a quality system.

It is strongly recommended that every manufacturer develop its quality systems to include the requirements of a manufacturing maintenance facility and apply for this approval. This approval, under FAR Part 145 Subpart D, is the simpler of the two approvals to obtain, and is primarily based on the quality systems established to control the manufacturer's manufacturing system. There will be additional training and documentation required, including creation of procedures, to obtain such an approval, but it is well worth the effort. The ability to service one's own products is a definite selling point within the aviation industry. Additionally, all documents pertaining to the accomplishment of work or indicating inspection (licensed mechanic/repairer) acceptance must be maintained as quality records. Keep in mind, though, that manufacturing maintenance facilities are not authorized to repair products and are not authorized to work on products other than their own. They are only authorized to perform maintenance and preventive maintenance on products of their own authorized production.

Domestic repair stations have more exacting requirements than MMFs. Repair stations are authorized to perform repairs, modifications, and alterations, in accordance with FAA-approved data, on the products for which they are rated. Supervision and inspection personnel shall be qualified. All inspectors and maintenance supervisors shall be licensed as mechanics or certified as repairmen, in accordance with FAR Part 65. The chief inspector for airframe repair stations should be licensed as an IA. The repair station also has additional facility requirements. These include the actual facility, tooling, library, and environmental controls.

Documentation requirements are also different than those for normal manufacturers. FAA Form 337 is used for documenting major repairs, alterations, and modifications, and FAA Form 8130-3 (1994 revision) can be used for returning product to service. Both of these forms must be completed by an authorized member of the repair station's staff.

NOTES

1. ANSI/ASQC Q9001-1994, *Quality Systems—Model for Quality Assurance in Design, Development, Production, Installation, and Servicing* (Milwaukee, Wis.: American Society for Quality Control, 1994), 9, para. 4.19, Servicing.

2. DOT/FAA, Federal Aviation Regulation Section 43.3 (i), *Maintenance, Preventive Maintenance, Rebuilding, and Alteration—Persons Authorized to Perform Maintenance, Preventive Maintenance, Rebuilding, and Alterations* (Washington, D.C.: DOT/FAA, 13 December 1988).

3. DOT/FAA, Federal Aviation Regulation Section 43.2 (b), *Maintenance, Preventive Maintenance, Rebuilding, and Alteration—Records of Overhaul and Rebuilding* (Washington, D.C.: DOT/FAA, 13 December 1988).

4. DOT/FAA, Federal Aviation Regulation Section 145.103, *Repair Stations—Privileges of Certificates* (Washington, D.C.: DOT/FAA, August 1993).

5. DOT/FAA, Federal Aviation Regulation Section 145.51, *Repair Stations—Privileges of Certificates* (Washington, D.C.: DOT/FAA, August 1993).

6. DOT/FAA, Federal Aviation Regulation Section 145.39 (d), *Repair Stations—Personnel Requirements* (Washington, D.C.: DOT/FAA, August 1993).

7. DOT/FAA, Federal Aviation Regulation Section 145.39 (e), *Repair Stations—Personnel Requirements* (Washington, D.C.: DOT/FAA, August 1993).

8. DOT/FAA, Federal Aviation Regulation Section 145.35 (b), *Repair Stations—Special Housing and Facility Requirements* (Washington, D.C.: DOT/FAA, August 1993).

9. DOT/FAA, Federal Aviation Regulation Section 145.35 (a) (4), *Repair Stations—Housing and Facility Requirements* (Washington, D.C.: DOT/FAA, August 1993).

10. DOT/FAA, Federal Aviation Regulation Section 145.71, *Repair Stations—General Requirements* (Washington, D.C.: DOT/FAA, August 1993).

11. DOT/FAA, Federal Aviation Regulation Section 145.63, *Repair Stations—Reports of Defects and Unairworthy Conditions* (Washington, D.C.: DOT/FAA, August 1993).

Chapter 21

STATISTICAL TECHNIQUES

In the present-day aviation industry, statistical techniques of inspection and process control are an everyday part of the business. Such statistical techniques include the use of sampling plans and the implementation of statistical process control techniques and software. In many cases, the implementation of such sampling and statistical techniques can provide an improvement in both processing results and inspection capacity. Through process improvement this can also have a positive effect on the financial performance of a company. However, there are instances in which the implementation of such techniques are not appropriate and can and will provide negative effects.

The use of statistical techniques is addressed in all three of the international quality standards. However, the use of these techniques is optional and is to be implemented only where appropriate. The international quality standards require that when such statistical techniques are implemented, procedures shall be established and maintained for identifying the need for statistical techniques required for establishing, controlling, and verifying process capability and product characteristics.

The FAA also addresses the use of statistical techniques; however, not as specifically as in the international quality standards. Within the majority of the FAA manufacturing approval regulations, the control of statistical techniques is implied through the requirement for procedures that control special processing. Because statistical techniques are considered special processes, the FARs require procedures to control them. However, in FAR section 21.303 (h)(5), under the quality requirements for a PMA manufacturer, the FAA does make specific mention of statistical techniques. The section states,

> Parts in process must be inspected for conformity with the design data at points in production where accurate determination can be made. Statistical quality control procedures may be employed where it is shown that a satisfactory level of quality will be maintained for a particular part involved.[1]

The FAA provides more direction for such controls within the various associated advisory circulars. Advisory Circular 21-1B addresses statistical techniques in various aspects of the manufacturing process. It also provides the interpretation of what the FAA feels is an acceptable inspection system. Under one of the many characteristics is the requirement for procedures that ensure that any defects which might be in a lot accepted under a statistical quality control plan will not result in an unsafe condition in an end product or spare article. This means that if a part is installed in an end-item product, and the conformity of that part cannot be verified through test or later inspection of the end-item product, that part is not appropriate for sampling inspection. So, prior to the implementation of sampling techniques, the manufacturer must be aware of the part's applications and later inspection and testing of end-item products.

The FAA also implies the use of statistical process control within special processes in the advisory circular. It states that

> *the integrity of processes and services utilized in the construction of articles and products is dependent upon the skill with which the work is performed, the capabilities of the equipment used, and the close control of temperatures, solutions, curing time, or other critical factors. A system to control all processes and services, such as welding, brazing, heat treatment, plating, etc., ensures that each process is performed by trained and qualified personnel and in accordance with approved specifications containing definitive standards of quality, and that periodic inspection of gages, solutions or any critical equipment is controlled and documented. As a method of control, statistical process control could be approved as an acceptable technique, providing it is correctly established and implemented.[2]*

Advisory Circular 21-1B also notes that manufacturers are also "responsible for ensuring that inspections and tests are extended to include their supplier's inspection and test of articles or services which cannot or will not be completely inspected upon receipt by the manufacturer."[3] This includes the use of any statistical techniques and the assurance that these techniques are properly applied.

Under the testing section of the advisory circular, it states that "where sampling inspection tests are utilized, other inspections and tests should be implemented as required to assure acceptance of conforming and safe products or articles."[4] Additionally, through the various sections of this advisory circular, the manufacturer is required to maintain all documents that are used in controlling the design configuration and conformity of parts and articles as quality records.

The use and control of statistical techniques is also an element of the ACSEP evaluation criteria.[5] So, in comparison to the international quality standards, the requirements of the FAA are similar, and are actually more exacting.

THE PROCEDURES

It is basically up to each individual manufacturer to decide to what extent it wishes to apply statistical techniques within its manufacturing process. Some may feel that the use of sampling inspection at receiving is sufficient for their applications. Others may feel that statistical process control should be implemented throughout the entire organization. Whatever is applicable for the individual organization, it must be documented in procedure. Normally, the quality assurance manual will address the use of such statistical techniques, but will not go into very much detail about application and methodology. The quality assurance manual should only provide a brief overview of the systems implemented. If there are no statistical control systems implemented, then they do not need to be addressed.

Individual procedures should be created to control the various types of statistical techniques. This will allow for the procedure to be revised and updated more easily, and will provide a stand-alone document to the operator of the techniques. The contents of a control procedure for statistical techniques, in addition to the standard requirements for procedures (such as purpose and scope), should include

- Definitions of the different types of statistical techniques
- Applicability of statistical techniques (receiving, in-process, testing, and so on)
- Identification of the need for statistical techniques
- Selection of sampling plans or appropriate charts (including appropriate software)
- Required training of personnel
- Requirements for suppliers, when applicable
- Retention of plans and inspection records as quality records

When the individual procedures have been created, they must be approved by the FAA prior to implementation. In addition, the contract may require approval by the customer prior to implementation on its products.

If a manufacturer develops its sampling inspection procedures and plans around MIL-STD-105D, it will probably have little difficulty in obtaining approval from both the FAA and the customer. This military standard has been widely used by the aviation industry for decades, and is the most recognized sampling standard in the world. It provides sample plans and charts and is a recommended document for every quality library.

Statistical process control (SPC) standards are a different story. There have been recent developments within the methodology of formulation of SPC that keep manufacturers on their toes. The use and implementation of SPC is much more complex than that of sampling inspection. For a manufacturer who is not experienced in the methods of SPC, caution is advised. The attendance of qualified training programs is the first step such manufacturers should take, followed by the selection of software and gradual implementation, where appropriate. Some larger airframe manufacturers will provide their suppliers with both training and software. However, there are numerous software programs available on the open market, and some are better than others. SPC is a process of evolution for each manufacturer, and its implementation should be carefully planned. Jumping into this process too quickly may prove to have a negative effect on both personnel morale and the process.

SUMMARY

The use of statistical processes is unique for each individual manufacturer. The statistical techniques must be molded to fit the individual processes and products of the manufacturer, and not the other way around. If statistical techniques are a requirement of a contract, the manufacturer and the customer should work together in developing acceptable techniques and finding appropriate applicability.

Statistical techniques are like any other special process. The process must be defined in a procedure, appropriate plans must be supplied to personnel, personnel must be appropriately trained, records must be appropriately maintained, and the process should be monitored through audit.

If appropriately applied and effectively developed, statistical techniques can and will provide positive results in processing, inspection capacity, and financial return.

NOTES

1. DOT/FAA, Federal Aviation Regulation Section 21.303 (h)(5), *Certification Procedures for Products and Parts—Replacement and Modification Parts* (Washington, D.C.: DOT/FAA, March 1993).

2. DOT/FAA, Advisory Circular 21-1B, *Production Certificates* (Washington, D.C.: DOT/FAA, 10 May 1976), 5, para. (9)(d)(3), Special Processing.

3. Ibid.

4. Ibid.

5. DOT/FAA, Federal Aviation Order 8100.7, *Aircraft Certification Systems Evaluation Program* (Washington D.C.: DOT/FAA, 30 March 1994), Appendix 6, Section 6.

CONCLUSION

In the previous 21 chapters of this book, a history of quality in aviation has been provided and the international quality standards have been compared, in detail, to the requirements of the various parts of the federal aviation regulations. In these comparisons, experienced aviation professionals will realize that the requirements of ANSI/ASQC Q9001 and ANSI/ASQC Q9002 are not much different than what the aviation industry has been doing for decades. However, this previous performance has not been because of the FAR requirements, but rather because companies wished to prevent nonconformance and implemented supplemental quality standards. The most predominantly used of these standards has been the MIL-Q-9858A.

Many companies may ask, why change their systems now? The answer is twofold. First, the FARs require only an inspection system and place no formal emphasis on internal audits and discrepancy prevention; however, the advisory circulars do. Without such tools imbedded into the system, the manufacturer will realize continued trends of nonconformance and deterioration of the bottom line. By developing internal systems that will identify problems before they become critical, the manufacturer will have the ability to correct the problem once and go about its business of streamlining the processes to enhance safety, production capability and capacity, and profits. Augmenting the FARs with MIL-Q-9858A is good, but the international quality standards are better. The international quality standards place more responsibility on management for quality and require internal auditing of all processes that affect quality. Second, the world economy is demanding compliance to these internationally recognized quality standards. Before too long, companies who are not certified or registered to one of the international quality standards will be excluded from the global marketplace. These are not empty threats, but rather the reality of global business. Companies are demanding the ability to forgo the lengthy process of supplier certification and want to get on with doing business. ISO 9000 quality system certification/registration will support such efforts.

For the aviation industry this still means that, because of FAR requirements, the manufacturer is responsible for its suppliers. However, with the exception of the special requirements of the FARs (depending on what type of manufacturing approval is applicable), it would be reasonable for the manufacturer to accept ISO 9000 quality system certification/registration as proof of a complying quality system. To reduce the

301

time needed to certify suppliers, the additional requirements of the FARs and process approvals can be approved through individual process audits. NASA and the Department of Defense, having recognized the ISO 9001 (ANSI/ASQC Q9001) quality standard as an acceptable alternative to the MIL-Q-9858A quality standard, are sending a message to U.S. industries. This acceptance may influence the FAA's decision-making process in recognizing the international quality standards. It is only a matter of time before ISO 9000 quality system certification/registration is recognized by the FAA.

Though it is purely the speculation of the author, it is foreseeable that the FAA may develop an approved list of registrars. This list may include registrars who are authorized to register aviation organizations to both the international quality standards and the applicable parts of the FARs. If this becomes the case, the registrars would be susceptible to audits by both the accrediting body (RAB, IQA-IRCA, and so on) as well as the FAA. The FAA would also have the continued authority to spot audit manufacturers at its discretion. The IQA-IRCA, in the United Kingdom, has taken the first steps in such a direction with the registration of lead auditors under the Aerospace Sector Certification Scheme (ASCS). Only personnel with credentials from the ASCS are allowed to perform audits of aerospace/aviation companies under the U.K. scheme.

Another scenario would be the FAA recognizing the ISO 9000 quality system certification/registration of the manufacturer, and performing a simplified audit to ensure that the additional FAA requirements are in compliance. Because there are only a few extra requirements (depending on the type of approval) the supplement audit would be a fraction of what it is today. With the great similarity of the ACSEP evaluation criteria to the international quality standards, it would appear that there is some interest on the side of the FAA to align its quality system requirements with that of global industry.

The benefits of both these scenarios are obvious. This is not to devalue the auditing abilities of the FAA's MIDO and FSDO representatives; they are multitasked and overburdened as it is. With the audits being performed by third-party registrars, the auditing functions would be performed by auditing professionals who have been extensively trained and certified for the performance of such audits. This would enhance safety by allowing the FAA to concentrate its efforts on the safety of flight, design, and special processing. Additionally, the potential cost savings to the taxpayer are obvious. Where the taxpayer has been paying the bill for such audit performance, it would now be the liability of the manufacturer. This may even open opportunities for joint ventures in countries where in the past the FAA has determined it to be too great a financial burden to perform such audits.

Even if the manufacturer has to foot the bill for certification/registration it benefits financially as well. Once all of industry accepts ISO 9000 quality system certification/registration, the need for multiple conformance to various customer quality standards is removed. By conforming to one quality standard, the manufacturer is faced with only one group of auditors, and only one set of standards. This will allow the manufacturer to streamline its internal processes and jettison redundant processes and documents. To the manufacturer, the cost of certification/registration should become irrelevant because of its need to ensure the organization's global competitiveness. Additionally, by having one global system, manufacturers who have in the past worked under military specification requirements as government contractors will have a simplified task when they diversify into commercial markets.

In realizing the benefits of international quality system compliance, manufacturers with vision should recognize the competitive advantages of developing or changing their internal systems to meet these international quality standards. After doing so, most manufacturers will wonder why they did not do so sooner. But remember to develop the systems with reality in mind. The organization should not be committed to steps and processes that are humanly impossible or organizationally disruptive. Standardize the operations of the organization and form procedures in such a manner as to meet the requirements of the international quality standards and applicable parts of the FARs, and the needs and wants of the customer. This can only be accomplished through committed, well-informed leadership.

Only after an organization has developed an effective quality system, regardless of standard base, can a successful effort be realized in implementing process improvements. Such improvements would include total quality management. Without a firm foundation of internal process controls and structured internal communication methods, the investment in organizational process improvement is surely ill-spent.

Appendix A

CROSS-REFERENCE MATRICES

ANSI/ASQC Q9001-1994 and FAR Cross-Reference

Q9001 elements	APIS	PC	PMA	DAS	TSO	Repair station	ACSEP evaluation questions
4.1.1.	—	—	—	—	—	—	1M1
4.1.2.1.	21.123	21.123	—	21.445	21.607	145.39	1Q1/1Q4
4.1.2.2.	21.123	21.143	21.303	21.439	—	145.35 145.37	1P3/1S3/1C3/ 5Q1/4Q7
4.1.2.3.	—	21.143	—	21.439	—	—	1Q2
4.1.3.	—	—	—	—	—	—	15M2
4.2.1.	21.123	21.143	—	21.441	21.607	145.45	1Q4
4.2.2.	—	21.143	—	21.441	21.607	145.45	—
4.2.3.	—	21.143	21.303	21.441	21.607	145.45	4P2/4P4
4.3.1.	—	—	—	—	—	—	—
4.3.2.	—	—	—	—	—	—	—
4.3.3.	—	—	—	—	—	—	—
4.3.4.	—	—	—	—	—	—	—
4.4.1.	—	—	—	21.441	21.605	—	2E2
4.4.2.	—	—	—	21.441	—	—	—
4.4.3.	—	—	—	21.441	—	—	2P1/2Q1/2S1
4.4.4.	—	—	—	21.441	21.605	—	—
4.4.5.	—	—	—	21.441	21.605	—	—
4.4.6.	—	—	—	—	—	—	—
4.4.7.	—	—	—	21.441	21.607	—	—
4.4.8.	21.125	21.143	21.303	21.463	21.607	145.57	4E2/4Q1
4.4.9.	21.125	—	21.303	—	21.611	—	2P1/2Q1/2S1
4.5.1.	—	—	—	21.441	—	—	3AE3/1Q4/1Q5
4.5.2.	—	—	—	21.441	—	—	2Q1/2P1/2S1/ 2E9/4P1/4P5

Continued on next page

Continued from previous page

Q9001 elements	APIS	PC	PMA	DAS	TSO	Repair station	ACSEP evaluation questions
4.5.3.	—	—	—	—	—	—	4P1/4P5
4.6.1.	21.125	21.143	—	—	21.143	—	10E1/10Q1/10Q2
4.6.2.	—	—	—	—	—	—	10Q1/10Q2/ 10Q3/10Q5/10E1
4.6.3.	21.125	—	—	—	—	—	10Q5/10Q6
4.6.4.1.	—	21.143	21.303	—	21.143	—	—
4.6.4.2.	—	21.143	—	—	21.615	—	10C1
4.7.	—	—	—	—	—	—	10Q4
4.8.	45.11	45.11	45.15	45.11	21.607	45.11	4P9/4P10
4.9.	21.125	21.143	21.303	—	21.607	145.45	4P3/4P4/4Q1
4.10.1.	21.125	21.143	21.303	—	21.607	145.45	10Q10/4Q1/5E1
4.10.2.2.	—	21.143	—	—	—	—	10Q10
4.10.2.3.	—	—	—	—	—	—	10Q11
4.10.3.	21.125	21.143	21.303	—	21.143	145.45	4Q10/4Q11
4.10.4.	21.125	21.143	21.303	21.441	21.143	145.63	4E1/4Q12
4.10.5.	21.125	—	21.303	21.493	21.613	145.61	8E1/8E2/8Q3
4.11.1.	—	—	—	—	—	145.45	7Q1/7Q2/ 7Q3/3AE1
4.11.2.	—	—	—	—	—	—	7Q4 through 7Q20
4.12.	45.11	45.11	45.15	45.11	21.607	45.11	4Q8/4Q9/4Q10
4.13.1.	21.125	21.143	21.303	—	21.607	145.45	11Q1/11S1/11C1
4.13.2.	21.125	21.143	21.303	—	21.143	145.45	11Q2/11Q3/ 11Q4/11Q5
4.14.1.	—	—	—	—	—	—	11Q6
4.14.2.	—	—	—	—	—	—	11M1
4.14.3.	—	—	—	—	—	—	11M1
4.15.1.	—	—	—	—	—	145.45	12P1/12E1
4.15.2.	21.125	—	21.303	—	21.125	145.35	9Q7/12Q1
4.15.3.	21.125	—	21.303	—	21.125	145.35	12Q2/12Q3/ 12Q4/12Q5/12Q7

Continued on next page

Continued from previous page

Q9001 elements	APIS	PC	PMA	DAS	TSO	Repair station	ACSEP evaluation questions
4.15.4.	—	—	—	—	—	145.35	12Q1/12Q6
4.15.5.	21.125	—	21.303	—	21.125	145.35	12Q1
4.15.6.	—	—	—	—	—	—	12Q6/12Q8
4.16.	21.125	—	21.303	21.125	21.613	145.61	1Q6
4.17.	—	—	—	—	—	—	15M1/15M2
4.18.	—	—	—	—	—	145.39	1P3/1Q3/1S3/ 1C3/4P6/5Q2/ 6Q2/6Q4/6Q6/ 8E4/9Q1
4.19.	—	—	—	21.477	—	145.45	1S1 and Section 17
4.20.1.	—	—	21.303	—	—	—	6Q5
4.20.2.	—	—	—	—	—	—	Section 6

Notes

Reference ANSI/ASQC Q9001 element 4.1.2.1., the corresponding FARs only require that the departments responsible for performing quality-related functions are described and their levels of authority defined.

Reference ANSI/ASQC Q9001 element 4.1.2.2., the corresponding FARs do not require internal audits.

Reference ANSI/ASQC Q9001 element 4.5.2., the corresponding FARs do not require a master list.

Reference ANSI/ASQC Q9001 element 4.6.4.2., the corresponding ACSEP criteria and FARs make no reference to customer inspection at the supplier's facility but they do require the right to FAA inspection.

The previous cross-reference matrix is solely the professional interpretation of the author and should be used solely as a reference in the development and assessment of aviation quality systems. There are numerous exceptions and conditions in the various requirements of both the FARs and the international quality standards. The individual chapters that discuss the various elements should be reviewed in conjunction with this matrix, to provide a better understanding of the correlations.

The FAA has also made official comparisons to the international quality standards. On 22 November 1994 the FAA's Production and Airworthiness Certification Division (AIR-200) released a memorandum to all of its managers at manufacturing inspection offices and aircraft certification offices. This memorandum provided the FAA field inspectors with a guide that readily depicts the FAR requirements, the corresponding ANSI/ASQC Q9001-1994 paragraphs and comments relative to their comparison by FAA production approval type. Since these comparisons were only applicable to FAA manufacturing approvals, the requirements for the repair station and DAS were not compared. Additionally, the requirements for TSOs are individual to the product and these comparisons were not published.

The following are the comparisons the FAA made. However, it should be remembered that the FAA published this memorandum to its internal departments only as guidelines and not as orders. The interpretation of each of the FAR and international quality standard elements can be made differently by each individual representative. The following matrices should be used as reference only in the development of individual quality systems.

Comparison of FAR Part 21 Subpart F with ANSI/ASQC Q9001-1994 Production Under Type Certificate Only

FAR	ANSI/ASQC Q9001-1994	Comments
21.125 (a)(1)	4.13.2.	FAR requirements go beyond Q9001 by specifying the establishment of an MRB and its composition.
21.125 (a)(2)	4.16.	FAR requirements go beyond Q9001 by specifying a two-year record retention period.
21.125 (b)(1)	4.6.4.2., 4.10.2.1.	Q9001 acceptable as long as "specified requirements" is understood to mean "type design data."
21.125 (b)(2)	4.8.	FAR requirements go beyond Q9001 by specifying the need to identify parts having physical and chemical properties that are not readily determined.
21.125 (b)(3)	4.15.5.	Q9001 appears adequate.
21.125 (b)(4)	4.9.	FAR requirements go beyond Q9001 by specifying that processes must be accomplished in accordance with acceptable industry or United States specifications.
21.125 (b)(5)	4.2.3., 4.10.3., 4.10.4.	Q9001 appears adequate.

Continued on next page

Continued from previous page

FAR	ANSI/ASQC Q9001-1994	Comments
21.125 (b)(6)	4.5.1.	FAR requirements go beyond Q9001 by specifying availability of design drawings (rather than "appropriate documents" as in Q9001) to manufacturing and inspection personnel (rather than the general quality system essentiality statement in Q9001).
21.125 (b)(7)	4.4. through 4.4.9., 4.5.3.	FAR requirements go beyond Q9001 by specifying control and approval of material substitutions.
21.125 (b)(8)	4.12., 4.13.	Q9001 appears adequate.
21.125 (b)(9)	4.13., 4.13.1.	FAR requirements go beyond Q9001 by specifying that nonconforming product must be processed through a materials review board.
21.125 (b)(10)	4.10.5., 4.16.	FAR requirements go beyond Q9001 by specifying a two-year record retention period.

Notes

The FAA analysis: In the opinion of the FAA, accreditation (registration) of a manufacturer to ANSI/ASQC Q9001-1994 would go a long way toward meeting FAR Part 21, Subpart F requirements. However, there are a number of FAR requirements not specifically addressed in Q9001 that would have to be complied with before approving production.

However, Q9001 exceeds FAR Part 21, Subpart F requirements in paragraphs 4.1.1. through 4.1.3., 4.2.3., 4.6.1. through 4.6.3., 4.7., 4.11.1. through 4.11.2., 4.14.1. through 4.14.3., 4.15.1., 4.15.2., 4.15.4., 4.15.6., and 4.17. through 4.20.2. Using AC 21-6A as an acceptable means of compliance, Q9001 would still exceed FAA requirements/guidance in paragraphs 4.1.1. through 4.1.3., 4.2.3., 4.6.1. through 4.6.3., 4.7., 4.14.1. through 4.14.3., 4.15.1., 4.15.4., 4.15.6., and 4.17. through 4.20.2. In the opinion of the FAA, FAA approval for production under FAR Part 21, Subpart F requirements and AC 21-6A would not be enough to comply

Comparison of FAR Part 21 Subpart G with ANSI/ASQC Q9001-1994 Production Certificate

FAR	ANSI/ASQC Q9001-1994	Comments
21.139	4.	Q9001 appears to meet the general intent.
21.143 (a)	4.2.1., 4.2.2.	FAR requirements go beyond Q9001 by specifying that data must be submitted for approval.
21.143 (a)(1)	4.1.2.	FAR requirements go beyond Q9001 by specifying that a chart must be submitted.
21.143 (a)(2)	4.6.4., 4.10.2.	FAR requirements go beyond Q9001 by emphasizing description of procedures for ensuring quality of product that cannot be completely inspected when delivered.
21.143 (a)(3)	4.9., 4.10.3., 4.10.4.	FAR requirements go beyond Q9001 by specifying that final test procedure and, for aircraft, manufacturer's production test procedures and checkoff list, be submitted for approval.
21.143 (a)(4)	4.13.	FAR requirements go beyond Q9001 by specifying the recording of review board decisions.
21.143 (a)(5)	4.4.9., 4.5.3.	FAR requirements go beyond Q9001 by specifying a system for informing inspectors of changes (in addition to design/document control in Q9001).
21.143 (a)(6)	4.2.3., 4.10.3.	FAR requirements go beyond Q9001 by specifying that a list or chart showing location and type of inspection stations be submitted for approval.
21.143 (b)	4.6.3., 4.6.4.	FAR requirements go beyond Q9001 by specifying availability of information regarding delegation of inspection authority to suppliers.

Notes

The FAA analysis: In the opinion of the FAA, accreditation (registration) of a manufacturer to ANSI/ASQC Q9001-1994 would go a long way toward meeting FAR Part 21, Subpart G requirements. However, there are a number of FAR requirements not specifically addressed in Q9001 that would have to be complied with before approving production.

However, Q9001 exceeds FAR Part 21, Subpart G requirements in paragraphs 4.3.1. through 4.3.4., 4.4.1. through 4.4.8., 4.5.1. and 4.5.2., 4.6.2., 4.7., 4.8., 4.10.5., 4.11.1. through 4.11.2., 4.12., and 4.14. through 4.20.2. Using AC 21-1B as an acceptable means of compliance, Q9001 would still exceed FAA requirements/guidance in paragraphs 4.3.1. through 4.3.4., 4.4.1. through 4.4.8., 4.7., 4.8., 4.10.5., 4.14., 4.15.1., 4.15.4. through 4.15.6., and through 4.20.2. In the opinion of the FAA, FAA approval for production under FAR Part 21 Subpart G requirements and AC 21-1B would not be enough to comply with the ANSI/ASQC Q9001-1994 requirements.

Comparison of FAR Part 21 Subpart K with ANSI/ASQC Q9001-1994 Parts Manufacturer Approval

FAR	ANSI/ASQC Q9001-1994	Comments
21.303 (h)	4.2.	Q9001 appears adequate.
21.303 (h)(1)	4.6.4., 4.10.2.1.	Q9001 appears adequate.
21.303 (h)(2)	4.8.	FAR requirements go beyond Q9001 by specifying the need to identify parts having physical and chemical properties that are not readily determined.
21.303 (h)(3)	4.15.3., 4.15.5.	Q9001 appears adequate.
21.303 (h)(4)	4.9.	Q9001 appears adequate.
21.303 (h)(5)	4.2.3., 4.10.3., 4.10.4., 4.20.	Q9001 appears adequate.
21.303 (h)(6)	4.5.2.	FAR requirements go beyond Q9001 by specifying availability of design drawings (rather than "appropriate documents" as in Q9001) to manufacturing and inspection personnel (rather than the general quality system essentiality statement in Q9001).
21.303 (h)(7)	4.4.1. through 4.4.9., and 4.5.3.	Q9001 appears adequate.
21.303 (h)(8)	4.12., 4.13.	Q9001 appears adequate.
21.303 (h)(9)	4.10.5., 4.16.	FAR requirements go beyond Q9001 by specifying a two-year record retention period.

Notes

The FAA analysis: In the opinion of the FAA, accreditation (registration) of a manufacturer to ANSI/ASQC Q9001-1994 would go a long way toward meeting FAR Part 21, Subpart K requirements. However, there are a number of FAR requirements not specifically addressed in Q9001 that would have to be complied with before approving production.

However, Q9001 exceeds FAR Part 21, Subpart K requirements in paragraphs 4.1., 4.2.3., 4.3., 4.6.1. through 4.6.3., 4.7., 4.11., 4.14., 4.15.1., 4.15.2., 4.15.4., 4.15.6., and 4.17. through 4.19. Using AC 21-303.1A as an acceptable means of compliance, Q9001 would still exceed FAA requirements/guidance in paragraphs 4.1., 4.2.3., 4.3., 4.6.3., 4.7., 4.14., 4.15.1., 4.15.2., 4.15.4., 4.15.6., and 4.17. through 4.19. In the opinion of the FAA, FAA approval for production under FAR Part 21 Subpart K requirements would not be enough to comply with ANSI/ASQC Q9001-1994 requirements.

GLOSSARY

AC, advisory circular. A document released by the FAA to provide clarification to the FARs.

ACO, aircraft certification office. The office within the FAA that is responsible for the certification of new and changed designs.

AD, airworthiness directive. A document issued by the FAA to the operator of the equipment requiring corrective or preventive action of a known or suspected deficiency.

ADCN, advance drawing change notice. An engineering document created to document engineering changes. Also sometimes called an SEO, or serialized engineering order.

ANSI, American National Standards Institute. The U.S. organization that represents the nation in matters of standardization.

APIS, approved production inspection system. An FAA production approval for manufacturers operating under a TC only.

A & P, airframe and powerplant. A mechanics' license issued by the FAA.

AQS, advanced quality system. The term Boeing Airplane Group uses to define its quality system requirements of D1-9000.

ASCS, Aerospace Sector Certification Scheme. An affiliate of the IQA-IRCA who is responsible for certifying aviation quality system auditors in the United Kingdom.

ASQC, American Society for Quality Control. The organization that represents the United States in matters of quality assurance/control.

ATA, Air Transport Association. Established in the 1930s to provide unity to the U.S. airlines.

CAA, Civil Aeronautics Authority. Created in 1938 to ensure safety and enforce regulation over all U.S. civil aviation.

CAA, Civil Aviation Authority. The British equivalent to the FAA.

C/A, corrective action. The process of investigating a discrepancy to identify its root cause and establish actions to prevent its recurrence.

CAB, Civil Aeronautics Board. Established in 1940 to control the rights of airlines and the routes they traveled.

CAB, corrective action board. A board within an organization whose primary responsibility is to review corrective actions for effectiveness.

CAIR, corrective action investigation report. A document that can be utilized to document the internal corrective and preventive action activities for a product nonconformance.

CAR, corrective action report. A document that can be utilized to document the internal corrective and preventive action activities for a system discrepancy.

DAR, designated airworthiness representative. An individual delegated by the FAA to perform certain airworthiness determinations and acceptance activities.

DAS, designated alteration station. Both a production and engineering delegation issued to organizations for the modification of aircraft, equipment, and components.

DCN, drawing change note. An engineering writing created to document engineering changes. Also called an EO, or engineering order.

DER, designated engineering representative. An individual delegated by the FAA to perform FAA engineering activities.

DL, discrepancy list. A preliminary review document of product nonconformances.

DMIR, designated manufacturing inspection representative. A delegation issued to a member of a manufacturer's inspection organization to perform acceptance inspections on behalf of the FAA.

DOT, Department of Transportation. Created in 1966 to centralize federal transportation agencies.

EO, engineering order. An engineering writing created to document engineering changes. Also sometimes called a DCN.

FAA, Federal Aviation Administration (formerly known as the Federal Aviation Agency). The U.S. federal authority responsible for the safety of air transport.

FARs, federal aviation regulations. The statutory rules of performance within the U.S. aviation industry.

FOCA, Federal Office for Civil Aviation. The Swiss equivalent to the FAA.

FRR, failure and rejection report. A formal (MRB) writing created to document major product nonconformances.

FSDO, flight standards district office. The office within the FAA that is responsible for the maintenance and safety of operating aircraft.

IA, inspection authorization. A licensed individual who is authorized to perform acceptance inspections of major repairs and alterations as well as perform annual and progressive inspections of aircraft and equipment.

IQA-IRCA, Institute for Quality Assurance-International Registrar of Certificated Auditors. The organization in the United Kingdom responsible for administering certification of quality system auditors.

ISO, International Organization for Standardization. The international group tasked with the international standardization of processes and standards.

JAA, Joint Airworthiness Authority. The European authority responsible for the safety of air transport.

JARs, joint airworthiness requirements. The European statutory rules of performance within the European aircraft industry.

JASANZ, Joint Accreditation System of Australia and New Zealand. The organization responsible for the ISO 9000 activities in that region.

LBA, Luftfahrt Bundesamt. The German equivalent to the FAA.

MAA, Manufacturers of Aircraft Association. Established in 1917 to administer cross-patent agreements.

MIDO, manufacturing inspection district office. The office within the FAA that is responsible for the production systems and product conformity of manufacturers and suppliers, as well as the MMFs.

ML, master list. A controlled document that lists the controlled documents of an organization and their current revision status.

MMF, manufacturer's maintenance facility. An authorization issued to a manufacturer from the FAA for the servicing of its own products.

MRB, material review board. The review team within the organization that determines the proper disposition for major product discrepancies.

MRF, material receipt form. A form that can be used to document the material receipt process.

MSDS, material safety data sheet. A document created by a material manufacturer identifying the hazards of a material and the proper first aid actions.

NACA, National Advisory Committee for Aeronautics. Established in 1915 to advise the U.S. president on matters relating to aviation, later replaced by NASA.

NASA, National Aeronautics and Space Administration. Established in 1958, absorbing the NACA and assuming responsibility for carrying out U.S. space flight missions.

NDT, nondestructive testing. A special process used to validate a product's conformity without damaging it.

NIST, National Institute of Standards and Technology. The U.S. federal agency responsible for the development and maintenance of national standards of measure.

NOR, notice of rejection. A document issued to a supplier notifying it of a discrepancy in the product or service provided. This document is for informational purposes only and does not require supplier response.

NTSB, National Transportation Safety Board. Created in 1966 to investigate accidents in transportation.

OEM, Original Equipment Manufacturer. In the aviation industry, the organization that holds FAA design and production approval for a particular product.

P/A, preventive action. The process of analyzing processes for activities that will prevent possible discrepancies from occurring.

PAB, Aircraft Production Board. Established in 1914 to control quality and schedules within the aviation industry for government contracts.

PAH, production approval holder. The holder of a PC, APIS, PMA, or TSOA.

PC, production certificate. The FAA production approval issued to qualified manufacturers of aircraft, engines, and propellers.

PI, principal inspector. The primary FAA representative assigned to a manufacturer to oversee product, facility, and system conformance.

PI, preliminary inspection. The initial inspection performed on a product's discrepancy to determine severity. Also known as preliminary review.

PMA, parts manufacturer approval. A production approval issued from the FAA to manufacturers who produce parts, equipment, and components under the design authority of a TC or an STC either through direct ownership of design or through licensing agreement.

PO, purchase order. A control document released to a supplier to procure a service or product.

PR, preliminary review. The initial inspection performed on a product's discrepancy to determine severity. Also known as preliminary inspection.

QA, quality assurance. The process or organization responsible for assuring the conformity of the system and the prevention activities of the organization.

QAM, quality assurance manual. The core quality document within an organization.

QAP, quality assurance procedures. The supplemental control documents relating to specific processes.

QC, quality control. The process or organization responsible for assuring the conformity of the product.

QSA, Quality Society of Australasia. The organization that represents the region of Australasia in quality matters. Similar to the ASQC.

QS-LA, quality systems lead auditor. An individual who is certified to perform and lead quality system audits of organizations. The international quality standards are typically used as the reference standard.

RAB, Registrar Accreditation Board. A division of the ASQC that administers ISO 9000 activities in the United States in association with ANSI.

RFQ, request for quotation. A document released to potential suppliers identifying the parameters of a desired service or product and requesting a bid to be submitted.

SB, service bulletin. A document created by the manufacturer and released to the equipment operator providing maintenance or modification instructions. Not normally FAA-approved data.

SCAN, supplier corrective action notice. A document issued to a supplier to pursue and document corrective and preventive actions.

SEO, serialized engineering order. An engineering document created to document an engineering change with limited effectivity. Sometimes called an ADCN.

STC, Supplemental Type Certificate. The FAA design approval for changes to TCs as well as stand-alone FAA design approval for aftermarket equipment and components.

TBO, time before overhaul. The time remaining on a component prior to required overhaul activities.

TC, Type Certificate. The FAA design approval document for aircraft, engines, and propellers.

TSO, Technical Standard Order. An FAA design specification for specific equipment or components.

TSOA, Technical Standard Order Approval. Both a design and production approval for products designed in accordance with a TSO.

BIBLIOGRAPHY

ANSI/ASQC Q9000-1-1994, *Quality Management and Quality Assurance Standards*. Milwaukee, Wis.: American Society for Quality Control, 1994.

ANSI/ASQC Q9001-1994, *Quality Systems: Model for Quality Assurance in Design/Development, Production, Installation, and Servicing*. Milwaukee, Wis.: American Society for Quality Control, 1994.

ANSI/ASQC Q9002-1994, *Quality Systems: Model for Quality Assurance in Production, Installation, and Servicing*. Milwaukee, Wis.: American Society for Quality Control, 1994.

ANSI/ASQC Q9003-1994, *Quality Systems: Model for Quality Assurance in Final Inspection and Test*. Milwaukee, Wis.: American Society for Quality Control, 1994.

ANSI/ASQC Q9004-1-1994, *Quality Management and Quality System Elements: Guidelines*. Milwaukee, Wis.: American Society for Quality Control, 1994.

ASQC Q90-1987, *Quality Management and Quality Assurance Standards*. Milwaukee, Wis.: American Society for Quality Control, 1987.

ASQC Q91-1987, *Quality Systems: Model for Quality Assurance in Design/Development, Production, Installation, and Servicing*. Milwaukee, Wis.: American Society for Quality Control, 1987.

ASQC Q92-1987, *Quality Systems: Model for Quality Assurance in Production and Installation*. Milwaukee, Wis.: American Society for Quality Control, 1987.

ASQC Q93-1987, *Quality Systems: Model for Quality Assurance in Final Inspection and Test*. Milwaukee, Wis.: American Society for Quality Control, 1987.

ASQC Q94-1987, *Quality Management and Quality System Elements: Guidelines*. Milwaukee, Wis.: American Society for Quality Control, 1987.

Berger, Roger W., and Thomas Pyzdek. *Quality Engineering Handbook*. New York: Marcel Dekker/ASQC Quality Press, 1992.

Brown, Carl A. *A History of Aviation*. Daytona Beach, Fla.: Embry-Riddle Aeronautical University, 1980.

Clements, Richard B. *Quality Manager's Complete Guide to ISO 9000: Interpretation, Application, Implementation, Registration, and Benefits of the ISO 9000 Standard*. Englewood Cliffs, N.J.: Prentice Hall, 1993.

Cottman, Ronald J. *A Guidebook to ISO 9000 and ANSI/ASQC Q90*. Milwaukee, Wis.: ASQC Quality Press, 1993.

DOT/FAA. Advisory Circular 20-62C, *Eligibility, Quality, and Identification of Approved Aeronautical Replacement Parts.* Washington, D.C.: DOT/FAA, 26 August 1976.

DOT/FAA. Advisory Circular 20-65, *U.S. Airworthiness Certificates and Authorizations for Operation of Domestic and Foreign Aircraft.* Washington, D.C.: DOT/FAA, 11 August 1969.

DOT/FAA. Advisory Circular 20-77, *Use of Manufacturers' Maintenance Manuals.* Washington, D.C.: DOT/FAA, 22 March 1972.

DOT/FAA. Advisory Circular 20-110H, *Index of Aviation Technical Standard Orders.* Washington, D.C.: DOT/FAA, 6 May 1993.

DOT/FAA. Advisory Circular 20-114, *Manufacturers' Service Documents.* Washington, D.C.: DOT/FAA, 22 October 1981.

DOT/FAA. Advisory Circular 21-ACSEP, *The Aircraft Certification Systems Evaluation Program.* Washington, D.C.: DOT/FAA, 17 August 1993.

DOT/FAA. Advisory Circular 21-1B, *Production Certificates.* Washington, D.C.: DOT/FAA, 10 May 1976.

DOT/FAA. Advisory Circular 21-2F, *Export Airworthiness Approval Procedures.* Washington, D.C.: DOT/FAA, 7 August 1987.

DOT/FAA. Advisory Circular 21-5L, *Announcement of Availability—Summary of Supplemental Type Certificates.* 1993 ed. Washington, D.C.: DOT/FAA, 7 May 1993.

DOT/FAA. Advisory Circular 21-9A, *Manufacturers Reporting Failures, Malfunctions, or Defects.* Washington, D.C.: DOT/FAA, 26 May 1982.

DOT/FAA. Advisory Circular 21-12A, *Application for U.S. Airworthiness Certificate, FAA Form 8130-6* (OMB 2120-0018). Washington, D.C.: DOT/FAA, 26 March 1987.

DOT/FAA. Advisory Circular 21-13, *Standard Airworthiness Certification of Surplus Military Aircraft and Aircraft Built from Spare and Surplus Parts.* Washington, D.C.: DOT/FAA, 5 April 1973.

DOT/FAA. Advisory Circular 21-15I, *Announcement of Availability: Aircraft, Aircraft Engines, and Propeller Type Certificate Data Sheets and Specifications.* DOT/FAA, 11 February 1993.

DOT/FAA. Advisory Circular 21.17-1A, *Type Certification—Airships.* Washington, D.C.: DOT/FAA, 30 October 1992.

DOT/FAA. Advisory Circular 21.17-2A, *Type Certification—Wing Gliders (Sailplanes), Including Powered Gliders.* Washington, D.C.: DOT/FAA, 10 February 1993.

DOT/FAA. Advisory Circular 21.17-3, *Type Certification of Very Light Airplanes Under FAR Para. 21.17 (b).* Washington, D.C.: DOT/FAA, 21 December 1992.

DOT/FAA. Advisory Circular 21-18, *Bilateral Airworthiness Agreements.* Washington, D.C.: DOT/FAA, 20 August 1982.

DOT/FAA. Advisory Circular 21-20, *Supplier Surveillance Procedures.* Washington, D.C.: DOT/FAA, 22 July 1982.

DOT/FAA. Advisory Circular 21-20A, *Supplier Surveillance Procedures.* Washington, D.C.: DOT/FAA, 25 July 1994.

DOT/FAA. Advisory Circular 21-22, *Injury Criteria for Human Exposure to Impact.* Washington, D.C.: DOT/FAA, 20 June 1985.

DOT/FAA. Advisory Circular 21-24, *Extending a Production Certificate to a Facility Located in a Bilateral Airworthiness Agreement Country.* Washington, D.C.: DOT/FAA, 14 April 1989.

DOT/FAA. Advisory Circular 21-25, *Approval of Modified Seats and Berths Initially Approved Under a Technical Standard Order.* Washington, D.C.: DOT/FAA, 24 April 1989.

DOT/FAA. Advisory Circular 21-26, *Quality Control for the Manufacture of Composite Structures.* Washington, D.C.: DOT/FAA, 26 June 1989.

DOT/FAA. Advisory Circular 21-27, *Production Certification Multinational/Multicorporate Consortia.* Washington, D.C.: DOT/FAA, 14 July 1989.

DOT/FAA. Advisory Circular 21-29A, *Detecting and Reporting Suspected Unapproved Parts.* Washington, D.C.: DOT/FAA, 16 July 1992.

DOT/FAA. Advisory Circular 21-31, *Quality Control for the Manufacture of Non-Metallic Compartment Interior Components.* Washington, D.C.: DOT/FAA, 15 November 1991.

DOT/FAA. Advisory Circular 21-32, *Control of Parts Shipped Prior to Type Certificate Issuance.* Washington, D.C.: DOT/FAA, 14 October 1992.

DOT/FAA. Advisory Circular 21-33, *Quality Assurance of Software Used in Aircraft or Related Products.* Washington, D.C.: DOT/FAA, 3 February 1993.

DOT/FAA. Advisory Circular 21-34, *Shoulder Harness–Safety Belt Installations.* Washington, D.C.: DOT/FAA, 4 June 1993.

DOT/FAA. Advisory Circular 21-35, *Computer Generated/Stored Records.* Washington, D.C.: DOT/FAA, 4 June 1993.

DOT/FAA. Advisory Circular 21-36, *Quality Assurance Controls for Product Acceptance Software.* Washington, D.C.: DOT/FAA, 11 August 1993.

DOT/FAA. Advisory Circular 21-39, *The Aircraft Certification Systems Evaluation Program.* Washington, D.C.: DOT/FAA, 31 August 1994.

DOT/FAA. Advisory Circular 21-303.1A, *Certification Procedures for Products and Parts.* DOT/FAA, 10 August 1972.

DOT/FAA. Advisory Circular 21.431-1A, *Designated Alteration Station Authorization Procedures.* Washington, D.C.: DOT/FAA, n.d.

DOT/FAA. Advisory Circular 23-11, *Type Certification of Very Light Airplanes with Powerplants and Propellers Certified to Parts 33 and 35 of the Federal Aviation Regulations.* Washington, D.C.: DOT/FAA, 2 December 1992.

DOT/FAA. Advisory Circular 25.1455-1, *Waste Water/Potable Water Drain System Certification Testing.* Washington, D.C.: DOT/FAA, 3 November 1985.

DOT/FAA. Advisory Circular 33-2B, *Aircraft Engine Type Certification Handbook.* Washington, D.C.: DOT/FAA, 30 June 1993.

DOT/FAA. Advisory Circular 43-2B, *Minimum Barometry for Calibration and Test of Atmospheric Pressure Instruments.* Washington, D.C.: DOT/FAA, 16 October 1980.

DOT/FAA. Advisory Circular 43-3, *Nondestructive Testing in Aircraft.* Washington, D.C.: DOT/FAA, May 1993.

DOT/FAA. Advisory Circular 43.9-1E, *Instructions for Completion of FAA Form 337.* Washington, D.C.: DOT/FAA, 21 May 1987.

DOT/FAA. Advisory Circular 43-9B, *Maintenance Records.* Washington, D.C.: DOT/FAA, 9 January 1984.

DOT/FAA. Advisory Circular 43-10A, *Mechanical Work Performed on U.S. and Canadian Registered Aircraft.* Washington, D.C.: DOT/FAA, 25 February 1983.

DOT/FAA. Advisory Circular 43-12A, *Preventive Maintenance.* Washington, D.C.: DOT/FAA, 28 October 1983.

DOT/FAA. Advisory Circular 43-17, *Methods, Techniques, and Practices Acceptable to the Administrator Governing the Installation, Removal, or Change of Identification Data and Identification Plates.* Washington, D.C.: DOT/FAA, 5 September 1979.

DOT/FAA. Advisory Circular 43-203B, *Altimeter and Static System Tests and Inspections.* Washington, D.C.: DOT/FAA, 20 June 1979.

DOT/FAA. Advisory Circular 65-23A, *Certification of Repairmen.* Washington, D.C.: DOT/FAA, 22 July 1987.

DOT/FAA. Advisory Circular 120-59, *Air Carrier Internal Evaluation Programs.* Washington, D.C.: DOT/FAA, 26 October 1992.

DOT/FAA. Advisory Circular 121-16, *Maintenance Certification Procedures.* Washington, D.C.: DOT/FAA, 9 November 1970.

DOT/FAA. Advisory Circular 121-21B, *Information Guide for Training Programs and Manual Requirements in the Air Transportation of Hazardous Materials.* Washington, D.C.: DOT/FAA, 3 January 1984.

DOT/FAA. Advisory Circular 125-1, *Operations of Large Airplanes Subject to Federal Aviation Regulation Part 125.* Washington, D.C.: DOT/FAA, 22 January 1981.

DOT/FAA. Advisory Circular 129-4, *Maintenance Programs for U.S. Registered Aircraft Under FAR Part 129.* Washington, D.C.: DOT/FAA, 1 March 1988.

DOT/FAA. Advisory Circular 135-10A, *Approved Aircraft Inspection Program.* Washington, D.C.: DOT/FAA, 22 December 1993.

DOT/FAA. Advisory Circular 140-6C, *The Development and Use of Major Repair Data Under Provisions of Special Federal Aviation Regulation No. 36.* Washington, D.C.: DOT/FAA, 3 February 1984.

DOT/FAA. Advisory Circular 145-3, *Guide for Developing and Evaluating Repair Station Inspection Procedures Manuals.* Washington, D.C.: DOT/FAA, 13 February 1981.

DOT/FAA. Advisory Circular 145.101-1B, *Application for Air Agency Certification—Manufacturer's Maintenance Facility.* Washington, D.C.: DOT/FAA, 30 November 1983.

DOT/FAA. Advisory Circular 183-33A, *Designated Airworthiness Representatives.* Washington, D.C.: DOT/FAA, 1 October 1985.

DOT/FAA. Federal Aviation Administration Order 8100.7, *Aircraft Certification Systems Evaluation Program.* Washington, D.C.: DOT/FAA, 30 March 1994.

DOT/FAA. Federal Aviation Administration Order 8130.21A, *Procedures for Completion and Use of FAA Form 8130-3.* Washington, D.C.: DOT/FAA, 3 January 1994.

DOT/FAA. Federal Aviation Regulation Part 21, *Certification Procedures for Products and Parts.* Washington, D.C.: DOT/FAA, March 1993.

DOT/FAA. Federal Aviation Regulation Part 145, *Repair Stations.* Washington, D.C.: DOT/FAA, August 1993.

"ISO 9000 Supporters Growing at NASA, DoD, FAA." *Quality Systems Update* 3, no. 6 (June 1993): 13.

Lamprecht, James L. *Implementing the ISO 9000 Series.* New York: Marcel Dekker, 1993.

Marrow, Mark. "ISO Gains Ground at Geneva Workshop." *Quality Digest,* 21 July 1993, 20.

MIL-STD-105D, *Sampling Procedures and Tables for Inspection by Attributes.* Washington, D.C.: Government Printing Office, 20 March 1964.

MIL-STD-1520C, *Corrective Action and Disposition System for Nonconforming Material.* Washington, D.C.: Government Printing Office, 3 July 1980.

MIL-STD-1535A, *Supplier Quality Assurance Program Requirements.* Washington, D.C.: Government Printing Office, 1 February 1974.

MIL-I-45208A, *Inspection System Requirements.* Washington, D.C.: Government Printing Office, 24 July 1981.

MIL-STD-45662, *Calibration Systems Requirements.* Washington, D.C.: Government Printing Office, 14 December 1984.

MIL-S-52779A, *Software Quality Assurance Program Requirements.* Washington D.C.: Government Printing Office, 5 April 1979.

MIL-Q-9858A, *Quality Program Requirements*. Washington, D.C.: Government Printing Office, 7 August 1981.

Rollo, V. Foster. *Aviation Law: An Introduction*. Lanham, Md.: Maryland Historical Press, 1985.

Rothery, Brian. *ISO 9000*. Brookfield, Vt.: Grower Press, 1993.

Stebbing, Lionel. *Quality Assurance: The Route to Efficiency and Competitiveness*. Chichester, West Sussex, England: Ellis Horwood, 1993.

Taneja, Nawal K. *Airlines in Transition*. Lexington, Mass.: Lexington Books, 1981.

Waylett, William, Jr. "What's So Different About ISO 9000?" *Quality Digest*, August 1992, 13.

Whempner, Robert J. *Corporate Aviation*. New York: McGraw-Hill, 1982.

INDEX

ANSI/ASQC Q9000 series,
requirements of—*continued*
contract review, 50
corrective action, 233
customer-supplied product, 134
delegation of authority, 40–41
design control, 73, 74, 75–76
drawings, 98
final inspection, 166, 167
final testing, 166
in-process inspection, 164
inspection and testing, 157
inspection and test status, 211
process control, 151
product handling, 247
product identification, 137–38
product storage, 249
purchase product verification, 127
purchasing, 109, 126
servicing, 285
traceability, 137–38
training, 275
ANSI/ASQC Q9000-1-1994, 14
ANSI/ASQC Q9001-1994, 14
alternative to MIL-Q-9858A, 302
elements of, 15–16
element 4.4.4, 79
element 4.4.4.6, 82
element 4.4.4.7, 82
element 4.4.4.8, 83
element 4.4.4.9, 87
element 4.4.5, 81
element 4.4.5.2, 98–99, 102, 106
element 4.4.5.3, 104
element 4.6.3, 126
element 4.6.4.1, 127
element 4.9, 151–52
element 4.14.2, 234
element 4.14.3, 235
element 4.17, 262, 263
FARs, cross referenced with, 305–11
ANSI/ASQC Q9002-1994, 14, 15–16
ANSI/ASQC Q9003-1994, xx, 14,
15–16
ANSI/ASQC Q9004-1-1994, 14, 20
APIS. *See* Approved production
inspection system

Approvals
for design, 69–73
of document control, 98–102
types of, 21–26
Approved data, 74
Approved production inspection
system (APIS), 22, 305–7, 313. *See
also* Production
under type certificate only
Approved supplier list, 124, 153
Archival records, 256–57
ASQC. *See* American Society for
Quality Control
Auditors, certified, 14, 262, 278, 281
Audits. *See also* Internal quality
audits; Quality assurance
ACSEP evaluations, 261
adherence, 265
calibration system, 208
compliance, 265
contract review, 66
corrective action, 119, 121–24,
237–39
deep, 265
discrepancies, 119, 121–24
external, 261
extrinsic, 261
FAA, 32–36, 302
final report, 269–72
follow-up, 268–69
nonconformances, 268–69
notification, 265, 266
planning, 116–19, 120
product handling, 252–53
purchasing control, 113–24
scheduling, 263–66
types of, 261, 265
Authority, of management, 39–41
Availability, of documents and
records, 94, 98–99, 102–4, 257–58

Bilateral agreements, between
countries, 112, 128–29, 183
Bogus parts, 162, 222
Bureau of Aircraft Production, 4
Buyer-furnished material. *See*
Customer-supplied product